T5-BBB-471

THE EPICURE'S COMPANION

BOOKS BY ANN SERANNE

The Epicure's Companion (*with John Tebbel*) • The Blender Cookbook (*with Eileen Gaden*) • The Complete Book of Home Preserving • Your Home Freezer • The Complete Book of Home Baking • The Art of Egg Cookery • Delectable Desserts •

BOOKS BY JOHN TEBBEL

Anthology

The Epicure's Companion (*with Ann Seranne*)

History

The American Indian Wars (*with Keith Jennison*) • George Washington's America • The Battle for North America (*editor*) •

Biography

The Inheritors • An American Dynasty • George Horace Lorimer and The Saturday Evening Post • The Marshall Fields • The Life and Good Times of William Randolph Hearst

Novels

The Conqueror • Touched with Fire • A Voice in the Streets

Medical

The Magic of Balanced Living • Your Body: How to Keep It Healthy

Textbook

Makers of Modern Journalism (*with Kenneth N. Stewart*)

THE EPICURE'S COMPANION

EDITED BY

ANN SERANNE

and JOHN TEBBEL

Illustrations by REESE BRANDT

DAVID McKAY COMPANY, INC. NEW YORK

THE EPICURE'S COMPANION

LIBRARY OF CONGRESS CATALOG CARD NUMBER: 62-20232

MANUFACTURED IN THE UNITED STATES OF AMERICA
VAN REES PRESS • NEW YORK

Typography by Charles M. Todd

For
KEITH JENNISON

ACKNOWLEDGMENTS

THE COMPILERS wish to thank the following holders of copyright for permission to reprint:

The Limited Editions Club for "My Lord Appetite," from *Gargantua and Pantagruel,* by François Rabelais, translated by Jacques Le Clercq.

Harcourt, Brace & World and Leonard Woolf for "Lunch Began with Sole," from *A Room of One's Own,* by Virginia Woolf, © 1929, by Harcourt, Brace & World, Inc.; © 1957 by Leonard Woolf; and "Boeuf en Daube," abridged from *To the Lighthouse,* by Virginia Woolf, © 1927, by Harcourt, Brace & World, Inc.; renewed, 1955, by Leonard Woolf. Reprinted by permission of the publishers.

Random House, Inc. for "Lunch at Combray," from *Swann's Way,* by Marcel Proust, translated by C. K. Scott Moncrieff; and to Chatto & Windus, Ltd., for Canadian rights.

A. D. Peters for "A Corner of Paris," from *Having Crossed the Channel,* by X. Marcel Boulestin; William Heinemann, Ltd., 1934

Hastings House for "The American Gastronome in France," from *Clementine in the Kitchen,* by Phineas Beck; Hastings House, Publishers, Inc.

Alfred A. Knopf, Inc. for "Gourmandizing in Nineteenth Century Russia," reprinted from *Dead Souls,* by Nikolai Gogol, translated by Constance Garnett, by permission of Alfred A. Knopf, Inc., copyright, 1923, by Mrs. Edward Garnett; copyright, 1950, by David Garnett. For distribution in Canada, reproduced by permission of the publishers, Chatto & Windus.

Alfred A. Knopf, Inc. for "Dinner at the Buddenbrooks'," reprinted from *Buddenbrooks,* by Thomas Mann, by permission of Alfred A. Knopf, Inc., copyright, 1924, 1952 by Alfred A. Knopf, Inc.

Alfred A. Knopf, Inc. for "The Great Black Duck Dinner," reprinted from *Paul Bunyan,* by James Stevens, by permission of Alfred A. Knopf, Inc., copyright, 1925, 1947 by Alfred A. Knopf, Inc.

Charles Scribner's Sons for "Eugene Discovers a Kitchen," reprinted with the permission of Charles Scribner's Sons from *Of Time and the River,* by Thomas Wolfe. Copyright 1935 by Charles Scribner's Sons.

The Viking Press, Inc. for "Dinner on the Beach," from *The Dharma Bums,* by Jack Kerouac; copyright 1958 by Jack Kerouac. Reprinted by permission of The Viking Press, Inc.

Adprint Limited for "Literary Men of Taste," from *The English at Table,* by John Hampson, published 1946 by Collins in the "Britain in Pictures" Series.

Executors of Mrs. C. F. Leyel for "Love Potions," from *The Magic of Herbs,* by Mrs. C. F. Leyel; and "Soul Medicines," from the same volume; also "Tisanes," from *Herbal Delights.*

Doubleday & Co., Inc. for "The Rivalry of Grasses," from *Six Thousand Years of Bread,* by H. E. Jacob, copyright 1944 by H. E. Jacob. Reprinted by permission of Doubleday & Co., Inc.

Houghton Mifflin Co. for "On a Tea-Drinker," from *To Think of Tea,* by Agnes Repplier, published by permission of Houghton Mifflin Co.

Hector Bolitho for "Loveliest of All Foods," and "Cannibalism," both from *The Glorious Oyster,* by Hector Bolitho, published by Horizon Press.

Doubleday & Co. for "Pork for Breakfast," from *Arundel,* by Kenneth Roberts, copyright, 1930, 1933, by Kenneth Roberts. Reprinted by permission of Doubleday & Co., Inc.

Simon and Schuster, Inc. for "Life of Carême," from *Grand Dictionnaire de Cuisine,* by Alexandre Dumas; © 1958 by Louis Colman, reprinted by permission of Simon and Schuster, Inc.

The New York Times for "Escoffier: Chef of Chefs," by Craig Claiborne, from The New York Times Magazine. Reprinted by permission of The New York Times.

A. D. Peters for "Recipe for Mixed Spices," from *Herbs, Salads and Seasonings,* by X. Marcel Boulestin and Jason Hill, published 1930, by William Heinemann Ltd., London. Reprinted by permission of A. D. Peters, London.

Lin Yutang for "The Chinese Cuisine," from *My Country and My People,* by Lin Yutang, published by The John Day Co. Reprinted by permission of the author.

The Macmillan Company for permission to reprint from *Notes on a Cellar-Book* by George Saintsbury.

TABLE OF CONTENTS

Part One

PLEASURES OF THE TABLE

Part Two

CUSTOMS AND MANNERS

Part Three

INGREDIENTS OF GOOD DINING

Part Four

SOME GASTRONOMIC ECCENTRICITIES

Part Five

LIFE WITH THE CHEFS

Part Six

SOME CURIOUS RECIPES

Part Seven

THE PHILOSOPHIC EPICURE

THE EPICURE'S COMPANION

PART 1

PLEASURES OF THE TABLE

Chapter One

SOME NOTABLE DINNERS

Of notable dinners in the literature of food there are enough to make a dozen anthologies, and the minute sampling offered here is no more than an hors d'oeuvre preceding the banquet laid out in the pages which follow. These were, one might say, *early* notable dinners for the most part, marking the outer boundaries of gastronomy.

Old, familiar friends are here. Trimalchio is inevitable in any collection of epicurean reminiscences, and one may as well greet him at once and sit by his side for a few moments of that banquet to end all banquets, which combined sex and ingestion in such overwhelming proportions. The Burnaby translation from which this excerpt is taken left the sex untranslated from Petronius's Latin. Times have changed and today the erotic caperings of these jaded Romans could not only be translated but would have a difficult time competing with contemporary figures in fiction. The ingestion, however, remains a thing of wonder, not unmixed with a nausea which would have been only good manners at Trimalchio's dinner. For pure gastronomic decadence, it can hardly be matched.

With relief we return to the healthy appetite of Lucius Apuleius, the Algerian who became a Latin novelist and thereby influenced the novel for centuries to come. In this excerpt from "The Golden Asse," or "Metamorphoses," the man turned into ass has been sold to two brothers, one a baker and the other a cook, a most fortunate transaction of which the Ass takes full advantage.

One of those whom Apuleius influenced was Giovanni Boccaccio (1313-1375), whose "Decameron," like "The Satyricon," is no longer considered erotica except in the classic sense. It is, indeed, pervaded by a certain morality that is forever restraining the libidinous gaiety of these Renaissance tales, told by a company of seven lovely girls and three handsome men as they spent the languorous summer of 1348 in flight from the plague-ridden city of Florence. The brief selection here demonstrates Boccaccio's genius for blending the satisfactions of all the senses and appetites in a genial souffle.

None of this elegance illuminates the plain prose of that great fifteenth century adventurer, Marco Polo, who began his fabulous journey to the court of Kublai Khan when he was only seventeen. No one believed his report of what he found there, not when he returned nor for centuries afterward. Today, embedded in his matter-of-fact diary, one finds a good reporter's account of life in China in that century. Marco was always interested in what people ate, and never more so than when he found himself in the presence of the Great Khan himself, whose public dining is described in this excerpt.

No ruler of men ever ate as well, however, as Gargantua, the man of appetites so lusty that his creator, François Rabelais, gave his name to the language as a symbol of them. Unfortunately the word "Rabelaisian," connoting these appetites, obscures for people who have never read his five books the fact that these gems of the early sixteenth century are really works of philosophy, interlaced with penetrating analyses of human character, and bound together with a gaiety which is buoyant and life-giving. The excerpts describe Gargantua, as a young man, learning how not to waste himself on idle occupations, and a dinner given for him by Pantagruel, his father.

"Salmon In May" is taken from one of the lesser-known novels of Thomas Love Peacock (1785-1866), the English poet and novelist whose lyric songs are better remembered than his novels, which are more worthy of remembrance. Even the short passage excerpted here demonstrates the wit, charming eccentricity and love of good living in which these tales abound.

In "The Vicomte de Bragelonne," we encounter two of the intrepid adventurers Alexandre Dumas immortalized in his 1844 classic, "The Three Musketeers." They were so popular that he had to carry on their exploits a year later in "Twenty Years After." Still the public would not let them go, and Dumas revived them once more in 1848, in the novel excerpted here. In this selection, Porthos is the hero of a gastronomic encounter with the King, but he is abetted, perhaps rescued from his own brashness, by D'Artagnan.

We close the first chapter with snippets from two famous diaries, those of John Evelyn and Samuel Pepys, who were friends, although they moved in somewhat different circles. Evelyn, an authentic gentleman, was comfortable in whatever circle he moved, and dined well in all of them, as one may observe from these two widely separated examples. When he ate with Pepys, he was in good company always, for the redoubtable Samuel, as his notable "Diary" tells us, ate well and prodigiously, no matter how much he might worry about what it cost. Judging by his descriptions of the little dinners he gave at home, one of which is given here, Mrs. Pepys must have spent in the kitchen all the time she could spare from quarreling and bedding with her husband.

Here, then, is our plate of nine hors d'oeuvres. The best dinners are yet to come.

Trimalchio's Feast

from The Satyricon of Petronius
(*translated by William Burnaby*)

IN THE PORCH stood the porter in a green livery, girt about with a cherry-colored girdle, garbling of pease in a silver charger; and overhead hung a golden cage with magpye in it, which gave us an All Hail as we entered. . . .

Then came a sumptuous antepast; for we were all seated, but only Trimalchio, for whom, after a new fashion, the chief place was reserved. Besides that, as part of the entertainment there was set by us a large vessel of metheglin, with pannier, in the one part of which were white olives, in the other black; two broad platters covered the vessel . . . and on them dormice strewed over with honey and poppy. There were also piping hot sausages on a silver gridiron, and under that large Damsons, with the kernels of pomegranates . . .

In the meantime while we were yet picking a relish here and there, a cupboard was brought in with a basket, in which was a hen carved in wood, her wings, lying round and hollow, as sitting on brood; when presently the consort struck up, and two servants fell a'searching the straw under her, and taking out some peahen's eggs, distributed them among the company. At this Trimalchio changing countenance, 'I commanded my friends,' said he, 'the hen to be set with peahen's eggs; and so help me Hercules, I'm afraid they may be half hatch't: however we'll try if they are yet suppable.'

The thing we received was a kind of shell of at least six pounds weight, made of paste, and molded into the figure of an egg, which we easily broke; and for my part, I was like to have thrown away my share; for it seemed to me to have a chick in it; till hearing an old guest of the tables saying it was some good bit or other, I searched further into it, and found a delicate fat wheatear, in the middle of a well peppered yoke; on this Trimalchio stopped his play for a while, and requiring the like for himself proclaimed if any of us would have any more metheglin, he was at liberty to take it; when of a sudden the musick gave the sign, and the first course was scrabled away by a company of singers and dancers; but in the rustle it happening that a dish fell on the floor, a boy took it up, and Trimalchio taking notice of it, pluck't him by the ears, and commanded him to throw it down again; on which the groom of the Chamber came with a broom and swept away the silver dish, with whatsoever else had fallen from the table.

When presently came in two long-haired blacks, with small leather bottles such as with which they strew sand on the stage, and gave us wine to wash our hands, but no one offered us water. We all admiring the finicalness of the entertainment, 'Mars,' said he, 'is a lover of justice, and therefore let every one have a table to himself, for having more elbow-room, these nasty stinking boys will be less troublesome to us'; and thereupon large double-ear'd vessels of glass close plaistered over, were brought up with labels about their necks, upon which was this inscription: OPIMIAN MUSCADINE OF AN HUNDRED YEARS OLD.

... We drank and admired everything, when in came a servant with a silver puppet, so jointed and put together that it turned every way; and being more than once thrown upon the table, cast itself into several figures; on which Trimalchio came out of his poetry ...

The applause we gave him was followed with a service, but respecting the place not so considerable as might have been expected; however, the novelty of the thing drew every man's eye upon it; it was a large charger, with the twelve Signs around it; upon every one of which the master cook had laid somewhat or other suitable to the Sign. Upon Aries, chick-pease (a pulse not unlike a ram's head); upon Taurus a piece of beef; upon Gemini a pair of pendulums and kidneys; upon Cancer a coronet; upon Leo an African fig; upon Virgo a well-grown boy; upon Libra a pair of scales, in one of which was a tart, in the other a custard; upon Scorpio a pilchard; upon Sagittari a greyhound; upon Capricorn a lobster; upon Aquarius a goose; upon Pisces two mullets and in the middle a plat of herbs, cut out like a green turf, and over them a honeycomb. During this, a lesser black carried about bread in a silver oven, and with a hideous voice, forced a bawdy song from a buffoon that stunk like asafoetida ...

Then the fourth consort struck up; at which the waiters fell a dancing and took off the upper part of the charger, under which was a dish of cramm'd fowl and the hinder paps of a sow that had farrowed but a day before, well powdered, and in the middle a hare, stuck in with finns of fish in his side, that he looked like a flying horse; and on the sides of the fish four little images that spouted a relishing sauce on some fish that lay near them, all of them brought from the River Euripus ...

The dish was by this time taken away and the guests grown merry with wine ... at last other servants came in and spread coverlets on the beds, on which were painted nets, men in ambush with hunting poles, and whatever appertained to hunting; nor could we yet tell what to make of it; when we heard a great cry without and a pack of beagles came and ran round the table, and after them a large tray, on which was a boar of the first magnitude, with a cap on his head (such as slaves at their making free, had set theirs in token of liberties); on his tusks hung two wicker baskets, the one full of dates, the other of almonds; and about him lay little pigs of marchpane, as if they were sucking; they signified a sow had farrowed and hang there as presents for the guests to carry away with them.

To the cutting up of this boar, here came not he that had carried about the fowl as before, but a swinging fellow with a two-handed beard, buskins on his legs, and a short embroidered coat; who drawing his wood-knife, made a large hole in the boar's side, out of which flew a company of blackbirds; then fowlers stood ready with their engines and caught them in a trice as they fluttered about the room. On which Trimalchio ordering to every man his bird, 'See,' said he, 'what kind of acorns this wild boar fed on.' When presently the boys took off the baskets and distributed the dates and almonds among the guests ...

The cloth being again taken away, upon the next musick were brought in three fat hogs with collars, and bells about their necks; and he that had the charge of them told us the one was two years old, the other three, and the third full grown. I took it at first to be a company of tumblers that the hogs, as the manner is, were to have shown us some tricks in a ring, till Trimalchio breaking my expectations, 'Which of them,' said he, 'will ye have for supper? For cocks, pheasants, and the like trifles are but country fare, but my cooks have coppers and will boil a calf whole.' And therewith commanding a cook to be called for, he prevented our choice by ordering him to kill the largest ...

Of a sudden the roof gave a crack, and the whole room shook. For my part I got on my feet, but all in confusion, for fear some tumbler might drop on my head; the same also were the rest of the guests; still gaping and expecting what new thing should come from the clouds: when straight the main beams opened, and a vast circle was let down, all round which hung golden garlands and alabaster pots of sweet ointments.

While we were required to take up these presents, I chanced to cast an eye upon the table, where there lay a fresh service of cheese-cakes and tarts, and in the midst of them a lusty rundlet, stuck round with all sorts of apples and grapes, as they commonly draw that figure.

We greedily reached our hands towards it, when of a sudden a new diversion gave us fresh mirth; for all the cheesecakes, apples and tarts upon the least touch threw out a delicious liquid perfume which fell upon us ...

This held a while till Trimalchio calling for a second service to entertain his new guests, the servants took away the tables that were before us, and having brought others, strewed the room with pindust, mixt with vermillion and saffron. And what I never saw before, the dust of a looking-glass ground to powder ...

On which a spruce boy that served us with warm water began to imitate a nightingale; till Trimalchio giving the word, a servant that waited on Habinas set up another humor ...

Nor had there ever been an end to this trumpery had not that last service of blackbirds, baked in good pie crust with raisins and chestnuts, been brought up, and after them quince peaches, so stuck with prickles that they looked like hedgehogs. Yet this might have been borne with if the next dish had not been such that we had rather have starved then touched it: for when it was set upon the table, and as we thought, a fat goose, with fishes and all kind of fowl round it, 'Whatever you see here,' said Trimalchio 'is all made of the same substance' ...

Quoth Trimalchio: 'Let me so grow in estate not bulk, as my cook made all of this out of one hog; there is not an excellenter fellow than himself; he shall, if he please, make ye a poll of ling of sow's tripe; a wood-culver of fat bacon; a turtle of a spring of pork; and a hen of a collar of brawn.'...

One of Trimalchio's guests described a good dinner ...

'But,' said Trimalchio, 'what had ye to eat?' 'I'll tell ye,' quoth Habinas, 'as near as I can, for my memory is not so good, but that sometimes I forget my own name: However, for the first dish we had a goodly porker, with a garland upon him, and puddings, goose giblets, lamb-stones, sweetbreads, and gizzards round him; there were also beets and household-bread of his own baking, for himself, which I would rather have than white; it makes a man strong, and I never complain of what I like. The next was a cold tart, with excellent warm honey, and that Spanish, running upon it. I eat little of the tart, but more of the honey; I tasted also the red pulse, and lupines, by the advice of Calvus, and several apples, of which I took away two in my handkerchief: for if I bring home nothing to my little she slave, I shall have snubs enough: this dame of mine puts me often in mind of her. We had also on a sidetable the haunch of a bear, which Scintilla tasting ere she was aware, had like to have thrown up her guts: I on the other hand eat a pound of it or better, for methought it tasted like boar's flesh; and said I, if a bear eats a man, why may not a man much more eat a bear? To be short, we had cream cheese, wine boil'd off to a third part, fry'd snails, chitterlings, liver, eggs, turnips, mustard, and a bowl that held a gallon. Don't disturb me, Palamedes; there were also handled about a basket of sugarcakes, of which we wantonly took some, and set away the gammon of bacon . . .'

Porthos on Lamb

from The Vicomte de Bragelonne

by Alexandre Dumas

THE KING, meanwhile, had sat down to the suppertable, and the not very large number of guests invited for that day had taken their seats, after the usual gesture intimating the royal permission to be seated. At this period of Louis XIV's reign, although etiquette was not governed by the strict regulations which subsequently were adopted, the French court had entirely thrown aside the traditions of good-fellowship and patriarchal affability which still existed in the time of Henry IV, and which the suspicious mind of Louis XIII had gradually replaced by the ceremonial semblance of a grandeur which he despaired of being able fully to realize.

The king, then, was seated alone at a small separate table, which, like the desk of a president, overlooked the adjoining tables. Although we say a small table, we must not omit to add that this small table was yet the largest one there. Moreover, it was the one in which were placed the greatest number and variety of dishes—consisting of fish, game, meat, fruit, vegetables, and preserves. The king was young and vigorous, very fond of hunting, addicted to all violent exercises of the body, and possessed, besides, like all the members of the Bourbon family, a rapid digestion and an appetite speedily renewed. Louis XIV was a formidable table-companion. He delighted to criticize his cooks; but when he honored them by praise and commendation, the honor was overwhelming. The king began by eating several kinds of soup, either mixed together or taken separately. He intermingled, or rather he isolated, the soups with glasses of old wine. He ate quickly and somewhat greedily.

Porthos, who from the beginning had out of respect been waiting for a jab of D'Artagnan's elbow, seeing the king make such rapid progress, turned to the musketeer and said in a low tone, "It seems as if one might go on now; his Majesty is very encouraging in the example he sets. Look!"—"The king eats," said D'Artagnan, "but he talks at the same time. Try to manage matters in such a manner that if he should happen to address a remark to you, he would not find you with your mouth full, for that would be very awkward." —"The best way, in that case," said Porthos, "is to eat no supper at all. And yet, I am very hungry, I admit; and everything looks and smells most inviting, as if appealing to all my senses at once."

"Don't for a moment think of not eating," said D'Artagnan; "that would put his Majesty out terribly. The king has a habit of saying that he who works well eats well, and he does not like to have people eat daintily at his table."—"But how can I avoid having my mouth full if I eat?" said Porthos.

"All you have to do," replied the captain of the musketeers, "is simply to swallow what you have in it, whenever the king does you the honor to address a remark to you."—"Very good," said Porthos; and from that moment he began to eat with a well-bred enthusiasm.

The king occasionally looked at the different persons who were at table with him, and as a connoisseur would appreciate the different dispositions of his guests. "M. du Vallon!" he said. Porthos was enjoying a ragout of hare, and swallowed half the back. His name pronounced in such a manner made him start, and by a vigorous effort of his gullet he absorbed the whole mouthful. "Sire," replied Porthos, in a stifled voice, but sufficiently intelligible, nevertheless.

"Let that fillet of lamb be handed to M. du Vallon," said the king. "Do you like browned meats, M. du Vallon?"—"Sire, I like everything," replied Porthos. D'Artagnan whispered, "Everything your Majesty sends me." Porthos repeated, "Everything your Majesty sends me,"—an observation which the king apparently received with great satisfaction.

"People who eat well work well," replied the king, delighted to have opposite him a guest of Porthos's capacity. Porthos received the dish of lamb and put a portion of it on his plate. "Well?" said the king.—"Exquisite," said Porthos, calmly.—"Have you as good mutton in your part of the country, M. du Vallon?" continued the king.—"Sire," said Porthos, "I believe that from my own province, as everywhere else, the best of everything is sent to Paris for your Majesty's use; but, on the other hand, I do not eat mutton in the same way your Majesty does."

"Ah! and how do you eat it?"—"Generally, I have a lamb dressed quite whole."—"Quite whole?"—"Yes, Sire."—"In what manner, then?"—"In this, Sire: my cook, who is a German, first stuffs the lamb in question with small sausages which he procures from Troyes, and larks which he procures from Pithiviers; by some means or other, with which I am not acquainted, he bones the lamb as he would bone a fowl, leaving the skin on, however, which forms a brown crust all over the animal. When it is cut in beautiful slices, in the same way that one would cut an enormous sausage, a rose-colored gravy issues forth, which is as agreeable to the eye as it is exquisite to the palate"; and Porthos finished by smacking his lips.

The king opened his eyes with delight, and, while cutting some of the *faisan en daube*, which was handed to him, he said: "That is a dish I should very much like to taste, M. du Vallon. Is it possible? —a whole lamb!"—"Yes, Sire."—"Pass those pheasants to M. du Vallon; I perceive that he is a connoisseur." The order was obeyed. Then, continuing the conversation, he said, "And do you not find the lamb too fat?"—"No, Sire; the fat falls down at the same time that the gravy does, and swims on the surface; then the servant who carves removes the fat with a silver spoon, which I have had made expressly for that purpose."

"Where do you reside?" inquired the king.—"At Pierrefonds, Sire."—"At Pierrefonds; where is that, M. du Vallon,—near Belle-Isle?"—"Oh, no, Sire; Pierrefonds is in the Soissonais."—"I thought that you alluded to the mutton on account of the salt marshes."—"No, Sire; I have marshes which are not salt, it is true, but which are not the less valuable on that account."

The king had now arrived at the *entrées,* but without losing sight of Porthos, who continued to play his part in his best manner. "You have an excellent appetite, M. du Vallon," said the king, "and you make an admirable table-companion."—"Ah, Sire, if your Majesty were ever to pay a visit to Pierrefonds, we would both of us eat our lamb together; for your appetite is not an indifferent one, by any means."

D'Artagnan gave Porthos a severe kick under the table, which made Porthos color up. "At your Majesty's present happy age," said Porthos, in order to repair the mistake he had made, "I was in the musketeers, and nothing could ever satisfy me then. Your Majesty has an excellent appetite, as I have already had the honor of mentioning, but you select what you eat with too much refinement to be called a great eater."

The king seemed charmed at his guest's politeness. "Will you try some of these creams?" he said to Porthos.—"Sire, your Majesty treats me with far too much kindness to prevent me from speaking the whole truth."—"Pray do so, M. du Vallon."—"Well, Sire, with regard to sweet dishes, I recognize only pastry, and even that should be rather solid; all these frothy substances swell my stomach, and occupy a space which seems to me too precious to be so badly tenanted."—"Ah, Messieurs," said the king, indicating Porthos by a gesture, "here is indeed a perfect model of gastronomy. It was in such a manner that our fathers, who so well knew what good living was, used to eat; while we," added his Majesty, "can do nothing but trifle with our food"; and as he spoke he took a fresh plate of chicken, with ham, while Porthos attacked a ragout of partridges and land-rails.

The cup-bearer filled his Majesty's glass to the brim. "Give M. du Vallon some of my wine," said the king. This was one of the greatest honors of the royal table. D'Artagnan pressed his friend's knee. "If you can only manage to swallow the half of the boar's head I see yonder," said he to Porthos, "I shall believe that you will be a duke and a peer within the next twelve-months."—"Presently," said Porthos, phlegmatically; "I shall come to it by and by."

Dining with John Evelyn

from the Diary of John Evelyn, 1620-1706

I WENT this afternoon with several of the Royal Society to a supper which was all dressed, both fish and flesh, in Monsieur Papin's digestors, by which the hardest bones of beef itself, and mutton, were made as soft as cheese, without water or other liquor, and with less than eight ounces of coals, producing an incredible quantity of gravy; and for close of all, a jelly made of the bones of beef, the best for clearness and good relish, and the most delicious that I had ever seen, or tasted. We eat pike and other fish bones, and all without impediment; but nothing exceeded the pigeons, which tasted just as if baked in a pie, all these being stewed in their own juice, without any addition of water save what swam about the digestor, as *in balneo;* the natural juice of all these provisions acting on the grosser substances, reduced the hardest bones to tenderness; but it is best descanted, with more particulars for extracting tinctures, preserving and stewing fruit, and saving fuel, in Dr. Papin's book published and dedicated to our Society, of which he is a member. He is since gone to Venice with the late Resident here (and also a member of our Society), who carried this excellent mechanic, philosopher, and physician, to set up a philosophical meeting in that city. This philosophical supper caused much mirth amongst us, and exceedingly pleased all the company. I sent a glass of the jelly to my wife, to the reproach of all that the ladies ever made of their best hartshorn.

I saw the magnificent entry of the French Ambassador Colbert, received in the Banqueting House. I had never seen a richer coach than that which he came in to Whitehall. Standing by his Majesty at dinner in the presence, there was of that rare fruit called the King-pine, growing in Barbadoes and the West Indies; the first of them I had ever seen. His Majesty having cut it up, was pleased to give me a piece off his own plate to taste of; but, in my opinion, it falls short of those ravishing varieties of deliciousness described in Captain Ligon's History, and others; but possibly it might be, or certainly was, much impaired in coming so far; it has yet a grateful acidity, but tastes more like the quince and melon than of any other fruit he mentions.

A Noble Dinner

from the Diary of Samuel Pepys

So MY POOR WIFE rose by five o'clock in the morning, before day, and went to market and bought fowls and many other things for dinner, with which I was highly pleased, and the chine of beef was down also before six o'clock, and my own jack, of which I was doubtful, do carry it very well. Things being put in order, and the cook come, I went to the office, where we sat till noon and then broke up, and I home, whither by the by comes Dr. Clerke and his lady, his sister, and a she-cozen, and Mr. Pierce and his wife, which was all my guests. I had for them, after oysters, at first course, a hash of rabbits, a lamb, and a rare chine of beef. Next a great dish of roasted fowl, cost me about 30 s., and a tart, and then fruit and cheese. My dinner was noble and enough. I had my house mighty clean and neat; my room below with a good fire in it;

my dining-room above, and my chamber being made a withdrawing-chamber; and my wife's a good fire also. I find my new table very proper, and will hold nine or ten people well, but eight with great room. After dinner the women to cards in my wife's chamber, and the Dr. and Mr. Pierce in mine, because the dining-room smoked unless I keep a good charcoal fire, which I was not then provided with. At night to supper, had a good sack posset and cold meat, and sent my guests away about ten o'clock at night, both them and myself highly pleased with our management of this day; and indeed their company was very fine, and Mrs. Clerke a very witty, fine lady, though a little conceited and proud. So weary so to bed. I believe this day's feast will cost me near £5.

Dining with the Great Khan

from The Travels of Marco Polo

[The Tartars] subsist entirely upon flesh and milk, eating the produce of their sport, and a certain small animal, not unlike a rabbit, which during the summer season is found in great abundance in the plains. But they likewise eat flesh of every description, horses, camels, and even dogs, provided they are fat. They drink mares' milk, which they prepare in such a manner that it has the qualities and flavor of white wine.

They make provision also of milk thickened and dried to the state of a paste, which is prepared in the following manner: They boil the milk, and skimming off the rich or creamy part as it rises to the top, put it into a separate vessel as butter; for so long as that remains in the milk, it will not become hard. The latter is then exposed to the sun until it dries. Upon going on service they carry with them about ten pounds for each man, and of this, half a pound is put, every morning, into a leathern bottle, with as much water as is thought necessary. By their motion in riding the contents are violently shaken, and a thin porridge is produced, upon which they make their dinner . . .

When His Majesty holds a grand and public court, those who attend it are seated in the following order: The table of the sovereign is placed on an elevation, and he takes his seat on the northern side, with his face turned towards the south; and next to him, on his left hand, sits the Empress. On his right hand are placed his sons, grandsons, and other persons connected with him by blood, upon seats somewhat lower, so that their heads are on a level with the Emperor's feet. The other princes and the nobility have their places at still lower tables; and the same rules are observed with respect to the females, the wives of the sons, grandsons, and other relatives of the Great Khan being seated on the left hand, at tables in like manner gradually lower; then follow the wives of the nobility and military officers: so that all are seated according to their respective ranks and dignities, in the places assigned to them, and to which they are entitled.

The tables are arranged in such a manner that the Great Khan, sitting on his elevated throne, can overlook the whole. It is not, however, to be understood that all who assemble on such occasions can be accommodated at tables. The greater part of the officers, and even of the nobles, on the contrary, eat, sitting upon carpets, in the halls; and on the outside stand a great multitude of persons who come from different countries, and bring with them many rare curiosities.

In the middle of the hall, where the Great Khan sits at table, there is a magnificent piece of furniture, made in the form of a square coffer, each side of which is three paces in length, exquisitely carved in figures of animals, and gilt. It is hollow within, for the purpose of receiving a capacious vase, of pure gold, calculated to hold many gallons. On each of its four sides stands a smaller vessel, containing about a hogshead, one of which is filled with mare's milk, another with that of the camel, and so of the others, according to the kinds of beverage in use. Within this buffet are also the cups or flagons belonging to His Majesty, for serving the liquors. Some of them are of beautiful gilt plate. Their size is such that, when filled with wine or other liquor, the quantity would be sufficient for eight or ten men.

Before every two persons who have seats at the tables, one of these flagons is placed, together with a kind of ladle, in the form of a cup with a handle, also of plate; to be used not only for taking the wine out of the flagon, but for lifting it to the head. This is observed as well with respect to the women as the men. The quantity and richness of the plate belonging to His Majesty is quite incredible.

Officers of rank are likewise appointed whose duty it is to see that all strangers who happen to arrive at the time of the festival, and are unacquainted with the etiquette of the court, are suitably accommodated with places; and these stewards are continually visiting every part of the hall, inquiring of the guests if there is anything with which they are unprovided, or whether any of them wish for wine, milk, meat, or other articles, in which case it is immediately brought to them by the attendants.

At each door of the grand hall, or of whatever part the Great Khan happens to be in, stand two officers of a gigantic figure, one on each side, with staves in their hands, for the purpose of preventing persons from touching the threshold with their feet, and obliging them to step beyond it. If by chance any one is guilty of this offense, these janitors take from him his garment, which he must redeem for money; or, when they do not take the garment, they inflict on him such number of blows as they have authority for doing. But, as strangers may be unacquainted with the prohibition, officers are appointed to introduce and warn them. This precaution is used because touching the threshold is regarded as a bad omen. In departing from the hall, as some of the company may be affected by the liquor, it is impossible to guard against the accident, and the order is not then strictly enforced.

The numerous persons who attend at the sideboard of His Majesty, and who serve him with victuals and drink, are all obliged to cover their noses and mouths with handsome veils or cloths of worked silk, in order that his victuals or his wine may not be affected by their breath. When drink is called for by him, and the page in waiting has presented it, he retires three paces and kneels down, upon which the courtiers, and all who are present, in like manner make their prostration. At the same moment all the musical instruments, of which there is a numerous band, begin to play, and continue to do so until he has ceased drinking, when all the company recover their posture. This reverential salutation is made as often as His Majesty drinks. It is unnecessary to say anything of the victuals, because it may well be imagined that their abundance is excessive.

When the repast is finished, and the tables have been removed, persons of various descriptions enter the hall, and amongst these a troop of comedians and performers on different instruments. Also tumblers and jugglers, who exhibit their skill in the presence of the Great Khan, to the high amusement and gratification of all the spectators. When these sports are concluded, the people separate, and each returns to his own house.

My Lord Appetite

from Gargantua and Pantagruel

by François Rabelais

(*translated by Jacques LeClercq*)

MEANWHILE MY LORD APPETITE put in an appearance and they sat down most opportunely to table.

At the beginning of the meal, they listened to the reading of some agreeable chronicle of chivalry in ancient times, until Gargantua gave the signal for wine to be served. Then, if they wished, the reading went on or they could talk merrily together. Often they discussed the virtues, property, efficacy, and nature of what was served at table: bread, wine, water, salt, meat, fish, fruit, herbs, roots, and their preparation. Thus Gargantua soon knew all the relevant passages in Pliny's *Natural History* . . . in the grammarian

Athenaeus' *Deipnosophistes* or *The Banquet of the Sages*, which treats of flowers, fruits, and their various uses . . . in Dioscorides' famous medical treatises, the Bible of apothecaries . . . in the *Vocabularium* by Julius Pollux, a grammarian and sophist of Marcus Aurelius' day, who wrote of hunting and fishing . . . in Galen's numerous dissertations upon alimentation . . . in the works of Porphyrius, the third-century Greek author of a *Treatise upon Abstinence from Meat* . . . in Oppian's two poems, *Cynegetica* which deals with venery and *Halieutica* with angling . . . in *Of Healthy Diet* by Polybius of Cos, disciple and son-in-law of Hippocrates . . . in Heliodorus of Emesa, Syrian Bishop of Tricca and a celebrated novelist of the fourth century . . . in Aristotle's essays on natural history . . . in the Greek works upon animals by Claudius Aelianus, a Roman contemporary of Heliogabalus . . . and in various other tomes . . . Often for surer authority as they argued, they would have the book in question brought to the table. Gargantua so thoroughly and cogently learned and assimilated all he heard that no physician of his times knew one-half so much as he.

They discussed the lessons they had learned that morning and topped their meal off with quiddany, a sort of quince marmalade and an excellent digestive. After which Gargantua picked his teeth with a fragment of mastic, washed his hands and daubed his eyes with cool clear water, and instead of saying grace, sang the glory of God in noble hymns, composed in praise of divine bounty and munificence . . .

Now the digestion of foods is a most important matter. There is the first stage, which occurs in the stomach, where the viands are changed into chyle; the second, in the liver, where the chyle is transformed into blood; the third, in the habit of the body, where the blood is finally converted into the substance of each part. So, whilst Gargantua awaited the first stage of digestion, they made a thousand delightful instruments, drew geometrical figures, and even applied the principles of astronomy . . .

* * *

Thereupon supper was prepared, and in honor of the special occasion they added to the regular menu sixteen oxen, three heifers, thirty-two calves, sixty-three young kids, ninety-five wethers, three hundred milch-sows soaked in sweet wine, eleven-score partridges, seven hundred woodcocks, four hundred capons from Loudun and Cornouailles in Brittany, six thousand pullets and as many pigeons again, six hundred crammed hens, fourteen hundred young hares, three hundred and three bustards, and one thousand and seven fat capons. As for venison, all they could obtain was eleven wild boars sent by the Abbot of Turpenay, eighteen fallow deer presented by My Lord of Grandmont, and sevenscore pheasants from My Lord of Les Essards. In addition, there were dozens of ringdoves and riverfowl, ducks, drakes, bitterns, curlews, plovers, francolins, sheldrakes, Poitou woodcocks, lapwings, shovellers, herons, moorhens, storks, orange flamingos, cranes, geese, ptarmigans, turkey hens, prepared with quantities of soups, broths, sauces and stew.

Beyond all doubt, here were victuals aplenty, cooked to a turn by Grangousier's cooks Wolfsauce, Hotchpot, and Lickjuice. The stewards, Jockbottle, Guzzletun, and Clearglass, kept their beakers brimful with wine.

* * *

Drawing close to the Gastrolaters, I noticed that they were followed by cohorts of fat varlets, bearing baskets, hampers, dishes, bags, pots, and kettles. Mandocus in the lead, they advanced, singing God knows what *dithyrambics* (wild songs), *craepalcomes* (chants of drunken revelry), and *epoenons* (canticles of praise). Opening their baskets and pots, they offered up to their god all manner of gifts, as listed below.

White hippocras or spiced wine, with toasts and sippets . . . plain white bread and bread of the snowiest dough . . . *carbonados* or grilled meats of six different varieties . . . *couscous,* an Arabian stew . . . haslets, pluck and fry . . . fricassées of nine sorts . . . bread and dripping, bread and cheese . . . gravy soup, hotchpotch, and potroast . . . shortbread and household loaf . . . *cabirotado* or grilled viands . . . cold loins of veal, spiced with ginger, meat pies and broths flavored with bay leaves . . . marrow bones of beef with cabbage . . . salmagundi, which is a mixed dish of chopped meat and pickled herring, with oil, vinegar, pepper, and onions . . .

Next came sausages, caparisoned with choice mustard, chitterlings, smoked oxtongue, salted meats of various sorts, pork's back with peas, pig's haslets, blood sausages, brain sausages, Bolognas, hams, boars' heads, dried venison with turnips, chicken livers on the spit, olives-in-oil.

Next, they poured into his maw the following fare: shoulder of mutton with garlic, meat pies with hot sauce, pork chops with onion sauce, roast capons basted in their own dripping, spring capons . . . goose, kid, fawn and deer, hare and leveret, partridge and choice young partridges, pheasant and delicate young pheasants, peacock and toothsome young peacocks . . . stork and storklet, woodcock, snipe, ortolan, turkey; gobbler, hen and pullet . . . ringdove, wood pigeon, pork with wine sauce, duck with onion sauce, blackbird, rail heron and excellent young herons, bustard and wild turkey, fig-pecker or *beccafico,* and Italian warbler fed on sweet fruits . . . young guinea hen, plover, goose and gosling, rockdove, wild duck, mavis, and flamingo . . .

Then, they fed Gaster pies and pasties of venison, lark, dormouse, roebuck, pigeon, chamois, capon, and bacon . . . hogsfeet in lard, fried piecrust, stuffed capons, cheese, and juicy peaches . . . artichoke, sea grouse, crier, crane, egret, teal, diver and loon, bittern and stakedriver, curlew, wood duck, waterhen with leeks, hedgehog, kid, shoulder of mutton with caper sauce . . . beef royal, breast of veal, boiled chicken and stuffed capon with blancmange, pullet and pullen, rabbit and cony, waterfowl, cormorant, francolin, ringdove, cottontail, porcupine, rail . . .

Next, they filled him with pastries, including cream tarts, fruit squares, sweet biscuits, sugar plums, fritters, tarts of sixteen varieties, waffles, pancakes, quince rolls, curds and cream, whipped cream, preserved myrobalans or prunes, and jellies.

And, finally, seventy-eight species of dry and liquid preserves and jams, sweetmeats of one hundred different colors, cream cakes, and light confections.

Apuleius Eats Well

from The Golden Asse
by Lucius Apuleius

When night came that Supper was done, and their business ended, they would bring many good morsels into their Chamber for themselves. One would bring Pigs, Chickens, Fish, and other good meates, the other fine bread, pastries, tarts, custards and other delicate Junkets dipped in honey. And when they had shut their Chamber doore, and went to the baines: (O Lord) how I would fill my guts with these goodly dishes: neither was I so much a foole, or so very an Asse, to leave the dainty meates, and to grind my teeth upon hard hay. In this sort I continued a great space, for I played the honest Asse, taking but a little of one dish, and a little of another, whereby no man distrusted me. In the end I was hardier and began to devour the whole messe of the sweet delicates, which caused the Baker and the Cooke to suspect, howbeit they nothing mistrusted me, but searched about to apprehend the theefe . . .

In the meane season, while I was fed with dainty morsels, I gathered together my flesh, my skin waxed soft, my hair began to shine, and was gallant on every part, but such faire and comely shape of my body, was cause of my dishonor, for the Baker and Cooke marveled to see me so slick and fine considering I did eat no hay at all. Wherefore on a time at their accustomed houre, they went to the baines and locked their Chamber doore. It fortuned that ere they departed away, they espied me through a hole, how I fell roundly to my victuals: then they marveled greatly and little esteemed the loss of their meate . . .

Then I perceiving every man laugh, was nothing abashed, but rather more bold, whereby I never rested eating, till such time as the master of the house commanded me to be brought into his parlor as a novelty, and there caused all kind of meates which were never touched to be set on the table, which I did greedily devour and made a cleane riddance of all the delicate meates. And to prove my nature wholly, they gave me such meates as every Asse doth abhorre: for they put before me beefe and vinegar, birds and pepper, fish and verjuice . . . Then one of the servants of the house said to his master, I pray you sir, give him some drink to his supper: Marry (quoth hee) I think thou saist true, for it may be that to his meate hee would drinke likewise a cup of wine. Hoe boy, wash yonder pot, and fill it with wine which done, carry it to the Asse, and say that I have drunke to him . . . But I (as soone as I beheld the cup) staied not long, but gathering my lips together, supped up all the wine at one draught. The master being right joyfull hereat caused the Baker and Cooke which had bought me to come before him, to whom he delivered four times as much for me as they paid.

A Banquet

from The Decameron

by Giovanni Boccaccio

AT EVERY time we were assembled together . . . you are not able to imagine what sumptuous hangings of tapestrie did adorn the Hall where we sate at meate, the Tables covered in such Royall manner, waited on my numberless noble and goodly attendants, both women and men, serving readily, at each man's command of the company. The Basins, Ewers, Pots, Flagons, and all the vessels else which stood before, and for the service of our diet being composed onely of Gold and Silver, and out of no worse did we both eate and drink: the viands being very rare and dainty, abounding in plenty and variety, according to the appetite of everie person, as nothing could be wished for but it was instantly obtained.

In good sadness, Sir, I am not able to remember and tell you (within the compass of a thousand years) what and how manie severall kindes of Musicall Instruments were continually played on before us: what multiplicity of wax lights burned in all partes of the roomes; neither the excessive store of rich Drugs, Marchpanes, Comfites, and rare Banquetting stuffe, consumed there at one Feasting, wherein there wanted no bounty of the best and purest wines . . .

Not any one man among us, but appeared by his apparell equall to the greatest Emperor on the earth, his robe most sumptuously embroidered with precious stones, Pearles, and Carbuncles, as the world affordeth not the like. But above all the rest, the delights and pleasures there are beyond my capacity to expresse, or (indeede) any comparison: as namely, store of goodly and beautifull women, brought hither from all parts of the world: always provided if men bee desirous of their company . . .

Now I am further to tell you, that after we have tasted a Cup of precious Wine, fed on a few delicate Comfites, and danced a dance or two to the rare Musicke: everyone taketh a Lady by the hand, of whom he pleaseth to make his election, and she conducteth him to her Chamber, in very grave and gracious manner. Concerning the Chambers there, each of them resembleth a Paradise to looke on, they are so faire and goodly, and no lesse odiferous in smell, than the sweetest perfumes in your Apothecaries shoppes, or the rare compounds of Spices, when they are beaten in an open mortar. And as for the Beds, they are infinitely richer, than the very costliest belonging to the Duke of Venice: yet (in such) each man is appointed to take his rest, the Musicke of rare Cymbals lasting all night long, much better to be by you considered, than in my rude eloquence expressed.

Adage

"Grace for supper, and grace for dinner,
Or you'll justly be thought a graceless sinner."

Salmon in May

from Crotchet Castle
by Thomas Love Peacock

The Rev. Dr. Folliott: Here is a very fine salmon before me: and May is the very *point nommé* to have salmon in perfection. There is a fine turbot close by, and there is much to be said in his behalf; but salmon in May is the king of fish.

Mr. Crotchet: That salmon before you, doctor, was caught in the Thames this morning.

Mr. MacQuedy: Eh! sir, on its own ground, your Thames salmon has two virtues over all others: first, that it is fresh; and, second, that it is rare; for I understand you do not take half-a-dozen in a year.

The Rev. Dr. Folliott: In some years, sir, not one. Mud, filth, gas dregs, lock-weirs, and the march of mind, developed in the form of poaching, have ruined the fishery. But when we do catch a salmon, happy the man to whom he falls.

Mr. MacQuedy: I confess, sir, this is excellent; but I cannot see why it should be better than a Tweed salmon at Kelso.

The Rev. Dr. Folliott: Sir, I will take a glass of Hock with you.

Mr. MacQuedy: With all my heart, sir. There are several varieties of the salmon genus: but the common salmon, the *salmo salar*, is only one species, one and the same everywhere, just like the human mind. Locality and education make all the difference.

Mr. Crocket, Jun.: Champagne, doctor?

The Rev. Dr. Folliott: Most willingly. But you will permit my drinking it while it sparkles. I hold it a heresy to let it deaden in my hand, while the glass of my *compotator* is being filled on the opposite side of the table. By-the-by, captain, you remember a passage in Athenaeus, where he cites Menander on the subject of fish sauce: (The captain was aghast for an answer that would satisfy both his neighbours, when he was relieved by the divine continuing.) The science of fish sauce, Mr. MacQuedy, is by no means brought to perfection; a fine field of discovery still lies open in that line.

Mr. MacQuedy: Nay, sir, beyond lobster sauce, I take it ye cannot go.

The Rev. Dr. Folliott: In their line, I grant you, oyster and lobster sauce are the pillars of Hercules. But I speak of the cruet sauces, where the quintessence of the sapid is condensed in a phial. I can taste in my mind's palate a combination, which, if I could give it reality, I would christen with the name of my college, and hand it down to posterity as a seat of learning indeed.

Chapter Two

EUTERPE DINES

Lyric poetry abounds with so much metrical talk of food that it is difficult to choose anything more than a small, representative selection, which the poems collected here comprise.

Plato's philosophic contemplation of the table is followed by a brief selection from Chaucer, then by a curiosity, an anonymous description of a fourteenth century feast. Porphyro's feast prepared for the fair Madeline on St. Agnes' Eve is too well known to require comment, except to say that the nice balance of passion and food seems credible only in the immortal hands of John Keats. It is a far lyric cry from Keats to the Reverend Sydney Smith's poetic recipe for roasting mutton.

Thomas Love Peacock's celebration of a fish feast has a timeless nostalgia about it, as well as a fine English flavor, and the chapter closes with Dr. King's directions for dessert without cheese, which is in reality a lyric salute to the end of a good meal.

Nor can I deem
Aught more delightful than the general joy
Of a whole people, when the assembled guests,
Seated in order in the royal hall,
Are listening to the minstrel, while the board
Is spread with bread and meats, and from the jars
The cup-bearer draws wine and fills the cups.
To me there is no more delightful sight.

—Plato

"To boille the chiknes with the marybones,
And poudre-marchant tart and galyngale;
Wel koude he knowe draughte of Londoun ale;
He koude rooste and sethe and boille and frye,
Maken mortreux and wel bake a pye . . .
For blankmanger, that made he with the bests."

—Geoffrey Chaucer

A Fourteenth Century Feast

(*Anonymous*)

The boar's head shall be brought with bays aloft,
Bucktails full broad in broths therewithal,
Venison with the fruments, and pheasants full rich,
Baked meats near by, on the board well set,
Chewets of chopped flesh, and chickens grilled;
Each several guest has six men's share.
Were this not enough, another course follows,
Roasts with rich sauces and royal spice,
Kids cleft in the back, quartered swans,
Tarts of ten inches, it tortures my heart
To see the board o'er-spread with blazing dishes,
As a rood arrayed with rings and with stones.
The third mess to me were a marvel to tell,
For all is Martinmass meat that I mostly know of,
Nought but worts with flesh-meat, without wild fowl,
Save a hen unto him that the house owneth;
And ye will have basted birds broach'd on a spit,
Baracle-geese and bitterns, and many billed snipes,
Larks and linnets, lapp'd in sugar,
Woodcocks and woodpeckers, full warm and hot,
Teals and titmice, to take what you please;
Caudels of conies, and custards sweet,
Dariols and dishmeats, that dearly cost,
Maumeny, as men call it, your maws to fill. . . .

The Feast of St. Agnes

from The Eve of St. Agnes
by John Keats

A CASEMENT high and triple-arch'd there was,
All garlanded with carven imag'ries
Of fruit, and flowers, and bunches of knot-grass . . .

Full on this casement shone the wintry moon,
And threw warm gules on Madeline's fair breast
As down she knelt for heaven's grace and boon . . .

Soon, trembling in her soft and chilly nest,
In sort of wakeful swoon, perplex'd she lay.
Until the poppied warmth of sleep oppress'd
Her soothed limbs, and soul fatigued away . . .

Stol'n to this paradise, and so entranced,
Porphyro gazed upon her empty dress,
And listened to her breathing, if it chanced
To wake into a slumberous tenderness . . .

Then by the bedside, where the faded moon
Made a dim, silver twilight, soft he set
A table, and half anguish'd threw thereon
A cloth of woven crimson, gold and jet . . .

And still she slept, an azure-lidded sleep,
In blanched linen, smooth and lavender'd,
While he from forth the closet brought a heap
Of candied apple, quince, and plum, and gourd:
With jellies soother than the creamy curd,
And lucent syrops, tinct with cinnamon;
Manna and dates, in argosy transferr'd
From Fez; and spiced dainties, every one,
From silken Samarkand to cedared Lebanon.

These delicates he heap'd with glowing hand
On golden dishes and in baskets bright
Of wreathed silver: sumptuous they stand
In the retired quiet of the night,
Filling the chilly room with perfume light.
"And now, my love, my seraph fair, awake!
Thou art my heaven, and I thy eremite;
Open thine eyes, for meek St. Agnes' sake."

Receipt to Roast Mutton

by the Reverend Sydney Smith

GENTLY STIR and blow the fire,
Lay the mutton down to roast,
Dress it quickly, I desire;
In the dripping put a toast,
That I hunger may remove;—
Mutton is the meat I love.

On the dresser see it lie;
Oh! the charming white and red!
Finer meat ne'er met the eye,
On the sweetest grass it fed;
Let the jack do swiftly round
Let me have it nicely brown'd.

On the table spread the cloth,
Let the knives be sharp and clean,
Pickles get and salad both,
Let them each be fresh and green.
With small beer, good ale, and wine,
O ye gods! how I shall dine!

Fish Feast

by Thomas Love Peacock

ALL DAY we sat, until the sun went down—
'Twas summer, and the Dog-star scorched the town—
At famed Blackwell, O Thames! upon thy shore,
Where Lovegrove's tables groan beneath their store;
We feasted full on every famous dish,
Dress'd many ways, of sea and river fish—
Perch, mullet, eels, and salmon, all were there,
And whitebait, daintiest of our fishy fare;
Then meat of many kinds, and venison last,
Quails, fruits, and ices, crowned the rich repast.
Thy fields, Champagne, supplied us with our wine,
Madeira's Island, and the rocks of Rhine.
The sun was set, and twilight veiled the land:
Then all stood up,—all who had strength to stand,
And pouring down, of Maraschino, fit
Libations to the gods of wine and wit,
In steam-wing'd chariots, and on iron roads,
Sought the great city, and our own abodes.

Dessert Without Cheese

MAKE YOUR TRANSPARENT sweet-meats truly nice,
With Indian sugar and Arabian spice;
And let your various creams encircl'd be
With swelling fruit just ravished from the tree.
Let plates and dishes be from China brought,
With lively paint and earth transparent wrought.
The feast now done, discourses are renewed,
And witty arguments with mirth pursu'd;
The cheerful master mid his jovial friends,
His glass to their best wishes recommends.
The grace-cup follows to his sovereign's health,
And to his country plenty, peace and wealth.
Performing then the piety of grace,
Each man that pleases reassumed his place.

—DR. KING, *The Art of Cookery*

Chapter Three

THE ENGLISH CUISINE

IT IS FASHIONABLE to regard the English cuisine today as execrable, compounded of soggy meat pies and dreadful boiled dishes. Even the traditional "roast beef of old England" has come to be regarded as a legend dispelled by generations of bad cooking offered to critical European and American travelers. Much of this is nonsense, of course. Provincial English cooking is doubtless no worse than it is in any other country, and in the great restaurants of London it is quite possible to find the *haute cuisine* available in most Western capitals.

The bad reputation of English cooking is harder to understand when one surveys the vast array of writing about food in English literature. No nation in modern times has written about its food with such gusto, not even the French, to whom food is more in the nature of a religion. One does not make fun of religion, and so there is a great deal more reverence than humor in French writing about food. But the English novelists and memoirists, particularly those of the nineteenth century, write with gaiety and gusto of their victuals, and occasionally with the special gift for social satire which seems to be a national talent.

Most of these English attributes are to be found in the works of William Makepeace Thackeray, that prolific chronicler of his country's life and manners. In the excerpts chosen here, Thackeray is at his best in the blend of gastronomy and love which is one of his many excellencies. In the account of his best beefsteak, he discloses himself as the complete trencherman, in whom food and love have become inextricably intermingled. "Memorials of Gourmandizing" is, indeed, a tasty monument to his lifelong love affair with food, and it is a pity it is not better known.

"The Haunch was a picture for painters to study,
The fat was so white, and the lean was so ruddy,
Tho' my stomach was sharp, I could scarce help regretting
To spoil such a delicate picture by eating."

—OLIVER GOLDSMITH, *Haunch of Venison*

Ottilia and the Oysters

from Fitz-Boodle's Confessions
by W. M. Thackeray

THE KEEN AIR has given me an appetite," said the dear angel, as we entered the supper-room; and to say the truth, fairy as she was, she made a remarkably good meal—consuming a couple of basins of white soup, several kinds of German sausages, some Westphalia ham, some white pudding, an anchovy-salad made with cornichons and onions, sweets innumerable, and a considerable quantity of old Steinwein and rum-punch afterwards. Then she got up and danced as brisk as a fairy; in which operation I, of course, did not follow her, but had the honor, at the close of the evening's amusement, once more to have her by my side in the sledge, as we swept in the moonlight over the snow. Kalsbraten is a very hospitable place as far as tea-parties are concerned, but I never was in one where dinners were so scarce. At the palace they occurred twice or thrice in a month; but on these occasions spinsters were not invited, and I seldom had the opportunity of seeing my Ottilia except at evening parties.

Nor are these, if the truth must be told, very much to my taste. Dancing I have foresworn, whist is too severe a study for me, and I do not like to play écarté with old ladies, who are sure to cheat you in the course of an evening's play.

But to have an occasional glance at Ottilia was enough; and many and many a napoleon did I lose to her Mamma, Madame de Schlippenschlopp, for the blest privilege of looking at her daughter. Many is the tea-party I went to, shivering into cold clothes after dinner (which is my abomination) in order to have one little look at the lady of my soul.

At these parties there were generally refreshments of a nature more substantial than mere tea—punch, both milk and rum, hot wine, consommé, and a peculiar and exceedingly disagreeable sandwich made of a mixture of cold white puddings and garlic, of which I have forgotten the name and always detested the savor.

Gradually the conviction came upon me that Ottilia ate a great deal.

I do not dislike to see a woman eat comfortably. I even think that an agreeable woman ought to be "*friande,*" and should love certain little dishes and knickknacks. I know that though at dinner they commonly take nothing, they have roast-mutton with the children at two, and laugh at their pretensions to starvation.

No! A woman who eats a grain of rice, like Amina in the "Arabian Nights," is absurd and unnatural; but there is a "modus in rebus": there is no reason why she should be a ghoul, a monster, an ogress, a horrid gormandiseress—faugh!

It was then, with a rage amounting almost to agony, that I found Ottilia ate too much at every meal. She was always eating, and always eating too much. If I went there in the morning, there was the horrid familiar odor of those oniony sandwiches; if in the afternoon, dinner had been just removed, and I was choked by reeking reminiscences of roast-meat. Tea we have spoken of . . . She gobbled up more cakes than any six people present; then came the supper and the sandwiches again, and the egg-flip and the horrid rum-punch.

She was as thin as ever, paler if possible than ever:—but, by heavens! her nose began to grow red!

Mon Dieu! How I used to watch and watch it! Some days it was purple, some days had more of the vermilion—I could take an affadavit that after a heavy night's supper it was more swollen, more red, than before.

I recollect one night when we were playing a round game (I had been looking at her nose very eagerly and sadly for some time), she of herself brought up the conversation about eating, and confessed that she had five meals a day.

"*That accounts for it!*" says I, flinging down the cards, and springing up and rushing like a madman out of the room. I rushed away into the night, and wrestled with my passion. "What! Marry," said I, "a woman who eats meat twenty-one times in a week, besides breakfast and tea. Marry a sarcophagus, a cannibal, a butcher's shop?—Away!" I strove and strove. I drank, I groaned, I wrestled and fought with my love—but it overcame me: one look at those eyes brought me to her feet again. I yielded myself up like a slave: I fawned and whined for her; I thought her nose was not so *very* red . . .

At this juncture the town of Hamburg sent his Highness the Grand Duke . . . a singular present: no less than a certain number of barrels of oysters . . .

In honor of the oysters and the new commercial treaty . . . his Highness announced a grand supper and ball, and invited all the quality of all the principalities round about. It was a splendid affair: the grand saloon brilliant with hundreds of uniforms and brilliant toilettes—not the least beautiful among them, I need not say, was Ottilia.

At midnight the supper-rooms were thrown open, and we formed into little parties of six, each having a table, nobly served with plate, a lacquey in attendance, and a gratifying ice-pail or two of champagne to *égayer* the supper. It was no small cost to serve five hundred people on silver, and the repast was certainly a princely and magnificent one . . .

The first course, of course, consisted of the oysters. Ottilia's eyes gleamed with double brilliancy as the lacquey opened them. There were nine apiece for us—how well I recollect the number!

I never was much of an oyster-eater, nor can I relish them *in naturabilis* as some do, but require a quantity of sauces, lemons, cayenne peppers, bread and butter, and so forth, to render them palatable.

By the time I had made my preparations, Ottilia, the captains, and the two ladies, had well-nigh finished theirs. Indeed Ottilia had gobbled up all hers, and there were only mine left in the dish.

I took one—IT WAS BAD. The scent of it was enough—they were all bad. Ottilia had eaten nine bad oysters.

I put down the horrid shell. Her eyes glistened more and more; she could not take them off the tray.

"Dear Herr George," she said, "*will you give me your oysters?*"

She had them all down—before I could say Jack Robinson! . . .

I left Kalsbraten that night, and have never been there since.

A White Dinner

from Pendennis

by W. M. Thackeray

I DECLARED MYSELF to her," said Alcide, laying his hand on his heart, "in a manner which was as novel as I am charmed to think it was agreeable. Where cannot Love penetrate, respectable Madame Frisbi? Cupid is the father of the invention! I inquired of the domestics what were the *plats* of which Mademoiselle partook with most pleasure; and built up my little battery accordingly. On a day when her parents had gone to dine in the world (and I am grieved to say that a grosser dinner in a restaurant, on the Boulevard, or in the Palais-Royal, seemed to form the delights of these unrefined persons), the charming Miss entertained some comrades of the pension; and I advised myself to send up a little repast suitable to so delicate young palates. Her lovely name is Blanche. The veil of the maiden is white, the wreath of roses she wears is white. I determined that my dinner should be as spotless as the snow. At her accustomed hour, and instead of the rude *gigot à l'eau* which was ordinarily served at her too simple table, I sent her up a little *potage à la Reine Blanche,* I called it—as white as her own tint—and confectioned with the most fragrant cream and almonds. I then offered up at her shrine a *filet de merlan à l'agnès,* and a delicate *plat,* which I have designated as *Éperlan à la Sainte Thérèse,* and of which my charming Miss partook with pleasure. I followed this by two little *entrées* of sweetbread and chicken; and the only brown thing which I permitted myself in the entertainment was a little roast of lamb, which I laid in a meadow of spinaches, surrounded with *croustillons,* representing sheep, and ornamented with daisies and other savage flowers. After this came my second service: a pudding *à la Reine Élisabeth* (who, Madame Frisbi knows, was a maiden princess); a dish of opal-colored plover's eggs, which I called *Nid de tourtereaux à la Roucoule;* placing in the midst of them two of those tender volatiles, billing each other, and confectioned with butter; a basket containing little *gâteaux* of apricots, which, I know, all young ladies adore; and a jelly of marasquin, bland, insinuating, intoxicating as the glance of beauty. This I designated *Ambroisie de Calypso à la Souveraine de mon Coeur*. And when the ice was brought in—an ice of *plombière* and cherries—how do you think I had shaped them, Madame Frisbi? In the form of two hearts united with an arrow, on which I had laid, before it entered, a bridal veil in cut paper, surmounted by a wreath of virginal orange-flowers. I stood at the door to watch the effect of this entry. It was but one cry of admiration. The three young ladies filled their glasses with the sparkling Ay, and carried me in a toast. I heard it, I heard Miss speak of me—I heard her say, 'Tell Monsieur Mirobolant that we thank him—we admire him—we love him!' My feet almost failed me as she spoke."

Fashionable London Dining in the Time of Swift

from The Four Georges
by W. M. Thackeray

When Lord Sparkish, Tom Neverout, and Colonel Allwit, the immortal personages of Swift's polite conversation, came to breakfast with my Lady Smart, at eleven o'clock in the morning, my Lord Smart was absent at the levée. His Lordship was at home to dinner at three o'clock to receive his guests; and we may sit down to this meal like the Barmecides's, and see the fops of the last century before us. Seven of them sat down at dinner, and were joined by a country baronet who told them they kept court hours. These persons of fashion began their dinner with a sirloin of beef, fish, a shoulder of veal, and a tongue. My Lady Smart carved the sirloin, my Lady Answerall helped the fish and the gallant Colonel cut the shoulder of veal. All made a considerable inroad on the sirloin and the shoulder of veal, with the exception of Sir John, who had no appetite, having already partaken of a beefsteak and two mugs of ale, besides a tankard of March beer as soon as he got out of bed. They drank a claret, which the Master of the house said should always be drunk after fish; and my Lord Smart particularly recommended some excellent cider to my Lord Sparkish, which occasioned some brilliant remarks from that nobleman. When the host called for wine, he nodded to one or other of his guests, and said "Tom Neverout, my service to you."

After the first course came almond-pudding, fritters, which the Colonel took with his hands out of the dish, in order to help the brilliant Miss Notable; chickens, black puddings, and soup; and the Lady Smart, the elegant mistress of the mansion, finding a skewer in a dish, placed it in her plate, with directions that it should be carried down to the cook and dressed for the cook's own dinner. Wine and small beer were drunk during this second course; and when the Colonel called for beer, he called the butler Friend, and asked whether the beer was good. Various jocular remarks passed from gentlefolk to the servants; at breakfast several persons had a word and a joke for Mrs. Betty, my lady's maid, who warmed the cream and had charge of the canister (the tea cost thirty shillings a pound in those days). When my Lady Sparkish sent her footman out to my Lady Match to come at six o'clock and play at quadrille, her ladyship warned the man to follow his nose, and if he fell by the way, not to stay to get up again. And when the gentleman asked the hall-porter if his lady was at home, that functionary replied, with manly waggishness, "She was at home just now, but she's not gone out yet."

After the pudding, sweet and black, the fritters and soup, came the third course, of which the chief dish was a hot venison pasty, which was put before Lord Smart, and carved by that nobleman. Besides the pasty, there was a hare, a rabbit, some pigeons, partridge, a goose, and a ham. Beer and wine were freely imbibed during this course, the gentlemen always pledging somebody, with every glass which they drank; and by this time the conversation between Tom

Neverout and Miss Notable had grown so brisk and lively, that the Derbyshire baronet began to think the young gentlewoman was Tom's sweetheart; on which Miss remarked, that she loved Tom "like pie." After the goose, some of the gentlemen took a dram of brandy, "which was very good for the wholesomes," Sir John said; and now having had a tolerably substantial dinner, honest Lord Smart bade the butler bring up the great tankard full of October to Sir John. The great tankard was passed from hand to hand and mouth to mouth, but when pressed by the noble host upon the gallant Tom Neverout, he said, "No, faith, my lord, I like your wine, and won't put a churl upon a gentleman. Your honor's claret is good enough for me." And so, the dinner over, the host said, "Hang saving, bring us up a ha'porth of cheese . . ."

The cloth was now taken away, and a bottle of Burgundy was set down, of which the ladies were invited to partake before they went to their tea. When they withdrew, the gentlemen promised to join them in an hour: fresh bottles were brought; the "dead men" meaning the empty bottles, removed; and "d'you hear, John? bring clean glasses," my Lord Smart said. On which the gallant Colonel Allwit said, "I'll keep my glass; for wine is the best liquor to wash glasses in."

Becky Sharp Attempts the Indian Cuisine

from Vanity Fair

by W. M. Thackeray

DOWNSTAIRS, then they went, Joseph very red and blushing, Rebecca very modest, and holding her green eyes downwards. She was dressed in white with bare shoulders as white as snow—the picture of youth, unprotected innocence, & humble, virgin simplicity. "I must be very quiet," thought Rebecca, "and very much interested about India."

Now we have heard how Mrs. Sedley had prepared a fine curry for her son, just as he liked it, and in the course of dinner a portion of this dish was offered to Rebecca. "What is it?" said she, turning an appealing look to Mr. Joseph.

"Capital," said he. His mouth was full of it; his face quite red with the delightful exercise of gobbling. "Mother, it's as good as my own curries in India."

"Oh, I must try some, if it is an Indian dish," said Miss Rebecca. "I am sure everything must be good that comes from there."

"Give Miss Sharp some curry, my dear," said Mr. Sedley laughing.

Rebecca had never tasted the dish before.

"Do you find it as good as everything else from India?" said Mr. Sedley.

"Oh, excellent," said Rebecca, who was suffering tortures with the cayenne pepper.

"Try a chili with it, Miss Sharp," said Joseph, really interested.

"A chili!" said Rebecca gasping, "Oh, yes!" She thought a chili was something cool, as its name imported, and was served some. "How fresh and green they look," she said, and put one into her mouth. It was hotter than the curry; flesh and blood could bear it no longer. She laid down her fork. "Water, for Heaven's sake, water!" she cried. Mr. Sedley burst out laughing (he was a coarse man from the Stock Exchange, where they love all sorts of practical jokes). "They are real Indian, I assure you," said he. "Sambo, give Miss Sharp some water."

The paternal laugh was echoed by Joseph, who thought the joke capital. The ladies only smiled a little, they thought poor Rebecca suffered too much. She would have liked to choke old Sedley, but she swallowed her mortification, as well as she had the abominable curry before it, and as soon as she could speak said with a comical, good-humored air—

"I ought to have remembered the pepper which the Princess of Persia puts in the cream-tarts in the Arabian Nights. Do you put cayenne into your cream-tarts in India, Sir?"

Old Sedley began to laugh, and thought Rebecca was a good-humored girl. Joseph simply said, "Cream-tarts, Miss? Our cream is very bad in Bengal. We generally use goat's milk, and gad! do you know, I've got to prefer it!"

"You won't like *everything* from India now, Miss Sharp," said the old gentleman; but when the ladies had retired after dinner, the wily old fellow said to his son, "Have a care, Joe, that girl is setting her cap at you."

Thackeray's Best Beefsteak

from Memorials of Gourmandizing

by W. M. Thackeray

AFTER THE SOUP, we had what I do not hesitate to call the very best beefsteak I ever ate in my life. By the shade of Heliogabalus! as I write about it now, a week after I have eaten it, the old, rich, sweet, piquant, juicy taste comes smacking on my lips again; and I feel something of that exquisite sensation I then had. I am ashamed of the delight which the eating of that piece of meat caused me. G---- and I had quarreled about the soup (I said so, and don't wish to return to the subject); but when we began on the steak, we looked at each other, and loved each other. We did not speak,—our hearts were too full for that; but we took a bit, and laid down our forks, and looked at one another, and understood each other. There were no two individuals on this wide earth,—no two lovers billing in the shade,—no mother clasping baby to her heart, more supremely happy than we. Every now and then, we had a glass of honest, firm, generous Burgundy, that nobly supported the meat. As you may fancy, we did not leave a single morsel of the steak; but when it was done, we put bits of bread into the silver dish, and wistfully sopped up the gravy. I suppose I shall never in this world taste anything so good again. But what then? What if I *did* like it excessively? Was my liking unjust or unmanly? Is my regret now puling or unworthy? No. "Laudo manentem!" as Titmouse says. When it is eaten, I resign myself, and can eat a two-franc dinner at Richard's without ill-humor and without a pang.

THE SECTION that follows begins with two dippings from the biography that reveals as much of the biographer as of his subject. There is a great deal of eating in Boswell's "Life", but most of the enjoyment of it seems to be in Johnson's capacious belly. Boswell may eat as much, but he does not have the doctor's intellectual appreciation of food. It may be that Boswell was so preoccupied with himself and sex that he found food a minor satisfaction. But as he truly remarks of Johnson, "No man eat more heartily . . . , or loved better what was nice and delicate . . ."

We will find Boswell and Johnson dining together several other times in these pages.

Easter Sunday with Johnson

from The Life of Samuel Johnson

by James Boswell

TO MY GREAT surprise he asked me to dine with him on Easter Day. I never supposed that he had a dinner at his house; for I had not then heard of any one of his friends having been entertained at his table. He told me, "I generally have a meat pie on Sunday: it is baked at a public oven, which is very properly allowed, because one man can attend it; and thus the advantage is obtained of not keeping servants from Church to dress dinners."

April 11, being Easter Sunday, after having attended divine service at St. Paul's, I repaired to Dr. Johnson's. I had gratified my curiosity much in dining with Jean Jacques Rousseau, while he lived in the wilds of Neufchâtel: I had as great a curiosity to dine with Dr. Samuel Johnson, in the dusky recess of a court in Fleet Street. I supposed we should have knives and forks, and only some strange, uncouth, ill-drest dish: but I found everything in very good order. We had no other company but Mrs. Williams and a young woman whom I did not know. As a dinner here was considered a singular phenomenon, and as I was frequently interrogated on the subject, my readers may perhaps be desirous to know our bill of fare. Foote, I remember, in allusion to Francis, the *negro,* was willing to suppose that our repast was *black broth*. But the fact was, that we had a very good soup, a boiled leg of lamb and spinach, a veal pie, and a rice pudding.

A Fine Veal

from The Life of Samuel Johnson

by James Boswell

THE CHEERING round of 'Dinner is upon the table' dissolved his reverie, and we all sat down without any symptom of ill-humor. There were present, beside Mr. Wilkes, and Mr. Arthur Lee, who was an old companion of mine when he studied physick at Edinburgh, Mr. (now Sir John) Miller, Dr. Lettsom, and Mr. Slater the druggist. Mr. Wilkes placed himself next to Dr. Johnson, and behaved to him with so much attention and politeness, that he gained upon him insensibly. No man eat more heartily than Johnson, or loved better what was nice and delicate. Mr. Wilkes was very assiduous in helping him to some fine veal. 'Pray give me leave, Sir: —It is better here—A little of the brown—Some fat, Sir—A little of the stuffing—Some gravy—Let me have the pleasure of giving you some butter—Allow me to recommend a squeeze of this orange; —or the lemon, perhaps, may have more zest.'—'Sir, Sir, I am obliged to you, Sir,' cried Johnson, bowing, and turning his head to him with a look for some time of 'surly virtue,' but, in a short while, of complacency.

Now follows an excursion into various quarters of eighteenth and nineteenth century England, beginning with a first visit to the pages of a magazine called "The Original", a weekly published in 1836 by an estimable gentleman named Thomas Walker, who deserves to be better known. He was a lawyer, a gourmet, a lover of refined pleasure. If there is little humor in his writing, it is nevertheless amiable and filled with a nice appreciation of living. The little weekly he wrote and published, "The Original", had a short life; it ran twenty-nine weeks, until death ended the life of its proprietor. But its short pieces, ranging over a varied list of topics, were entertaining, if minor, examples of the essayist's art which flowered in that century. The whitebait dinner is one of the more famous.

Leaving lawyer Walker, we join an old friend, Robinson Crusoe, whose meals were hardly epicurean but who gloried in and gave thanks to a bountiful Nature that provided him with a full table and averted starvation. Then we are in Anthony Trollope's England, luxuriating in another kind of bounty that shows us how the clergy of Barsetshire, unlike those of America, lived in an Episcopalian luxury appalling to a Baptist. The Abbot lived even better at Strawberry Hill, as a sample of Walpole's voluminous accounting demonstrates. How austere Lord Byron's diet appears by comparison —and how much of the times his deception about it discloses.

That the supposedly unimaginative English are capable of gastronomic flamboyance is revealed in the brief portrait of Twistleton Fiennes, the late Lord Saye and Sele, and far more so in the excerpt from Tobias Smollett's "Peregrine Pickle", an eighteenth century novel in which an ambitious doctor attempts to re-create the glories of Rome in an English kitchen, at a dinner whose climax might have been the handiwork of Mack Sennett.

Mr. Walker's Whitebait Dinner at Blackwell

from The Original
by Thomas Walker

As, like other people I suppose, I can write most easily upon what is freshest in my mind, I will give you, dear reader, an account of a dinner I have ordered this very day at Lovegrove's, at Blackwell, where, if you never dined, so much the worse for you. This account will serve as an illustration of my doctrines on dinner-giving better than a long abstract discourse. The party will consist of seven men beside myself, and every guest is asked for some reason—upon which good-fellowship mainly depends, for people brought together unconnectedly had, in my opinion, better be kept separate. Eight I hold to be the golden number, never to be exceeded without weakening the efficacy of concentration. The dinner is to consist of turtle followed by no other fish but whitebait, which is to be followed by no other meat but grouse, which are to be succeeded simply by apple fritters and jelly, pastry on such occasions being quite out of place. With the turtle, of course, there will be punch, with the whitebait champagne, and with the grouse claret. The two former I have ordered to be particularly well iced, and they will all be placed in succession upon the table, so that we can help ourselves as we please. I shall permit no other wines, unless, perchance, a bottle or two of port, if particularly wanted, as I hold variety of wines a great mistake. With respect to the adjuncts, I shall take care that there is cayenne, with lemons cut in halves, not in quarters, within reach of every one, for the turtle, and that brown bread and butter in abundance is set upon the table for the whitebait. It is no trouble to think of these little matters beforehand, but they make a vast difference in convivial contentment. The dinner will be followed by ice and a good dessert, after which coffee and one glass of liqueur each, and no more; so that the present may be enjoyed rationally without introducing retrospective regrets. If the master of a feast wishes his party to succeed, he must know how to command, and not let his guests run riot, each according to his own wild fancy. Such, reader, is my idea of a dinner, of which I hope you approve; and I cannot help thinking that if Parliament were to grant me £10,000 a year, in trust, to entertain a series of worthy persons, it would promote trade and increase the revenue more than any hugger-mugger measure ever devised.

I shall begin this article with stating that the dinner at Blackwell, mentioned in my last number, was served according to my directions, both as to the principal dishes and the adjuncts, with perfect exactness, and went off with corresponding success. The turtle and whitebait were excellent; the grouse not quite of equal merit; and the apple fritters so much relished, that they were entirely cleared, and the jelly left untouched. The only wines were champagne and claret, and they both gave great satisfaction. As soon as the liqueurs were handed round once, I ordered them out of the room; and the only heresy committed was by one of the guests asking for a glass of bottled porter, which I had not the presence of mind instantly to forbid. There was an opinion broached that some flounders water-zoutched, between the turtle and whitebait, would have been an improvement—and perhaps they would. I dined again yesterday at Blackwell as a guest, and I observed that my theory as to adjuncts was carefully put in practice, so that I hope the public will be a gainer.

At Table with Robinson Crusoe

from Robinson Crusoe
by Daniel Defoe

I FOUND IN the low grounds, hares as I thought them to be, and foxes, but they differed greatly from all other kinds I had met with; nor could I satisfy myself to eat them, though I killed several: but I had no need to be venturous; for I had no want of food, and of that which was very good too: especially these three sorts, goats, pigeons, and turtle or tortoise; which, added to my grapes, Leadenhall market could not have furnished a better table than I, in proportion to the company: and though my case was deplorable enough, yet I had great cause for thankfulness, that I was not driven to any extremities for food; but rather plenty, even to dainties . . .

But this was not all; for now I not only had goat's-flesh to feed on when I pleased, but milk too, a thing which indeed in my beginning I did not so much as think of, and which, when it came into my thoughts, was really an agreeable surprise; for now I set up my dairy, and had sometimes a gallon or two of milk in a day. And as Nature, who gives supplies of food to every creature, dictates even naturally how to make use of it, so I, that had never milked a cow, much less a goat, or seen butter or cheese made, very readily and handily, though after a great many essays and miscarriages, made me both butter and cheese at last, and never wanted it afterwards.

How mercifully can our great Creator treat his creatures, even in those conditions in which they seem to be overwhelmed in destruction! How can he sweeten the bitterest providences, and give us cause to praise him for dungeons and prisons! What a table was here spread for me in a wilderness, where I saw nothing at first but to perish for hunger!

It would have made a stoic smile, to have seen me and my little family sit down to dinner: there was my majesty, the prince and lord of the whole island; I had the lives of all my subjects at absolute command; I could hang, draw, give liberty, take it away, and no rebels among all my subjects!

Then to see how like a king I dined too, all alone, attended by my servants! Poll, as if he had been my favorite, was the only person permitted to talk to me; my dog, which was now grown old and crazy, and found no species to multiply his kind upon, sat always at my right hand; and two cats, one on one side the table, and one on the other, expecting now and then a bit from my hand as a mark of special favor.

Breakfast at the Rectory

from The Warden

by Anthony Trollope

AND NOW LET us observe the well-furnished breakfast parlor at Plumstead Episcopi, and the comfortable air of all the belongs of the rectory. Comfortable they certainly were, but neither gorgeous nor even grand; indeed considering the money that had been spent there, the eye and taste might have been better served; there was an air of heaviness about the rooms which might have been avoided without any sacrifice of propriety; colors might have been better chosen and lights more perfectly diffused; but perhaps in doing so the thorough clerical aspect of the whole might have been somewhat marred. At any rate it was not without ample consideration that those thick, dark, costly carpets were put down; those embossed but sombre papers hung up; those heavy curtains draped so as to half exclude the light of the sun. Nor were these oldfashioned chairs, bought at a price far exceeding that now given for more modern goods, without a purpose. The breakfast service on the table was equally costly and equally plain. The apparent object had been to spend money without obtaining brilliancy or splendor. The urn was of thick and solid silver, as were also the tea-pot, coffee-pot, cream-ewer, and sugar-bowl; the cups were old, dim dragon china, worth about a pound a piece, but very despicable in the eyes of the uninitiated. The silver forks were so heavy as to be disagreeable to the hand, and the bread-basket was of a weight really formidable to any but robust persons. The tea consumed was the very best, the coffee the very blackest, the cream the very thickest; there was dry toast and buttered toast, muffins and crumpets; hot bread and cold bread, white bread and brown bread, homemade bread and baker's bread, wheaten bread and oaten bread; and if there be other breads than these, they were there; there were eggs in napkins, and crispy bits of bacon under silver covers; and there were little fishes in a little box, and deviled kidneys frizzling on a hot-water dish;—which, by-the-by, were placed closely contiguous to the plate of the worthy archdeacon himself. Over and above this, on a snow white napkin, spread upon the side-board, was a huge ham and a huge sirloin; the latter having laden the dinner table on the previous evening. Such was the ordinary fare at Plumstead Episcopi.

A Banquet at Strawberry Hill

from a letter of Horace Walpole

YOUR POOR BEASMAN, the Abbot of Strawberry, whose glories verge towards their setting, has been more sumptuous today than ordinary, and banqueted their representative majesties of France and Spain . . .

The refectory was never so crowded . . . A violent shower in the morning laid the dust, brightened the green, refreshed the roses, pinks, orange flowers, and the blossoms with which the acacias are covered. A rich storm of thunder and lightning gave a dignity of coloring to the heavens; and the sun appeared enough to illuminate the landscape, without basking himself over it at his length. During dinner there were French horns and clarionets in the cloister, and after coffee I treated them with an English, and to them very new collation—a syllabub milked under the cows, that were brought to the brow of the terrace. Thence they went to the printing house, and saw a new, fashionable French song printed. They drank tea in the gallery, and eight went away to Vauxhall. They really seemed quite pleased with the place and the day; but I must tell you, the treasury of the Abbey will feel it, for without magnificence, all was handsomely done.

Dinner with Lord Byron

from Table Talk

by Samuel Rogers

NEITHER MOORE NOR myself had ever seen Byron when it was settled that he should dine at my house . . . When we sat down to dinner I asked Byron if he would take soup? "No, he never took soup."—"Would he take fish?" "No, he never took fish."—Presently I asked if he would eat some mutton? "No, he never ate mutton."—I then asked if he would take a glass of wine? "No, he never tasted wine."—It was now necessary to inquire what he *did* eat and drink; and the answer was, "Nothing but hard biscuits and soda-water." Unfortunately, neither hard biscuits nor soda-water were at hand; and he dined upon potatoes bruised down on his plate and drenched with vinegar.—My guests stayed till very late discussing the merits of Walter Scott and Joanna Baillie.—Some days after, meeting Hobhouse, I said to him, "How long will Lord Byron persevere in his present diet?" He replied, "Just as long as you continue to notice it." I did not then know, what I now know to be a fact—that Byron, after leaving my house, had gone to a club in St. James's Street, and eaten a hearty meat-supper.

A British Sybarite

from Reminiscences

by Gronow

TWISTLETON FIENNES, the late Lord Saye and Sele . . . was a very eccentric man, and the greatest epicure of his day. His dinners were worthy of the days of Vitellius or Heliogabalus. Every country, every sea, was searched and ransacked to find some new delicacy for our British Sybarite. I remember, at one of his breakfasts, an omelette being served which was composed entirely of golden pheasants' eggs. He had a very strong constitution, and would drink absynthe and curacao in quantities which were perfectly awful to behold. These stimulants produced no effect upon his brain; but his health gradually gave way under the excesses of all kinds in which he indulged. He was a kind, liberal, and good-natured man, but a very odd fellow. I shall never forget the astonishment of a servant I had recommended to him. On entering his service, John made his appearance as Fiennes was going out to dinner, and asked his new master if he had any orders. He received the following answer—"Place two bottles of sherry by my bedside, and call me the day after tomorrow."

The Doctor's Dinner

from The Adventures of Peregrine Pickle
by Tobias Smollett

THE DOCTOR WITH an air of infinite satisfaction began:—This here, gentlemen, is a boiled goose, served up in a sauce composed of pepper, lovage, coriander, mint, rue, anchovies, and oil! I wish for your sakes, gentlemen, it was one of the geese of Ferrara, so much celebrated among the ancients for the magnitude of their livers, one of which is said to have weighed upwards of two pounds: with this food, exquisite as it was, did the tyrant Heliogabalus regale his hounds. But I beg pardon, I had almost forgotten the soup, which I hear is so necessary an article at all tables in France. At each end there are dishes of the *salacacabia* of the Romans; one is made of parsley, pennyroyal, cheese, pine-tops, honey, vinegar, brine, eggs, cucumbers, onions, and hen-livers; the other is much the same as the *soupe-maigre* of this country. Then there is a loin of veal boiled with fennel and caraway seed, on a pottage composed of pickle, oil, honey, and flour, and a curious *hachis* of the lights, liver and blood of an hare, together with a dish of roasted pigeons. Monsieur le Baron, shall I help you to a plate of this soup?—The German, who did not at all approve of the ingredients, assented to the proposal, and seemed to relish the composition; while the marquis was in consequence of his desire accommodated with a portion of the *soupe-maigre;* and the count supplied himself with a pigeon . . .

The Frenchman, having swallowed the first spoonful, made a pause; his throat swelled as if an egg had stuck in his gullet, his eyes rolled, and his mouth underwent a series of involuntary contractions and dilations. Pallet, who looked steadfastly at this connoisseur, with a view of consulting his taste, before he himself would venture upon the soup, began to be disturbed at these emotions, and observed, with some concern, that the poor gentleman seemed to be going into a fit; when Peregrine assured him these were symptoms of ecstasy, and, for further confirmation, asked the marquis how he found the soup. It was with infinite difficulty that his complaisance could so far master his disgust, as to enable him to answer, "Altogether excellent, upon my honor!" And the painter, being certified of his approbation, lifted the spoon to his mouth without scruple; but far from justifying the eulogium of his taster, when this precious composition diffused itself upon his palate, he seemed to be deprived of all sense and motion, and sat like the leaden statue of some river god, with the liquor flowing out at both sides of his mouth . . .

The Doctor, alarmed at this indecent phenomenon, earnestly inquired into the cause of it; and when Pallet recovered his recollection, and swore that he would rather swallow porridge made of burning brimstone, than such an infernal mess as that which he had tasted, the physician, in his own vindication, assured the company that, except the usual ingredients, he had mixed nothing in the soup but some salammoniac instead of the ancient nitrum, which could not now be procured; and appealed to the marquis, whether such a succedaneum was not an improvement of the whole. The unfortunate *petit-maître,* driven to the extremity of his condescension, acknowledged it to be a masterly refinement; and deeming himself obliged, in point of honor, to evince his sentiments by his practice, forced a few more mouthfuls of this disagreeable potion down his throat, till his stomach was so much offended that he was compelled to start up of a sudden; and, in the hurry of his elevation, overturned his plate into the bosom of the baron. The emergency of his occasion would not permit him to stay and make apologies for this abrupt behavior; so that he flew into another apartment, where Pickle found him puking, and crossing himself with great devotion; and a chair, at his desire, being brought to the door, he slipped into it, more dead than alive . . . When our hero returned to the dining-room the places were filled with two pyes, one of dormice liquored with syrup of white poppies which the Doctor had substituted in the room of toasted poppyseed, formerly eaten with honey, as a dessert; and the other composed of a hock of pork baked in honey.

Pallet hearing the first of these dishes described, lifting up his hands and eyes, and with signs of loathing and amazement, pronounced, "A pye made of dormice and syrup of poppies—Lord in Heaven! What beastly fellows those Romans were!"

All the Doctor's invitations and assurances could not prevail upon his guests to honor the *hachis* and the goose; and that course was succeeded by another. "That which smokes in the middle," said he, "is a sow's stomach, filled with a composition of minced pork, hog's brains, eggs, pepper, cloves, garlick, aniseed, rue, oil, wine, and pickle. On the right-hand side are the teats and belly of a sow just farrowed, fried with sweet wine, oil, flour, lovage, and pepper. On the left is a fricassee of snails, fed, or rather purged, with mulk. At that end, next Mr. Pallet, are fritters of pompions, lovage, origanum, and oil; and here are a couple of pullets, roasted and stuffed in the manner of Apicius."

The painter, who had by wry faces testified his abhorrence of the sow's stomach, which he compared to a bagpipe, and the snails which had undergone purgation, no sooner heard him mention the roasted pullets, than he eagerly solicited the wing of a fowl; but scarce were they set down before him, when the tears ran down his cheeks, and he called aloud in a manifest disorder, "Z—ds! This is the essence of a whole bed of garlic!" That he might not, however, disappoint or disgrace the entertainer, he applied his instruments to one of the birds, and when he opened up the cavity, was assailed by such an irruption of intolerable smells, that, without staying to disengage himself from the cloth, he sprung away, with an exclamation of "Lord Jesus!" and involved the whole table in havoc, ruin and confusion.

Before Pickle could accomplish his escape, he was soused with the syrup of the dormous-pye, which went to pieces in the general wreck; and as for the Italian count, he was overwhelmed by the sow's stomach, which bursting in the fall, discharged its contents upon his leg and thigh, and scalded him so miserably, that he shrieked with anguish, and grinned with a most ghastly and horrible aspect . . .

The Doctor was confounded with shame and vexation. He expressed his sorrow for the misadventure and protested there was nothing in the fowls which could give offense to a sensitive nose, the stuffing being a mixture of pepper, lovage, and asafoetida, and the sauce consisting of wine and herring-pickle, which he had used instead of the celebrated garum of the Romans.

THERE IS ENOUGH eating in the pages of Charles Dickens to provoke a severe case of literary indigestion if it were not done with a master hand. Surely the glories of eating in nineteenth century England were never celebrated so joyously!

Out of the innumerable tables where people are eating in Dickens' novels, we have chosen four meals, although other morsels are distributed through later portions of the book. One depicts poor David Copperfield's unequal contest with a hungry and ingenious waiter, followed by two entertainments before and with Dora. Another is a description of a Pickwickian meal (the Pickwick Club appeared to be forever eating).

Feast, then, with Charles Dickens, a man who knew and loved food and loved to write about it.

A Waiter Out-Eats David Copperfield, and Other Scenes from His Domestic Life

from David Copperfield
by Charles Dickens

THE COACH WAS in the yard, shining very much all over, but without any horses to it as yet; and it looked in that state as if nothing was more unlikely than its ever going to London. I was thinking this, and wondering what would ultimately become of my box, which Mr. Barkis had put down on the yard-pavement by the pile (he having driven up the yard to turn his cart), and also what would ultimately become of me, when a lady looked out of a bow-window where some fowls and joints of meat were hanging up, and said:

"Is that the little gentleman from Blunderstone?"

"Yes, ma'am," I said.

"What name?" inquired the lady.

"Copperfield, ma'am," I said.

"That won't do," returned the lady. "Nobody's dinner is paid for here in that name."

"Is it Murdstone, ma'am?" I said.

"If you're Master Murdstone," said the lady, "why do you go and give another name first?"

I explained to the lady how it was, who then rang a bell, and called out, "William? show the coffee-room!" upon which a waiter came running out of a kitchen on the opposite side of the yard to show it, and seemed a good deal surprised when he found he was only to show it to me.

It was a large long room, with some large maps in it. I doubt if I could have felt much stranger if the maps had been real foreign countries, and I cast away in the middle of them. I felt it was taking a liberty to sit down, with my cap in my hand, on the corner of the chair nearest the door; and when the waiter laid a cloth on purpose for me, and put a set of casters on it, I think I must have turned red all over with modesty.

He brought me some chops and vegetables, and took the covers off in such a bouncing manner that I was afraid I must have given him some offense. But he greatly relieved my mind by putting a chair for me at the table, and saying very affably, "Now, six-foot! come on!"

I thanked him, and took my seat at the board; but found it extremely difficult to handle my knife and fork with anything like dexterity, or to avoid splashing myself with the gravy, while he was standing opposite, staring so hard, and making me blush in the most dreadful manner every time I caught his eye. After watching me into the second chop, he said:

"There's half a pint of ale for you. Will you have it now?"

I thanked him, and said, "Yes." Upon which he poured it out of a jug into a large tumbler, and held it up against the light, and made it look beautiful.

"My eye!" he said. "It seems a good deal, don't it?"

"It does seem a good deal," I answered with a smile. For it was quite delightful to me to find him so pleasant. He was a twinkling-eyed, pimple-faced man, with his hair standing upright all over his head; and as he stood with one arm akimbo, holding up the glass to the light with the other hand, he looked quite friendly.

"There was a gentleman here yesterday," he said—"a stout gentleman, by the name of Topsawyer—perhaps you know him?"

"No," I said, "I don't think—"

"In breeches and gaiters, broad-brimmed hat, gray coat, speckled choker," said the waiter.

"No," I said bashfully, "I haven't the pleasure—"

"He came in here," said the waiter, looking at the light through the tumbler, "ordered a glass of this ale—would order it—I told him not—drank it, and fell dead. It was too old for him. It oughtn't to be drawn, that's the fact."

I was very much shocked to hear of this melancholy accident, and said I thought I had better have some water.

"Why, you see," said the waiter, still looking at the light through the tumbler, with one of his eyes shut up, "our people don't like things being ordered and left. It offends 'em. But *I'll* drink it, if you like. I'm used to it, and use is everything. I don't think it'll hurt me, if I throw my head back, and take it off quick. Shall I?"

I replied that he would much oblige me by drinking it, if he thought he could do it safely, but by no means otherwise. When he did throw his head back, and take it off quick, I had a horrible fear, I confess, of seeing him meet the fate of the lamented Mr. Topsawyer, and fall lifeless on the carpet. But it didn't hurt him. On the contrary, I thought he seemed the fresher for it.

"What have we got here?" he said, putting a fork into my dish. "Not chops?"

"Chops," I said.

"Lord bless my soul!" he exclaimed, "I didn't know they were chops. Why, a chop's the very thing to take off the bad effects of that beer! Ain't it lucky?"

So he took a chop by the bone in one hand, and a potato in the other, and ate away with a very good appetite, to my extreme satisfaction. He afterwards took another chop, and another potato; and after that another chop, and another potato. When he had done, he brought me pudding, and having set it before me, seemed to ruminate, and to become absent in his mind for some moments.

"How's the pie?" he said, rousing himself.

"It's a pudding," I made answer.

"Pudding!" he exclaimed. "Why, bless me, so it is! What!" looking at it nearer, "you don't mean to say it's a batter-pudding?"

"Yes, it is indeed."

"Why, a batter-pudding," he said, taking up a tablespoon, "is my favorite pudding! Ain't that lucky? Come on, little 'un, and let's see who'll get most."

The waiter certainly got most. He entreated me more than once to come in and win; but what with his tablespoon to my teaspoon, his dispatch to my dispatch, and his appetite to my appetite, I was left far behind at the first mouthful, and had no chance with him. I never saw any one enjoy a pudding so much, I think; and he laughed, when it was all gone, as if his enjoyment of it lasted still . . .

Poor Copperfield was constantly being cheated of good eating. Much later in his adventures, we find him gastronomically deprived by love as effectively as he had been earlier by perfidy, poverty and inhumanity. Here, before his marriage to the unfortunate Dora, we discover him as the host of a ghastly dinner which the resourceful Mr. Micawber succeeds in rescuing.

Until the day arrived on which I was to entertain my newly-found old friends, I lived principally on Dora and coffee. In my love-lorn condition, my appetite languished; and I was glad of it, for I felt as though it would have been an act of perfidy towards Dora to have a natural relish for my dinner. The quantity of walking exercise I took was not in this respect attended with its usual consequence, as the disappointment counteracted the fresh air. I have my doubts, too, founded on the acute experience acquired at this period of my life, whether a sound enjoyment of animal food can develop itself freely in any human subject who is always in torment from tight boots. I think the extremities require to be at peace before the stomach will conduct itself with vigor.

On the occasion of this domestic little party, I . . . provided a pair of soles, a small leg of mutton, and a pigeon-pie . . . At the appointed time my three visitors arrived together—Mr. Micawber with more shirt collar than usual, and a new ribbon to his eye-glass; Mrs. Micawber with her cap in a whity-brown paper parcel; Traddles carrying the parcel, and supporting Mrs. Micawber on his arm . . .

. . . I informed Mr. Micawber that I relied upon him for a bowl of punch, and led him to the lemons. His recent despondency, not to say despair, was gone in a moment. I never saw a man so thoroughly enjoy himself amid the fragrance of lemon-peel and sugar, the odor of burning rum, and the steam of boiling water, as Mr. Micawber did that afternoon. It was wonderful to see his face shining at us out of a thin cloud of these delicate fumes, as he stirred, and mixed, and tasted, and looked as if he were making, instead of punch, a fortune for his family down to the latest posterity . . .

I suppose—I never ventured to inquire, but I suppose—that Mrs. Crupp, after frying the soles, was taken ill. Because we broke down at that point. The leg of mutton came up very red within, and very pale without; besides having a foreign substance of a gritty nature sprinkled over it, as if it had had a fall into the ashes of that remarkable kitchen fire-place. But we were not in a condition to judge of this fact from the appearance of the gravy, forasmuch as the "young gal" had dropped it all upon the stairs—where it remained, by-the-by, in a long train, until it was worn out. The pigeon-pie was not bad, but it was a delusive pie; the crust being like a disappointing head, phrenologically speaking—full of lumps and bumps, with nothing particular underneath. In short, the banquet was such a failure that I should have been quite unhappy—about the failure, I mean, for I am always unhappy about Dora—if I had not been relieved by the great good-humor of my company, and by a bright suggestion from Mr. Micawber.

"My dear friend Copperfield," said Mr. Micawber, "accidents will occur in the best-regulated families; and in families not regulated by that pervading influence which sanctifies while it enhances the—a—I would say, in short, by the influence of Woman, in the lofty character of Wife, they may be expected with confidence, and must be borne with philosophy. If you will allow me to take the liberty of remarking that there are few comestibles better, in their way, than a devil, and that I believe, with a little division of labor, we could accomplish a good one if the young person in attendance could produce a gridiron, I would put it to you that this little misfortune may be easily repaired."

There was a gridiron in the pantry, on which my morning rasher of bacon was cooked. We had it in, in a twinkling, and immediately applied ourselves to carrying Mr. Micawber's idea into effect. The division of labor to which he had referred was this: Traddles cut the mutton into slices; Mr. Micawber (who could do anything of this sort to perfection) covered them with pepper, mustard, salt, and cayenne; I put them on the gridiron, turned them with a fork, and took them off, under Mr. Micawber's direction; and Mrs. Micawber heated, and continually stirred, some mushroom ketchup in a little saucepan. When we had slices enough done to begin upon, we fell to, with our sleeves still tucked up at the wrists, more slices sputtering and blazing on the fire, and our attention divided between the mutton on our plates and the mutton then preparing.

What with the novelty of this cookery, the excellence of it, the bustle of it, the frequent starting up to look after it, the frequent sitting down to dispose of it as the crisp slices came off the gridiron hot and hot, the being so busy, so flushed with the fire, so amused, and in the midst of such a tempting noise and savor, we reduced the leg of mutton to the bone. My own appetite came back miraculously. I am ashamed to record it, but I really believe I forgot Dora for a little while. I am satisfied that Mr. and Mrs. Micawber could not have enjoyed the feast more, if they had sold a bed to provide it. Traddles laughed as heartily, almost the whole time, as he ate and worked. Indeed we all did, all at once, and I dare say there never was a greater success.

Dora, "elevated to the lofty character of Wife," failed to improve the quality of Copperfield's entertaining. Indeed, Traddles was subjected to an oyster dinner which failed of the happy ending provided by Micawber.

One of our first feats in the housekeeping way was a little dinner to Traddles. I met him in town, and asked him to walk out with me that afternoon. He readily consenting, I wrote to Dora, saying I would bring him home. It was pleasant weather, and on the road we made my domestic happiness the theme of conversation. Traddles was very full of it; and said that, picturing himself with such a home, and Sophy waiting and preparing for him, he could think of nothing wanting to complete his bliss.

I could not have wished for a prettier little wife at the opposite end of the table, but I certainly could have wished, when we sat down, for a little more room. I did not know how it was, but though there were only two of us, we were at once always cramped for room, and yet had always room enough to lose everything in. I suspect it may have been because nothing had a place of its own, except Jip's pagoda, which invariably blocked up the main thoroughfare. On the present occasion, Traddles was so hemmed in by the pagoda and the guitar-case and Dora's flower-painting, and my writing-table, that I had serious doubts of the possibility of his using his knife and fork; but he protested, with his own good-humor, "Oceans of room, Copperfield! I assure you, oceans!"

There was another thing I could have wished—namely, that Jip had never been encouraged to walk about the tablecloth during dinner. I began to think there was something disorderly in his being there at all, even if he had not been in the habit of putting his foot in the salt or the melted butter. On this occasion he seemed to think he was introduced expressly to keep Traddles at bay, and he barked at my old friend, and made short runs at his plate, with such undaunted pertinacity, that he may be said to have engrossed the conversation.

However, as I knew how tender-hearted my dear Dora was, and how sensitive she would be to any slight upon her favorite, I hinted no objection. For similar reasons I made no allusion to the skirmishing plates upon the floor; or to the disreputable appearance of the castors, which were all at sixes and sevens, and looked drunk; or to the further blockade of Traddles by wandering vegetable dishes and jugs. I could not help wondering in my own mind, as I contemplated the boiled leg of mutton before me, previous to carving it, how it came to pass that our joints of meat were of such extraordinary shapes, and whether our butcher contracted for all the deformed sheep that came into the world; but I kept my reflections to myself.

"My love," said I to Dora, "what have you got in that dish?"

I could not imagine why Dora had been making tempting little faces at me, as if she wanted to kiss me.

"Oysters, dear," said Dora timidly.

"Was that *your* thought?" said I, delighted.

"Ye-yes, Doady," said Dora.

"There never was a happier one!" I exclaimed, laying down the carving knife and fork. "There is nothing Traddles likes so much!"

"Ye-yes, Doady," said Dora, "and so I bought a beautiful little barrel of them, and the man said they were very good. But I—I am afraid there's something the matter with them. They don't seem right." Here Dora shook her head, and diamonds twinkled in her eyes.

"They are only opened in both shells," said I. "Take the top one off, my love."

"But it won't come off," said Dora, trying very hard, and looking very much distressed.

"Do you know, Copperfield," said Traddles, cheerfully examining the dish, "I think it is in consequence—they are capital oysters, but I *think* it is in consequence—of their never having been opened."

They never had been opened; and we had no oyster-knives, and couldn't have used them if we had; so we looked at the oysters, and ate the mutton. At least we ate as much of it as was done, and made up with capers. If I had permitted him, I am satisfied that Traddles would have made a perfect savage of himself, and eaten a plateful of raw meat, to express enjoyment of the repast. But I would hear of no such immolation on the altar of friendship; and we had a course of bacon instead—there happening, by good fortune, to be cold bacon in the larder.

A Pickwickian Meal

from The Posthumous Papers of the Pickwick Club

by Charles Dickens

After a great many jokes about squeezing the ladies' sleeves, and a vast quantity of blushing at sundry jocose proposals that the ladies should sit in the gentlemen's laps, the whole party were stowed down in the barouche; and the stout gentleman proceeded to hand the things from the fat boy (who had mounted up behind for the purpose) into the carriage.

"Now, Joe, knives and forks." The knives and forks were handed in, and the ladies and gentlemen inside, and Mr. Winkle on the box, were each furnished with those useful instruments.

"Plates, Joe, plates." A similar process employed in the distribution of the crockery.

"Now, Joe, the fowls. Damn that boy; he's gone to sleep again. Joe! Joe!" (Sundry taps on the head with a stick, and the fat boy, with some difficulty, roused from his lethargy.) "Come, hand in the eatables."

There was something in the sound of the last word which roused the unctuous boy. He jumped up; and the leaden eyes which twinkled behind his mountainous cheeks, leered horribly upon the food as he unpacked it from the basket.

"Now make haste," said Mr. Wardle; for the fat boy was hanging fondly over a capon, which he seemed wholly unable to part with. The boy sighed deeply, and, bestowing an ardent gaze upon its plumpness, unwillingly consigned it to his master.

"That's right—look sharp. Now the tongue—now the pigeon-pie. Take care of that veal and ham—mind the lobsters—take the salad out of the cloth—give me the dressing." Such were the hurried orders which issued from the lips of Mr. Wardle, as he handed in the different articles described, and placed dishes in everybody's hands, and on everybody's knees, in endless number.

"Now an't this capital?" inquired that jolly personage, when the work of destruction had commenced.

"Capital!" said Mr. Winkle, who was carving a fowl on the box.

"Glass of wine?"

"With the greatest pleasure."

"You'd better have a bottle to yourself, up there, hadn't you?"

"You're very good."

"Joe!"

"Yes, sir." (He wasn't asleep this time, having just succeeded in abstracting a veal patty.)

"Bottle of wine to the gentleman on the box. Glad to see you, sir."

"Thank'ee." Mr. Winkle emptied his glass, and placed the bottle on the coach-box, by his side.

"Will you permit me to have the pleasure, sir?" said Mr. Trundle to Mr. Winkle.

"With great pleasure," replied Mr. Winkle to Mr. Trundle: and then the two gentlemen took wine, after which they took a glass of wine round, ladies and all.

FROM Pickwick and the London of Dickens, it is no more than a walk into the next room to meet Robert Surtees, a contemporary of Dickens, whose Mr. Jorrocks inspired the creation of Mr. Pickwick. Like Thomas Walker, Robert Smith Surtees was a magazine proprietor, the owner, editor and principal writer for his own publication, "The New Sporting Magazine."

Jorrocks first appeared in its pages in 1831, the ludicrous hero of a series of sketches, who came to be loved and quoted from one end of the Empire to the other. The series was collectively titled, "Jorrocks' Jaunts and Jollities," with the extravagant subtitle, "or the Hunting, Shooting, Racing, Driving, Sailing, Eating, Eccentric and Extravagant Exploits of that renowned Sporting Citizen, Mr. John Jorrocks of St. Botolph Lane and Great Coram Corner." The great Phiz himself illustrated the series.

M. F. K. Fisher calls Jorrocks "one of the great fool-heroes, infectiously and ridiculously and lovably absurd. He ate and talked and drank with irresistible gusto." There were some, of course, who found him easily resistible, not caring much for Jorrocks as the low-comedy character he proved to be. But he holds up well for his admirers, after more than 125 years, perhaps because Surtees was, like Dickens, a superb reporter of the social scene.

But here is Jorrocks, the sporting grocer. Let him speak for himself.

Mr. Jorrocks' Little Dinner

from Handley Cross

by Robert Smith Surtees

THE FOOTMAN presently returned, followed by a very smiling comely-looking personage, dressed in black silk, with sky-blue ribbons in her jaunty little cap and collar, who proceeded in a most voluble manner to express with her hands, and tongue, and eyes, Sir Archibald's regrets that he had been suddenly summoned to town, adding that he had left word that they were to make the expected guest as comfortable as possible, and show him every possible care and attention.

'Ah, well, that's summut like,' smiled Mr. Jorrocks, with a jerk of his head, thinking what a good-looking woman she was. In another instant he was on the top step of the entrance beside her, giving her soft hand a sly squeeze as she prepared to help him out of his reversible coat. 'Take the quad to the stable,' said he to the footman, 'and bid 'em take great care on 'im'—adding, with a leer at the lady, 'gave a'most a 'undred for him.' So saying, hack-like, the horse was left to take its chance, while our fat friend followed the fair lady into the library.

'I'll have a fire lighted directly,' observed she, looking round the spacious apartment, which, like many bachelors' company rooms, felt pretty innocent of fuel.

'Fiddle the fire!' exclaimed Mr. Jorrocks, 'fiddle the fire! dessay you've got a good 'un in your room—*I'll go there!'*

'Couldn't for the world,' whispered Mrs. Markham, with a shake of head, glancing her large hazel eyes lovingly upon Jorrocks. 'What if Sir Archey should hear!'

'Oh, he'll *never* hear,' rejoined our friend confidently.

'*Wouldn't* he?' retorted Mrs. Markham; 'you don't know what servants are if you think that. Bless ye! they watch me just as a cat watches a mouse.'

'Well, then, you must come in to *me*,' observed Mr. Jorrocks, adding—'I can't be left mopin' alone, you know.'

'It must be after they've gone to bed, then,' whispered the lady.

A hurrying housemaid now appearing with a red-hot poker, Mrs. Markham drew back and changed the whispering conversation into an audible:

'And please, sir, what would you like to 'ave for dinner, sir?'

'Oh, I don't care,' shrugged Mr. Jorrocks; 'wot 'ave you got?'

'There's soup, and fish, and meat, and game, and poultry; whatever you like to 'ave, I dare say.'

'Humph,' mused Mr. Jorrocks, wishing the housemaid further, 'I'll 'ave a bit o' fish, with a beefsteak, and a fizzant to follow, say—'

'No soup?' observed Mrs. Markham.

'No; I doesn't care nothin' 'bout soup, 'less it's turtle,' replied he with a toss of his head.

'I'm afraid there is no turtle, sir,' replied Mrs. Markham, well knowing there was not. 'Gravy, macaroni, mulligatawny.'

'No, jest fish, and steak, and fizzant,' rejoined Mr. Jorrocks. 'Cod and hoister sauce, say—and p'r'aps a could o' dozen o' hoisters to begin with—jest as a whet, you know.'

'Any *sweets?*' asked the lady significantly.

'No, I'll 'ave my sweets arter,' winked Mr. J., licking his lips.

'Open tart, apple fritters, omelette, anything of that sort?' continued she; intimating with her eye that the loitering housemaid might hear his answer.

'No; I'll fill up the chinks wi' cheese,' replied Mr. Jorrocks, stroking his stomach.

'And wine?' asked the housekeeper; adding, 'the butler's away with Sir Archey, but I 'ave the key of the cellar.'

'That's all right!' exclaimed our friend, adding, 'I'll drink his 'ealth in a bottle of his best.'

'Port?' asked Mrs. Markham.

'Port in course,' replied Mr. J., with a hoist of his eyebrows, adding, 'but, mind, I doesn't call the oldest the best—far from it—it's oftentimes the wust. No,' continued he, 'give me a good fruity wine; a wine with a grip o' the gob, that leaves a mark on the side o' the glass; not your weak woe-begone trash, that would be water if it wasn't wine.'

'P'r'aps you'd like a little champagne at dinner,' suggested Mrs. Markham.

'Champagne,' repeated Mr. Jorrocks thoughtfully, 'champagne! well, I wouldn't mind a little champagne, only I wouldnt like it hiced; doesn' want to 'ave all my teeth set a-chatterin' i' my 'ead; havn't got so far advanced in gentility as to like my wine froze—I'm a Post Hoffice Directory, not a Peerage man,' added he with a broad grin.

'Indeed,' smiled Mrs. Markham, not exactly understanding the simile.

'Folks talk about the different grades o' society,' observed Mr. Jorrocks, with a smile and a pshaw, 'but arter all's said and done there are but two sorts o' folks i' the world, Peerage folks and Post

Hoffice Directory folks—Peerage folks, wot think it's all right and proper to do their tailors, and Post Hoffice Directory folks wot think it's the greatest sin under the sun not to pay twenty shillins i' the pund—the greatest sin under the sun 'cept kissin' and then tellin',' added he, in an undertone, with a wink, as he drew his hand across his jolly lips.

'Well, then, you'll have it iced,' observed Mrs. Markham in a tone for the housemaid to hear. 'Just a few minutes' plunge in the pail,—enough to dull the glass, p'r'aps?' continued she.

'Well,' mused our friend, 'as you are mistress o' the revels, I'll leave that to you, and I make no doubt,' added he, with another sly squeeze of her soft hand, now that the housemaid's back was turned, 'I shall fare uncommon well.'

And Mrs. Markham, seeing that the maid was bent on outstaying her, sailed away with a stately air, ordering her, in a commanding tone, to 'bring some wood to the fire.'

And Mr. Jorrocks, we need scarcely say, had a very good dinner, and spent his evening very pleasantly.

FEW OF US think of Virginia Woolf as a contributor to the literature of food, yet she brought to those paragraphs in her novels which dealt with eating the same quiet, sensitive, introverted contemplation that graced all her work. It is perceptive, intellectual appreciation of food, far from the gusto of Dickens.

The two excerpts offered here, taken from two of her best known works, are short but representative. In "Boeuf en Daube," from "To the Lighthouse," the appreciation of the dish is interwoven with the subtle crosscurrents of emotion in those who eat it. In the luncheon scene, from "A Room of One's Own," only a fragment of which is quoted, the descriptive paragraph has the sharpness of a miniature.

Boeuf en Daube

abridged from To the Lighthouse
by Virginia Woolf

SHE WAS NOW beginning to feel annoyed with them for being so late; it was inconsiderate of them, and it annoyed her on top of her anxiety about them, that they should choose this very night to be out late, when, in fact, she wished the dinner to be particularly nice, since William Bankes had at last consented to dine with them; and they were having Mildred's masterpiece—Boeuf en Daube. Everything depended upon things being served up the precise moment they were ready. The beef, the bayleaf, and the wine—all must be done to a turn. To keep it waiting was out of the question. Yet of course tonight, of all nights, out they went, and they came in late, and things had to be sent out, things had to be kept hot; the Boeuf en Daube would be entirely spoilt. . . .

"We went back to look for Minta's brooch," he said, sitting down by her . . . "we" did this, "we" did that. They'll say that all their lives, she thought, and an exquisite scent of olives and oil and juice rose from the great brown dish as Marthe, with a little flourish, took the cover off. The cook had spent three days over that dish. And she must take great care, Mrs. Ramsay thought, diving into the soft mass, to choose a specially tender piece for William Bankes. And she peered into the dish, with its shiny walls and its confusion of savoury brown and yellow meats, and its bay leaves and its wine, and thought. This will celebrate the occasion—a curious sense rising in her, at once freakish and tender, of celebrating a festival, as if two emotions were called up in her, one profound—for what could be more serious than the love of man for woman, what more commanding, more impressive, bearing in its bosom the seeds of death; at the same time these lovers, these people entering into illusion glittering eyed, must be danced round with mockery, decorated with garlands.

"It is a triumph," said Mr. Bankes, laying his knife down for a moment. He had eaten attentively. It was rich; it was tender. It was perfectly cooked. How did she manage these things in the depth of the country? he asked her. She was a wonderful woman. All his love, all his reverence had returned; and she knew it.

"It is a French recipe of my grandmother's" said Mrs. Ramsay, speaking with a ring of great pleasure in her voice. Of course it was French. What passes for cookery in England is an abomination (they agreed). It is putting cabbages in water. It is roasting meat till it is like leather. It is cutting off the delicious skins of vegetables. "In which," said Mr. Bankes, "all the virtue of the vegetable is contained." "And the waste," said Mrs. Ramsay. "A whole French family could live on what an English cook throws away . . ."

"Yes," she assured William Bankes, "there is plenty for everybody."

"Andrew," she said, "hold your plate lower, or I shall spill it."

"Then cheese with fruite, on the table set,
With bisketes or caroways, as you may get.
Wyne to them fyll, els ale or beare,
But wyne is metest, if any there were."

—SEAGER, *Schoole of Vertue*

Lunch Began with Sole

from A Room of One's Own
by Virginia Woolf

. . . Lunch on this occasion began with soles, sunk in a deep dish, over which the college cook had spread a counterpane of the whitest cream, save that it was branded here and there with brown spots like the spots on the flanks of a doe. After that came the partridges, but if this suggests a couple of bald brown birds on a plate you are mistaken. The partridges, many and various, came with all their retinue of sauces and salads, the sharp and the sweet, each in its order; their potatoes, thin as coins but not so hard; their sprouts, foliated as rosebuds but more succulent. And no sooner had the roast and its retinue been done with than the silent serving-man, the Beadle himself, perhaps in a milder manifestation, set before us, wreathed in napkins, a confection which rose all sugar from the waves.

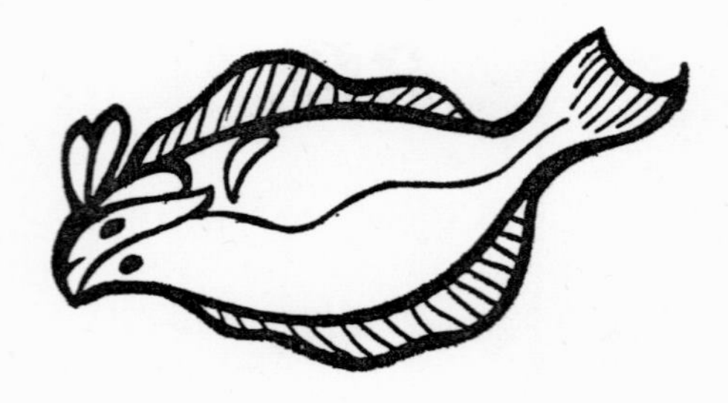

Chapter Four

THE FRENCH CUISINE

PERHAPS THE BEST writing about food, in a purely literary sense, has been done by the French. The great French novels are full of it, and of course it is almost always taken with the utmost seriousness. Frenchmen do not ordinarily joke about food; they have too much respect for it, as befits a nation whose cuisine is equaled in variety and subtlety only by the Chinese, who are also quite humorless about gastronomy.

Instead of trying to extract a representative sample of French writing, which would have been next to impossible, considering the profusion of material, we have chosen to view French cooking from a variety of angles, some conventional and some not, and not all the work of French writers.

It is appropriate, however, to begin with the best and most-quoted of French writers on food, Anthelme Brillat-Savarin, whose name is a landmark in gastronomy. He died a little more than 136 years ago, but his name, reputation and writings live on; his master work, "The Physiology of Taste," was reissued as a paperback only recently. In this book, the first compilation of a gastronomic code, Brillat-Savarin set forth the rules relating to food and drink, in respect to quality, combination, conservation, preparation and presentation. By its publication he meant, he said, "to protect man's life by means of the best nourishment," and "to increase the total sum of his pleasures."

Brillat-Savarin's high opinion of the good eater is evident in the following excerpt from "The Physiology of Taste."

"In the reign of Louis XIV, men of letters were drunkards; they conformed with the fashion, and on this point the memoirs of the time are highly edifying. Nowadays they are gourmands, a notable change for the better."

Some of the book's wisdom, couched in Brillat-Savarin's genial style, shines from the excerpts that follow. The first is an adventure in a French village, in which Brillat-Savarin charms himself into a splendid dinner. The other is the charming tale of a young married couple whose hunger in the late night hours was not for each other, but for the good dinner they had missed as the consequence of indulgence in an oyster breakfast.

Traveler's Luck

from The Physiology of Taste

by Anthelme Brillat-Savarin

One day, mounted on my good horse *La Joie,* I was crossing the genial slopes of the *Jura.*

It was in the worst days of the Revolution, and I was on my way to *Dôle,* to see Representative Prôt, and to obtain from him, if possible, a safe-conduct which should serve to keep me out of prison, and in all likelihood from going thence to the scaffold.

At eleven o'clock in the morning I halted at an inn in the small township or village of *Mont-sous-Vaudrey;* and having first attended to the wants of my mount, walked into the kitchen, where a sight met my gaze which no traveler can ever have beheld without emotion.

In front of the glowing fire a spit was slowly turning, most admirably decked with quails, yea, kings among quails, and as well with those little green-footed landrails which excel in plumpness. This choice game was yielding its last drops on to a mighty round of roast, the fashioning whereof proclaimed a sportsman's hand; and close beside it, ready cooked, lay one of those well-nourished leverets which *Parisians* know not, and the smell of which would fill a church as sweetly as any incense.

'Good!' said I to myself, much cheered by the sight of these things: 'Providence has not yet utterly forsaken me. Here's one more flower to pluck by the wayside; there will always be time to die.'

Then, addressing mine host, a man of giant frame, who throughout my examination had been walking to and fro across the kitchen, with his hands behind his back, whistling: 'My friend,' said I, 'what good things are you going to offer me for dinner?' 'Good things only, *monsieur,* and none else,' he answered: 'good *bouilli,* good potato soup, good shoulder of mutton, and good haricot beans.'

At this unexpected reply, a shiver of disappointment ran through all my limbs; the reader knows that I never eat *bouilli,* because it is meat deprived of its juices; beans and potatoes are alike obesigenous; my teeth, I felt, were not of tempered steel for the rending of mutton: the menu, in a word, was expressly designed to break my heart, and all my woes descended on me once again.

Mine host looked knowingly at me, and seemed to divine the cause of my disappointment. . . . 'And for whom, pray, are you keeping all this fine game?' I inquired, with an air of extreme vexation. 'Alas, *monsieur,*' he sympathetically answered, 'it is not mine to dispose of; it all belongs to some legal gentlemen, who have been here these ten days past, employed on a valuation which concerns a certain very wealthy lady; they finished their work yesterday, and are celebrating the happy event with a feast; breaking out, as we say in these parts.' '*Monsieur,*' I replied, after a moment's reflection, 'be so good as to tell these gentlemen that a man of good company begs, as favor, to be allowed to join them at dinner; that he will bear his share of the cost; and above all, that he will be profoundly indebted to them.' I said: he departed and did not return.

But a few moments later, a short, fat, fresh-complexioned, chubby, sprightly little man came in, prowled round the kitchen, shifted one or two pots and pans, raised the lid of a casserole, and went out again.

'Good,' said I to myself: 'the brother tiler, sent to take stock of me.' And I began to hope, for experience had already taught me that my exterior is not repellent.

Nevertheless my heart was beating like that of a candidate waiting to be told that he has been plucked, when the host reappeared, and announced that the gentlemen were highly flattered by my proposal, and only waited for me to join them before they sat down to table.

I danced out of the room, met with the most flattering reception, and within a few minutes had taken root.

What a dinner that was! I will not describe it in detail; but honorable mention is surely due to a chicken fricassee of the most distinguished craftsmanship, such as can only be met with in country places, and so richly dowered with truffles that it would have made old *Tithonus* brisk again.

The roast has been described already; its taste did not fall short of its appearance; it was done to a turn, and the difficulty I had experienced in attaining to it still further enhanced its savor.

Dessert was composed of a vanilla *crème,* choice fruit, and excellent cheese. And all these good things we washed down first with a light wine of the hue of garnets; then with Hermitage; after that with a straw-colored wine as soft as it was generous; and the whole was crowned with some first-rate coffee, confectioned by the sprightly tiler, who also used a free hand in respect of certain Verdun liqueurs, which he produced from a species of tabernacle of which he had the key.

Not only was the dinner good, it was very gay also.

Having talked awhile, with due circumspection, of the affairs of the day, my gentlemen fell to making jests at one another's expense, in a manner which enlightened me as to a part of their biographies; they said little of the business which had brought them together; good stories were told, and songs sung, to which I responded with some unpublished verses of my own, and even delivered some lines impromptu, which were received with generous applause; here they are:

Air: *du Maréchal Ferrant.*

Oh, 'tis a pleasant thing and sweet
When kindly folk the traveler greet,
And merriment and wine flow free;
With such good fellows and such cheer,
How gladly could I tarry here,
Secure from all anxiety,
Four days,
Fourteen days,
Forty days,
A year, nor go
While the bless'd Fates detain'd me so!

If I record these verses here, it is not that I much admire them; I have written better in my time, thanks be to Heaven! and could improve these if I chose; but I prefer to leave them in their impromptu shape, in hopes that the reader will agree with me that he who could make so merry, with a revolutionary gang at his elbow, had the heart and head of a true *Frenchman*.

We must have been at least four hours at table, when the question arose of how best to finish the day: and it was decided to take a long walk, for digestion's sake, and thereafter to play a game of ombre while waiting for the evening meal, which was already commandeered in the form of a dish of trout and the still very desirable remnants of our dinner.

To each of these proposals I was obliged to say no; the sun, declining towards the horizon, warned me to be moving. My companions pressed me to stay, as warmly as politeness would allow of, and only gave way upon my assuring them that my journey was not entirely a matter of pleasure.

As the reader will have guessed, they would hear no word about my share of the reckoning; they refrained from putting awkward questions to me, and all came out to see me mount; and so we parted, after exchanging the heartiest farewells.

If any of those who used me so hospitably that day is still living, and this book should fall into his hands, I wish him to know that more than thirty years later this chapter was penned with the liveliest feelings of gratitude.

The Pullet of Bresse

from The Physiology of Taste
by Brillat-Savarin

On one of the early days of January in this present year, 1825, a young married couple, *Mme.* and *M. de Versy* by name, were guests at a *full-dress* oyster breakfast; my readers will know what that means.

Such meals are charming, not only on account of the tempting dishes they are composed of, but also because of the gaiety which usually distinguishes them; they have one disadvantage, however, namely, that they upset the rest of the day's arrangements. And so it was on the present occasion. When dinner-time arrived, the pair took their places at table; but it was a mere formality; *Madame* swallowed a mouthful of soup, *Monsieur* drank a glass of wine and water; some friends came in, a game of whist was played, the evening drew to a close, and one bed received the twain.

About two o'clock in the morning, *M. de Versy* awoke; he was restless; he yawned; he tossed and turned so, that his wife grew alarmed, and asked him, was he unwell. "No, my dear, but I seem to be hungry; I was dreaming of that beautiful Bresse chicken we so shamefully neglected at dinner." "My dear, to confess the truth, I am as hungry as you are, and if you have been dreaming of that chicken, why, it must be sent for and eaten." "Oh nonsense! The whole house is asleep, and tomorrow we shall be a laughing-stock." "If the whole house is asleep, the whole house shall wake up, and we shall not be laughed at, for the simple reason that no one will know about it. And besides, who knows if between now and tomorrow one of us may not starve to death? I don't intend running the risk. I am going to ring for *Justine*."

No sooner said than done; and the poor girl who had supped well and was sleeping as only those can sleep who are nineteen years old and untroubled by love, was rudely awakened.

She arrived all untidy, with half-closed eyes, and sat down still yawning and stretching her arms.

But this had been an easy task; it still remained to rouse the cook and there was an affair indeed. For she was a blue ribbon, and crusty in proportion; she grunted, neighed, growled, snorted, and roared; in the end, however, she got out of bed, and set her vast circumference in motion.

Meanwhile *Mme. de Versy* had slipped into a camisole, and her husband also made himself presentable. *Justine* spread a cloth upon the bed, and brought in the indispensable adjuncts to an improvised feast.

And when all was ready, the chicken appeared, to be rent asunder on the instant and remorselessly devoured.

Following this first exploit, husband and wife shared a plump Saint-German pear, and ate some orange marmalade.

In the *entr'actes* they drained a bottle of Graves wine to the dregs, and repeatedly declared, with variations, that never had they made a more delightful meal.

However, the meal came to an end, as all things must in this world below; *Justine* cleared away the incriminating evidence, and went back to bed; and the conjugal curtain once more hid the festive pair.

Next morning *Mme. de Versy* ran to her friend, *Mme. de Franval,* and recounted all that had passed in the night; and it is to that lady's indiscretion that the public owes the present revelation.

She invariably insists that *Mme. de Versy,* when she came to the end of her narration, coughed twice and very positively blushed.

To be wanting in the sense of taste is to have a stupid mouth, just as one may have a stupid mind.

—Guy de Maupassant.

It was only natural that the Rothschilds, the richest and most powerful family in Europe, if not the world, should have in their kitchen, at least for a time, the most noted of chefs, Carême, whose personality and career will be considered at length in later pages.

Lady Morgan, a visitor to the Rothschild mansion in Paris, describes here what it was like to dine in what must have been the utmost in gastronomic luxury.

A Carême Dinner at the Rothschilds'

from The Letters of Lady Morgan

I DID NOT HEAR the announcement of *Madame est servie* without emotion. We proceeded to the dining-room, not as in England by the printed orders of the red-book, but by the law of the courtesy of nations, whose only distinctions are made in favor of the greatest strangers. The evening was extremely sultry, and in spite of Venetian blinds and open verandahs, the apartments through which we passed were exceedingly close. A dinner in the largest of them threatened much inconvenience from the heat; but on this score there was no ground for apprehension. The dining-room stood apart from the house, in the midst of orange trees: it was an elegant oblong pavilion of Greek marble, refreshed by fountains that shot in air through scintillating streams, and the table, covered with the beautiful and picturesque dessert, emitted no odor that was not in perfect conformity with the freshness of the scene and fervor of the season. No burnished gold reflected the glaring sunset, no brilliant silver dazzled the eyes; porcelain, beyond the price of all precious metals by its beauty and its fragility, every plate a picture, consorted with the general character of sumptuous simplicity which reigned over the whole, and showed how well the master of the feast had consulted the genius of the place in all.

To do justice to the science and research of a dinner so served would require a knowledge of the art equal to that which produced it; its character, however, was, that it was a season—that it was up to its time—that it was in the spirit of the age—that there was no *perruque* in its composition, no trace of the wisdom of our ancestors in a single dish—no high-spiced sauces, no dark-brown gravies, no flavor of cayenne and allspice, no tincture of catsup and walnut pickle, no visible agency of those vulgar elements of cooking of the good old times, fire and water. Distillations of the most delicate viands, extracted in silver dews, with chemical precision—'on tepid clouds of rising steam'—formed the *fond* of all. EVERY MEAT PRESENTED ITS OWN NATURAL AROMA—EVERY VEGETABLE ITS OWN SHADE OF VERDURE: the *mayonnaise* was fried in ice (like Ninon's description of Sévigné's heart) and the tempered chill of the *plombière* (which held the place of the eternal *fondu* and *soufflées* of our English tables) anticipated the stronger shock, and broke it, of the exquisite avalanche, which with the hue and odor of fresh-gathered nectarines, satisfied every sense and dissipated every coarser flavor.

With less genius than went to the composition of this dinner, men have written epic poems; and if crowns were distributed to cooks, as to actors, the wreaths of Pasta or Sontag (divine as they are) were never more fairly won than the laurel which should have graced the brow of Carême for this specimen of the intellectual perfection of an art, the standard and gauge of modern civilization. Cruelty, violence and barbarism, were the characteristics of the men who fed upon the tough fibres of half-dressed oxen; humanity, knowledge, and refinement, belong to the living generation, whose tastes and temperance are regulated by the science of such philosophers as Carême, and such Amphitryons as his employers!

I prefer a tender *gigot*
Which, without pomp or show,
Is accompanied by an entourage
Of lettuce and of *haricot*.

—Berchoux

THE REMAINDER of these French excursions need no individual introductions. They can be brought on as separate, and for the most part, familiar courses.

Here, first, is Quentin Durward in France, in which we observe French cuisine through the eyes of an Englishman, who is no less appreciative because of his separation by the Channel. Then comes Daudet's gluttonous clergyman, and another frolic with the irrepressible Jorrocks, who is not at all abashed by the manners and food of another country, and finds himself as able to eat himself into a stupor in France as at home.

From the multitudinous, detailed wining and dining in "Remembrance of Things Past," we pluck one of Proust's gems, which, contained within one long paragraph, may stand for his approach to food.

Of J. K. Huysmans, his friend and doctor, de Lézinier, once wrote: "The frugality of his stomach and the austerity of his appetite had refined the aristocracy of his palate . . . he chose his food and wines primarily for their taste, and then for their health-sustaining properties." A man of such special and refined tastes, Huysmans nevertheless depicts the jaded young hero of "Against the Grain" in an orgy of sensuousness on the eve of his departure from Paris for London, where he expects to return to a simpler life.

Another and far more familiar aspect of Paris is X. M. Boulestin's account of a perfect and perfectly French meal, in an odd corner of the city. It is the kind of discovery every tourist dreams of.

The section concludes with the report of an American "tourist"—but what a tourist! Samuel Chamberlain's gastronomic tours of France and Italy, illustrated with his own splendid photographs, are famous in the literature of food, as are many of the other volumes he and his gourmet family have written. He has lived in France at various times, and has written about one of these residences in "Clementine in the Kitchen," under the pseudonym, Phineas Beck. The book is the gastronomic diary of an American family (the Beck-Chamberlains) in France. Clementine was their faithful, red-cheeked *cuisinière* who presided over their kitchen for nearly ten years. "Snails in the Garden" describes the incident which disclosed to the Becks that in Clementine they had found a treasure to make the heart of any gourmet sing with rapture.

An Englishman Dines in France

from Quentin Durward
by Sir Walter Scott

THE DINNER, in particular, was exquisite. The soup, although bearing the term of *maigre,* which Englishmen use in scorn, was most delicately flavored, and the matelot of pile and eels reconciled me, though a Scottishman, to the latter. There was even a *petit plat of bouilli* for the heretic, so exquisitely dressed as to retain all the juices, and, at the same time, rendered so thoroughly tender, that nothing could be more delicate. The *potage,* with another small dish or two, was equally well arranged. But what the old *maître d'hôtel* valued himself upon as something superb, smiling with self-satisfaction, and in enjoyment of my surprise, as he placed it on the table, was an immense *assiettée* of spinach not smoothed into a uniform surface, as by our uninaugurated cooks upon your side of the water, but swelling into hills and declining into vales, over which swept a gallant stag, pursued by a pack of hounds in full cry, and a noble field of horsemen and buglehorns, with whips held upright, and brandished after the manner of broadswords—hounds, huntsmen, and stag being all very artificially cut out of toasted bread. Enjoying the praises which I failed not to bestow on this *chef d'oeuvre,* the old man acknowledged it had cost the best part of two days to bring to perfection; and added, giving honor where honor was due, that an idea so brilliant was not entirely his own, but that Monsieur himself had taken the trouble to give him several valuable hints, and even condescended to assist in the execution of some of the most capital figures. The marquis blushed a little at this *éclaircissement,* which he might probably have wished to suppress, but acknowledged he had wished to surprise me with a scene from the popular poem of my country, *Miladi Lac.* I answered, that 'So splendid a cortege much more resembled a *grand chasse* of Louis Quatorze than of a poor King of Scotland, and that the paysage was rather like Fontainebleau than the wilds of Callander.' He bowed graciously in answer to this compliment, and acknowledged that recollections of the costume of the old French court, when in its splendor, might have misled his imagination—and so the conversation passed on to other matters.

Our dessert was exquisite: the cheese, the fruits, the salad, the olives, the *cerneaux,* and the delicious white wine, each in their way were *impayables;* and the good marquis, with an air of great satisfaction, observed, that his guest did sincere homage to their merits. 'After all,' he said, 'and yet it is but confessing a foolish weakness—but, after all, I cannot but rejoice in feeling myself equal to offering a stranger a sort of hospitality which seems pleasing to him. Believe me, it is not entirely out of pride that we *pauvres revenants* live so very retired, too many of us wander about the halls of our fathers, rather like ghosts of their deceased proprietors than like living men restored to their own possessions; yet it is rather on your account, than to spare our own feelings, that we do not cultivate the society of our foreign visitors. We have an idea that your opulent nation is particularly attached to *faste* and to *grand chère*—to your ease and enjoyment of every kind; and the means of entertainment left to us are, in most cases, so limited, that we feel ourselves totally precluded from such expense and ostentation. No one wishes to offer his best where he has reason to think it will not give pleasure; and as many of you publish your journals, *monsieur le marquis* would not probably be much gratified by seeing the poor dinner which he was able to present to *milord Anglois* put upon permanent record.'

I interrupted the marquis, that were I to wish an account of my entertainment published, it would be only in order to preserve the memory of the very best dinner I ever had eaten in my life. He bowed in return, and presumed that 'I either differed much from the national taste, or the accounts of it were greatly exaggerated.' He was particularly obliged to me for showing the value of the possessions which remained to him. 'The useful,' he said, 'had no doubt survived the sumptuous at Hautlieu as elsewhere. Grottoes, statues, curious conservatories of exotics, temple and tower, had gone to the ground; but vineyard, the *potager*, the orchard, the *étang*, still existed;' and once more he expressed himself 'happy to find that their combined productions could make what even a Briton accepted as a tolerable meal. I only hope,' he continued, 'that you will convince me your compliments are sincere by accepting the hospitality of the Chateau de Hautlieu as often as better engagements will permit during your stay in their neighborhood.'

I readily promised to accept an invitation offered with such grace as to make the guest appear the person conferring the obligation.

The Chaplain's Gluttony

from Letters from My Mill

by Alphonse Daudet

"TWO TRUFFLED TURKEYS, Garrigou?"

"Yes, reverend sir, two magnificent turkeys, crammed with truffles. I know something about it, since it is I who helped to stuff them. One would think that their skins must burst in roasting, they are stretched so tight—"

"Jesu-Maria! I who so love truffles! Quick! give me my surplice, Garrigou. And what else did you see in the kitchen beside the turkeys?"

"Oh! all sorts of good things. We have done nothing since noon but pluck pheasants, lapwings, pullets, and grouse. Their feathers were flying everywhere. Then they have brought from the pond eels, golden carp, trout, and—"

"How big were the trout, Garrigou?"

"As big as that, reverend sir. Enormous!"

"Oh, ye gods! It seems to me that I can see them. Have you put the wine in the cruets?"

"Yes, reverend father, I have put the wine in the cruets. But, pshaw! it is not so good as that which you will drink presently, when you come from the midnight Mass. If you could see in the château dining-room all those blazing decanters, full of wine of every color! And the silver plate, the chased epergnes, the flowers, the candelabra! Never again will be seen such a supper! The marquis has invited all the nobles in the neighborhood. There will be at least forty of you at table, you are very happy to be one of them, reverend father! Simply from having smelled those fine turkeys, the odor of the truffles follows me everywhere. Meuh!"

"Come, come, my child. Let us beware of the sin of gluttony, especially on the night of the Nativity. Go light the tapers quickly, and ring the first bell for Mass; for it is almost midnight, and we must not be late."

This conversation was carried on one Christmas Eve in the year of grace sixteen hundred and something, between the Reverend Dom Balaguère, ex-prior of Barnabites, now salaried chaplain of the lords of Trinquelage, and his little clerk Garrigou, or at least what he believed to be his little clerk Garrigou, for you must know that the devil, that night, had taken on the round face and the unformed features of the young sacristan, that he might the better lead the reverend father into temptation, and cause him to commit an appalling sin of gluttony. Therefore, while the suppositious Garrigou (hum! hum!) was lustily ringing the bell of his lordship's chapel, the reverend father finished putting on his chasuble in the little sacristy of the château, and, with his mind already excited by all these gastronomic descriptions, kept repeating to himself, as he robed—

"Roast turkeys! Golden carp! Trout as big as that!"

Jorrocks in France

from Jorrocks' Jaunts and Jollities
by Robert Smith Surtees

AT LENGTH the diligence got its slow length dragged not only to Abbéville, but to the sign of the 'Fidèle Berger'—or 'Fiddle Burger,' as Mr. Jorrocks pronounced it—where they were to dine . . .

The diligence being a *leetle* behind time as usual, the soup was on the table when they entered. The passengers quickly ranged themselves round, and, with his mouth watering as the female *garçon* lifted the cover from the tureen, Mr. Jorrocks sat in the expectation of seeing the rich contents ladled into the plates. His countenance fell fifty per cent as the first spoonful passed before his eyes. 'My wig, why it's water!' exclaimed he—'water I do declare, with worms in it—I can't eat such stuff as that—it's not man's meat—oh! dear, oh! dear, I fear I've made a terrible mistake in coming to France! Never saw such stuff as this at Bleaden's or Birch's, or anywhere in the city.' 'I've traveled three hundred miles,' said the fat man, sending his plate from him in disgust, 'and never tasted such a mess as this before.' 'I'll show them up in *Bell's Life,'* cried Mr. Jorrocks; 'and look what stuff is here—beef boiled to rags! Well, I never, no never, saw anything like this before. Oh! I wish I was is Great Coram Street again.—I'm sure I can't live here—I wonder if I could get a return chaise—waiter—gars*oo*n—cuss! . . .'

Oh! Heavens! grant your poor Jorrocks but one request, and that is the contents of a single sentence. 'I want a roasted or boiled leg of mutton, beef, hung beef, a quarter of mutton, mutton chops, veal cutlets, stuffed tongue, hog's pudding, white sausage, chicken with rice, a nice fat roast fowl, roast chicken with cressy, roast or boiled pigeon, a fricassee of chicken, sweetbread, goose, lamb, calf's cheek, calf's head, fresh pork, salt pork, cold meat, hash.—But where's the use of titivating one's appetite with reading of such luxuries? . . . Oh! dear, oh! dear, I shall die of hunger I see—I shall die of absolute famine, my stomach thinks my throat's cut already!' In the height of his distress in came two turkeys and a couple of fowls, and his countenance shone forth like an April sun after a shower. 'Come, this is better,' said he; 'I'll trouble you, sir, for a leg and a wing, and a bit of the breast, for I'm really famished'—oh, hang! the fellow's a Frenchman and I shall spend half the day in looking it out in my dictionary. Oh, dear, oh, dear, where's the dinner dialogue!—well, here's something to the purpose. 'I will send you a bit of this fowl.' 'A little bit of the fowl cannot hurt you.'—'No, nor a great bit either.'—'Which do you like best, a leg or a wing?' '*Qu'aimez vous le mieux, la cuisse ou l'aile?*' Here the Countess Benvolio, who had been playing a good knife and fork herself, pricked up her ears, and, guessing at Jorrocks's wants, interceded with her countryman and got him a plateful of fowl. It was soon disposed of, however, and half a dish of hashed hare or cat, that was placed within reach of him shortly after, was quickly transferred into his plate . . .

Presently there was a large dish of stewed eels put on. 'What's that?' asked Jorrocks of the man. '*Poisson*' was the reply. '*Poison!* why, you infidel, have you no conscience?' 'Fish,' said the Countess. 'Oh aye, I smell—eels—just like what we have at the eel-pie house at Twickenham—your ladyship, I am thirsty—ge soif, in fact.' 'Ah, *bon,*' said the Countess laughing, and giving him a tumblerful of claret. 'I've traveled three hundred thousand miles,' said the fat man, 'and never saw claret drunk in that way before.' 'It's not werry good, I think,' said Mr. Jorrocks, smacking his lips; 'if it was not claret I would sooner drink port.' Some wild ducks and *fricandeau de veau* which followed were cut up and handed round, Jorrocks helping himself plentifully to both, as also to *pommes de terre à la maître d'hôtel,* and bread at discretion . . . Just when Jorrocks began to think he had satisfied nature, in came a roast leg of mutton, a beefsteak, 'à la G--d dam,' and a dish of larks and snipes . . . He again set to, and 'went a good one' at both mutton and snipes, but on pulling up, he appeared somewhat exhausted . . . He had not got through it all yet however. Just as he was taking breath, a *garçon* entered with some custards and an enormous *omelette soufflée* whose puffy brown sides bagged over the tin dish that contained it. 'There's a tart!' cried Mr. Jorrocks. 'Oh my eyes, what a swell! Well suppose I must have a shy at it.—"In for a penny, in for a pound!" as we say at the Lord Mayor's feed. Know I shall be sick, but, however, here goes' . . . The first dive of the spoon undeceived him as he heard it sound at the bottom of the dish. 'Oh, lauk, what a go! All puff, by Jove!—a regular humbug—a balloon pudding in short! I won't eat such stuff—give it to Mouncheer there,' rejecting the offer of a piece. 'I like the solids;—will trouble you for some of that cheese, sir, and don't let it taste of the knife. But what do they mean by setting the dessert on before the cloth is removed?' . . .

'You shall take some dessert,' said the Countess, handing him over some peaches and biscuits. 'Well, I'll try my hand at it if it will oblige your ladyship, but I really have had *almost* enough.' 'And some apricot,' said she, helping him to a couple of fine juicy ones. 'Oh, thank you, my lady, thank you, my lady, I'm *nearly* satisfied.' '*Vous ne mangez pas,*' said she, giving him half a plate of grapes. 'Oh, my lady, you don't understand me—I *can't* eat any more—I am regularly high and dry—chock full—*bursting in fact.*' Here she handed him a plate of sponge cakes mixed with bon-bons and macaroons, saying '*Vous êtes un pauvre mangeur—vous ne mangez rien, Monsieur.*' 'Oh, dear, she does not understand me, I see.—Indeed, my lady, I *can not* eat any more.—Ge would-era, se ge could-era, mais ge can-era pas!' 'Well now, I've traveled three hundred thousand miles, and never heard such a bit of French as that before,' said the fat man, chuckling.

There is a most delectable little part of the turkey which the French euphoniously call *le sot l'y laisse*. Grimod de la Reynière, the celebrated gourmet, was wont to say that it was the most exquisite morsel of flesh in the world.

—Frank Schloesser, in *The Greedy Book*

Lunch at Combray

from Swann's Way

by Marcel Proust

FROM THE DAY on which fine weather definitely set in at Combray—the proud hour of noon, descending from the steeple of Saint-Hilaire which it blazoned for a moment with the twelve points of its sonorous crown, would long have echoed about our table . . . and we would still be found seated in front of our Arabian Nights plates, weighted down by the heat of the day, and even more by our heavy meal. For the permanent foundation of eggs, cutlets, potatoes, preserves and biscuits, whose appearance on the table she no longer announced to us, Françoise would add—as the labor of fields and orchards, the harvest of the tides, the luck of the market, the kindness of the neighbors, and her own genius might provide; and so effectively that our bill of fare, like the quatrefoils that were carved on the porches of cathedrals in the thirteenth century, reflected to some extent the march of the seasons and the incidents of human life—a brill, because the fish-woman had guaranteed its freshness; a turkey, because she had seen a beauty in the market . . . cardoons with marrow, because she had never done them for us that way before; a roast leg of mutton, because the fresh air made one hungry and there would be plenty of time for it to "settle down" in the seven hours before dinner; spinach, by way of a change; apricots, because they were still hard to get; gooseberries, because in another fortnight there would be none left; raspberries, which Mr. Swann had brought specially; cherries, the first to come from the cherry tree which had yielded none for the last two years; a cream-cheese, of which in those days I was extremely fond; an almond cake, because she had ordered one the evening before; a fancy loaf, because it was our turn to "offer" the holy bread. And when all these had been eaten, a work composed expressly for ourselves, but dedicated more particularly to my father who had a fondness for such things—a cream of chocolate, inspired in the mind, created by the hand of Françoise, would be laid before us, light and fleeting as an occasional piece of music, into which she had poured the whole of her talent. Anyone who refused to partake of it, saying: "No, thank you, I have finished, I am not hungry," would at once have been lowered to the level of the Philistines who, when an artist makes them a present of one of his works, examine its weight and material, whereas what is of value is the creator's intention and his signature. To have left even the tiniest morsel in the dish would have shown as much discourtesy as to rise and leave a concert hall while the piece was still being played, and under the composer's very eyes.

A Young Rake Sates Himself in the Paris Fleshpots

from Against the Grain

by J. K. Huysmans

HE ACQUIRED the reputation of an eccentric, which he enhanced by wearing costumes of white velvet, and gold-embroidered waist-coats, by inserting, in place of a cravat, a Parma bouquet in the opening of his shirt, by giving famous dinners to men of letters, one of which, a revival of the eighteenth century, celebrating the most futile of his misadventures, was a funeral repast.

In the dining-room, hung in black and opening on the transformed garden with its ash-powdered walks, its little pool now bordered with basalt and filled with ink, its clumps of cypresses and pines, the dinner had been served on a table draped in black, adorned with baskets of violets and scabiouses, lit by candelabra from which green flames blazed, and by chandeliers from which wax tapers flared.

To the sound of funeral marches played by a concealed orchestra, nude Negresses, wearing slippers and stockings of silver cloth with patterns of tears, served the guests.

Out of black-edged plates they had drunk turtle soup and eaten Russian rye bread, ripe Turkish olives, caviar, smoked Frankfort black pudding, game with sauces that were the color of licorice and blacking, truffle gravy, chocolate cream puddings, nectarines, grape preserves, mulberries, and black-heart cherries; they had sipped, out of dark glasses, wines from Limagnes, Roussillon, Tenedos, Val de Penas, and Porto, and after the coffee and walnut brandy had partaken of kvas and porter and stout.

The farewell dinner to a temporarily dead virility—this was what he had written on invitation cards designed like bereavement notices.

* * *

The fiacre stopped in front of the tavern. Once more, Des Esseintes alighted and entered a long dark plain room, divided into partitions as high as a man's waist—a series of compartments resembling stalls. In this room, wider towards the door, many beer pumps stood on a counter, near hams having the color of old violins, red lobsters, marinated mackeral, with onions and carrots, slices of lemon, bunches of laurel and thyme, juniper berries and long peppers swimming in thick sauce.

One of these boxes was unoccupied. He took it and called a young black-suited man who bent forward, muttering something in a jargon he could not understand. While the cloth was being laid, Des Esseintes viewed his neighbors. There were islanders . . . with cold *faïence* eyes, crimson complexions, thoughtful or haughty airs. They were reading foreign newspapers. The only ones eating were unescorted women in pairs, robust English women with boyish faces, large teeth, ruddy apple cheeks, long hands and legs. They attacked, with genuine ardor, a rumpsteak pie, a warm meat dish cooked in mushroom sauce and covered with a crust, like a pie.

After having lacked appetite for such a long time, he remained amazed in the presence of these hearty eaters whose voracity whetted his hunger. He ordered oxtail soup and enjoyed it heartily. Then he glanced at the menu for the fish, ordered a haddock and, seized with a sudden pang of hunger at the sight of so many people relishing their food, he ate some roast beef and drank two pints of ale, stimulated by the flavor of a cow-shed which this fine, pale beer exhaled.

His hunger persisted. He lingered over a piece of blue Stilton cheese, made quick work of a rhubarb tart, and to vary his drinking quenched his thirst with porter, that dark beer which smells of Spanish licorice but which does not have its sugary taste.

He breathed deeply. Not for years had he eaten and drunk so much. This change of habit, this choice of unexpected and solid food had awakened his stomach from its long sleep. He leaned back in his chair, lit a cigarette and prepared to sip his coffee, into which gin had been poured.

A Corner of Paris

from Having Crossed the Channel

by X. Marcel Boulestin

THE TAXI-DRIVER did not try to hide his surprise and his dissatisfaction; he went on grumbling and muttering to himself while racing along the crowded streets; evidently his bad temper spoilt his usual accuracy; he missed two pedestrians and one car. We could not help sympathizing with him; it was no joke being left miles away in the wilds of La Villette, where there would be no prospect of a "fare" back till he reached a more civilized quarter. Yet it was civilization we were pursuing in these rough parts, civilization in the guise of a perfect meal. We had been promised wonders by one whose opinion was invaluable, wonders—that is, the genuine good cooking, the finer traditions, the food one had dreamt of or tasted once, by chance, in some remote corner of France still unspoilt by progress.

It was odd somehow to have to go to the Boulevard de La Villette, of all places in Paris, in order to find a meal which would be both perfect and perfectly French. Our cab went on through streets which appeared sometimes sordid, sometimes frankly provincial; at last we reached a large avenue: on one side there were small houses, on the other big buildings, walls with gates at intervals, the *Abattoirs,* where all the cattle to be eaten in Paris are slaughtered.

Suddenly, in this dreary avenue, an oasis, as it were: a few trees in tubs, three *café-restaurants,* little tables on the pavement, a real *coin de province.* The smallest of the three establishments, the "Cochon d'Or" was our goal.

The moment we entered and saw the customers, the *patron,* the bill of fare, the wine-list, we knew we had not been deceived. We had hors-d'oeuvre, none of your moldy sardines, anemic tomatoes and washed-out potato salad, but slices of cold sausages and home-made potted meat, *Terrine* Maison. There was no doubt about it. "*Ça y est, c'est ça,*" murmured my friend. It was fatal, final, a great light, so to speak; discussion was useless, choice forbidden. We left it to the *patron,* all politeness and efficiency, who came himself to serve us. Obviously he had not time to waste. Our fate was decided in a few seconds; surrender was the only way. We surrendered abjectly, beautifully, extravagantly.

It was a simple meal, but the simplicity was that of perfection and with an amount of refinement all unexpected and quite out of keeping with the table manners of the customers. But they knew what to eat if, according to polite standards, they did not know how to eat it. The meat, of course, was of the finest quality and grilled, as it should be, on charcoal, the birds were roasted on a spit in front of an open fire, the salad seasoned with oil made of crushed walnuts, the fired potatoes, as a matter of course, *soufflées* and coffee admirable. The wine-list was imposing. We gave it several chances; the Romanèche rosé was obviously the genuine article bought by the *patron* from the same grower, year after year, and the Haut Brion, 1908, all that it should be, especially against a background of Port-Salut cheese. But it was odd to see these farmers finishing their luncheon with ices and Coupe-Jacques like so many schoolgirls. It seemed somehow all wrong, a touch of "modernism" with its suggestion of "Smartness," entirely out of place in this temple of Tradition.

The American Gastronome in France

from Clementine in the Kitchen
by Phineas Beck

WITHIN A WEEK after the bright-eyed Clementine came to preside over our kitchen in Senlis the Beck family realized what a treasure it had found. One cool evening, after her dishes were washed, we watched Clementine take an exploratory stroll out to the garden gate, a rather picturesque bit of rural architecture with a steep tile roof. It had been a rainy day, and the ground was humid under her feel as she disappeared around the corner wall. Suddenly she came into view again, visibly excited. She rushed up to us wide-eyed, then gulped and regained her composure before breaking the news.

"*Mais Madame, vous avez des escargots dans votre jardin! Des centaines d'escargots!*" This breathless bit of information came as a thunderbolt to the innocent Beck family, though we should have guessed what was destroying our young lettuce plants. We rushed down to the garden wall in the semi-obscurity. An incredible evening promenade of snails greeted us—dozens and hundreds of them. They had grown reckless, perhaps because of the long immunity which our innocence had given them, and deserting their daytime retreats in the deep recesses of the wall, they had come out in droves. The moist terrain doubtless made smooth and agreeable traction. They clung to the branches of our dwarf pear tree like baubles on a Christmas evergreen. They paraded over our newly spaded vegetable beds, carrying their ochre-colored shells lightly and leaving silvery trails behind them, intent upon devouring tender young green shoots. Some of them merely basked on the stone wall, apparently enjoying the moist evening air. With peasant enthusiasm at getting something for nothing, Clementine plucked them up from the ground with joyful rapidity, and the whole family joined in the hunt. In no time we all had a good-sized pail full.

When, we asked, would we be able to feast upon our find? Clementine looked surprised at our ignorance.

"Oh, not yet, Madame. First they must fast themselves. They should be kept captive for a week. *Then* we can sample them."

To give the snails enough parading space to divest themselves of their impurities, Clementine hit upon the idea of allotting a cardboard shoebox to each three or four dozen snails. For several days these boxes stayed unnoticed in a corner of the kitchen, each securely tied with string. But Clementine had not counted upon the disintegrating effect of snail moisture upon cardboard. And one memorable night the boxes softened up enough to permit a wholesale escape.

Our first intimation of it came about midnight, when strange crackling noises occasionally arose from the kitchen. The family cat, usually a phlegmatic animal, seemed to be disturbed, and made restless sounds. When we finally paddled downstairs in our slippers, a rare sight awaited us. Every one of the snails was on parade again, over the floor, the sink, the table, icebox and gas stove. Many of them had loftier aspirations, and were proceeding up the walls and across the ceiling. Here the traction was not so good, apparently. Many of the snails had lost their grip and fallen to the floor, shell and all, making the peculiar crackling noise we had heard upstairs. It took an hour of ingenious acrobatics and cautious stepping to disrupt this truant flight, but finally we had them all assembled, except for the cracked and fallen ones, in a well-sealed wooden crate. Clementine was a trifle red-faced the next morning, and hastily removed the traces of silvery scum from the kitchen. She had another bad moment when she began to wipe the breakfast dishes and found the dish towel alive with errant snails.

This variety of snail was the smaller *petit gris,* of course, and not the magnificent creature that deigns only to live in Burgundy. The *petit gris* is a forager, working hard for what he gets. The real Burgundian snail, however, leads a charmed existence until his hour of reckoning arrives. He is encouraged to gorge himself upon the lush, fat leaves of the Pinot and Gamay grape vines in the Burgundy valley, since he leaves the grapes strictly alone. The effect of such a mass attack on the leaves is very noticeable. Frequently only the dried leaf structure remains. Here again the snail serves the wine grower well. By removing the body of the leaves he has opened up a path for the ardent rays of the September sun, so vital to the fruition of the grapes.

When it came time to prepare our *petit gris,* I was curious about the authoritative recipe, and asked Clementine if she knew of one. With a troubled look she brought out her green-covered cook book and gave it to me.

"It's in here, Monsieur, and it is very good. But I should warn you that the monsieur who wrote the recipe is long-winded and full of silly words. I think he's something of a '*farceur.*' "

The recipe which greeted my astonished eyes is such a unique document that I can't resist sharing it with you. It is written by Georges Lecomte. With only a few deletions, here is a fairly accurate translation:

ESCARGOTS DE BOURGOGNE

"You ambush them in the morning, while they are parading nonchalantly on the humid leaf, when their slow, fleshy promenade makes one think of the throat of a voluptuous woman shuddering under a gross and clumsy caress. The snail, sticky and thick, carries its light shell with a facetious air, and projects or contracts its horns so lasciviously elastic, as the mood pleases him. He irritates you a little with his tactics of a gluttonous beast, rampant on his well-filled stomach, and everlastingly on the same greedy quest.

"So, between two indignant fingers you imprison this shell, fallacious as a crinoline, and you pull, in order to disengage the adherent flesh from the leaf to which it is sticking. The beast beats the air in distress with its bewildered tentacles, and then retreats glowering into its kiosk, like a much-teased maiden who rushes sobbing to her bedroom. But no pity! These melodramatic gestures no longer move the soul of a gourmet.

"You next cloister your snail in a cool cellar and, regardless of its own ideas on hygiene, you invariably nurse him for eight days on green and succulent lettuce, exactly as you stuff a nursing mother with lentils in order to have better milk, even though the good woman is refractory regarding such fattening fare. On such favorable tidbits our beasts are to enrich themselves. And what noble flesh it makes—rich, velvety, worthy of a princely banquet!

"From there on, cease to regard these slugs as living creatures. Like an ogre, with your cutlass in your teeth, you begin the bold hunt for these voluptuaries who lounge on their divans of lettuce. They would like to make you tender hearted with their imploring horns. Ignore them. Place them at once in a *terrine* with salt and vinegar. *Ah, dame!* There will be convulsions, if not tears! With your hands you manfully move this seething mass to make it foam. Secretions which are too bitter or too listless escape from tissues thus sharply attacked. Then you pour repeated torrents of water upon them to sweep away the scum. And when, upon the beasts thus purged, only a last crystal glaze remains, limpid as spring water, you collect your immobile mass of snails, cringing terrified in the corners of their shells, and you throw them to their final torture in an earthen crock bubbling with boiling water. You cook them for a half hour or so, until your instinct signals that you may exhume the rich meat from the shells. Ah, since this last adventure, our beasts have ceased to be self-indulgent foragers, and their antennae formerly so proudly retractable, are now very melancholy little things. But what of that? You have the ferocious heart of a fanatic now!

"Quickly drain these corpses, still in refuge at the fat end of their dwelling. Then, without any pusillanimity, pull them from their retreat. If you are very refined, give them a supreme *toilette* in several baths of hot water. Having arrived at this paroxysm of murder, you have, of course, no further scruples. So, with the cold eye of a torturer, you contemplate these soft submissive snails and, as one possessed of a cruel frenzy, you strip off their green outer skins.

"All that remains for you is the delicate routine of an artist, a sumptuous chef. *C'est charmant*. In a radiant copper casserole you spread out this flesh which has ceased to suffer, accompanied by the traditional and poetic bouquet of bay leaf, parsley and thyme. In order that the vegetable garden and the wine cellar may join in the festivities, you add a handsome golden brown onion, the sliver of a section of garlic and the sunshine of a glass of cognac. Then you dilute this appetizing mixture in water, and let it simmer over a calm, tranquil little fire for six or seven hours. And then, what aromas arise as you lift off the cover! Your snails are impregnated with all of these fine substances. Let them cool peacefully, like a wise man would handle precious bits of porcelain. In each shell pour adroitly one unctuous spoonful of *jus de viande*. As soon as you think the snails are cold, make a pious restitution to each one, by putting it in a shell thus prepared. And when the animal, unaware of the fine nectar into which it is being plunged, reclines gracefully in the sauce, block up the opening of the shell with a thick layer of beaten butter, joyously sown with chives, shallots, salt, pepper and chopped parsley. In a special circular plate place these little domes sheltering their savory preparations and heat them in a hot oven. May the butter melt and run, so that all of these aromas will penetrate well into the meat.

"Then, your soul rejoiced, your eyes sparkling, you have only to regale yourself with this truly exquisite dish, despite the abominable animal which furnishes the pretext."

Clementine, though very distrustful of Monsieur Lecomte's fine words, admitted that his recipe was worthy of the best Burgundian master cooks, and she followed it closely. She insists that six or seven hours is too long to cook them, but admits that the *ciboulette* and shallots in the butter are more subtle than garlic, which almost everyone uses. At all events, the result which we tasted ten days after the discovery in the garden was utterly superb. My good spouse, who had shuddered on the brink of tasting a snail for almost five years, fell overboard with a vengeance, after the first taste. We had to be stern to stop little Phinney at two dozen. I had known snails during the war—had gone to a snail party with a group of *poilus,* in fact, where twenty of us polished off some eight hundred snails which they had prepared with loving care and magnificent dosages of garlic. Plenty of red *pinard,* bread, strong cheese, black coffee and blacker cigarettes had gone with them. When I crept back into the barracks at midnight, my breath had been sufficient to awaken all of my slumbering fellow doughboys, and to stir up a fine flurry of profanity. But I had never known snails like these!

Chapter Five

TASTINGS FROM OTHER CUISINES

WE HAVE NO disposition to ignore the food of other countries than England, France and our own—indeed, some of them will be considered in other sections of this anthology—but there is a limit to the appetite of even the most gluttonous anthologist. However, there are a few plates it would be a shame to leave untouched.

One is Flaubert's vivid description of a Carthaginian feast from "Salambo"—eating on a heroic scale. Another is the cuisine of imperial Russia, represented first by two short excerpts from the journals of those indefatigable English girls,

Martha and Catherine Wilmot, who explored the delights of Moscow with typical British thoroughness. Our other Russian excerpt comes from an unlikely source, Nikolai Gogol's "Dead Souls," a masterwork of the most penetrating satire and irony, in which the Russia of mid-nineteenth century is laid bare with a scalpel. This is not heroic eating, in the manner of Flaubert, but simple gourmandizing as practiced by the rich land owners of Russia.

There follows another view of gourmandizing, from the pages of Eugène Sue's curious novel, "Gluttony."

The chapter closes with an excerpt from another masterwork, Thomas Mann's "Buddenbrooks." Here the gluttony of Gogol's Russia is transferred to Germany, proving that the steady stuffing of the well-to-do middle class in the last century was very much the same everywhere.

A Carthaginian Feast

from Salambo

by Gustave Flaubert

(*translated by Powys Mathers*)

MEN OF ALL NATIONS were there, Ligurians and Lusitanians, Balearic Islanders, Negroes, and fugitives from Rome . . .

They lay upon cushions; they squatted around huge trays, and so ate; others, lying upon their bellies, reached out for lumps of meat and gorged themselves, leaning on their elbows in the placid posture of lions dismembering their prey. Late-comers, leaning against the trees, watched the low tables half hidden under their scarlet coverings, and awaited their turn.

Since Hamilcar's kitchens were inadequate, the Council had provided slaves, dishes and couches. Oxen were roasting at great clear fires in the middle of the garden, which thus looked like a battlefield when the dead are being burned. Loaves dusted with aniseed vied with huge cheeses heavier than disks, and great bowls of wine with mighty water tankards, set close to gold filigree baskets full of flowers. Their eyes gleamed wide in delight at being at last free to gorge to their hearts' content; and here and there they were beginning to sing.

First they were served with birds in green sauce upon plates of red clay, decorated in black relief; then with every kind of shell-fish that is found on the Punic coasts, with broths thickened with wheat, beans and barley, and with cumin-spiced snails upon yellow amber dishes.

After this the tables were loaded with meats: antelopes still with their horns, peacocks still with their feathers, whole sheep cooked in sweet wine, camels' and buffaloes' haunches, hedgehogs in garum sauce, fried grasshoppers, and pickled dormice. Great pieces of fat were floating amid saffron in bowls of Tamrapanni wood. Everywhere was a lavish abundance of pickles, truffles, and asafoetida. There were pyramids of fruit tumbling upon honeycombs; and they had not forgotten to serve some of those silky-coated, red, fat-paunched little dogs, fattened on olive lees: a Carthaginian dish which was an abomination to other peoples. Their stomachs' greed was titillated by the excitement and wonder of such novel fare. The Gauls, with their long hair coiled upon the top of their heads, snatched at watermelons and lemons, and crunched them peel and all. Negroes who had never seen a crawfish, tore their faces on its red spines. The Greeks, who were smooth-shaven and whiter than marble, threw the leavings of their plates behind them; while herdsmen from Brutium, clad in wolf-skins, ate in silence, their faces buried in their plates.

Night fell. The awning over the cypress avenue was drawn back, and torches were brought.

Dining in Moscow, 1804

from The Russian Journals of Martha and Catherine Wilmot

YESTERDAY WE WENT at twelve o'clock to Count Ostrowman's . . . Immediately on entering we were led to a table where what is called a Breakfast was displayed—that is, little odds and ends of dried fish, or Caviar, of Cheese, Bread, etc., and *eau de vie* were presented to us to give us an appetite for dinner which was announced almost immediately. We assembled in the Hall . . . surrounded by a sort of gallery which was filled with Men, Women, Dwarfs, children, Fools, and enraged musicians who sang and played with such powerful effect as to deafen those whom Heaven had spared . . .

A Trumpet sounded and "blew a blast so loud and dread" that every tongue was silenced . . . A crystal vase filled with champagne was presented to the Master of the Castle. He stood up and quaffed the sparkling draught to the health of the Lady of the feast. The Trumpet sounded a second tune, the Goblet was presented to Princess Dashkaw who went thro' the same ceremony. A third time the Trumpet sounded and a third person quaffed from the same crystal vase to the same toast. In short the ceremony was repeated for every individual, and as there were a party of forty-six you may judge the time which all the pomp and parade took up . . .

Many a bad dinner I made from the mere fatigue of being offered fifty or sixty different dishes by servants who come one after the other and flourish ready carv'd fish, flesh, fowl, vegetables, fruits, soups of fish, etc., before your eyes, wines, liqueures, etc., in their turn. Seriously the profusion is beyond anything I ever saw . . .

At a very agreeable sledging party . . . which was given nominally for the Princess (Dashkaw) we were a few minutes late, and could scarcely gain admittance for the number of traineaus that were in the court and afterwards for the number of guests that were in the apartments. Soon after chocolate and cakes were handed, and then breakfast opened on our astonished optics in another room, which consisted of hot and cold soups, meat, fish, fowls, ices, fruits, etc. The dessert was in another room, dry'd fruits, cakes, and *eau de vie*. At length forty traineaus, each drawn by six horses at least, quitted the House. In each traineau were four people, two ladies and two gentlemen attended by two footmen and two or three postillions, etc. The *coup d'oeuil* was superb. We drove like lightning round the town . . . each animating his coachman to unheard of exertions to pass the traineau which was before him . . . After parading with indefatigable speed for two hours and a half we returned to M. Kumberline's, arranged our dresses as well as we could, drank tea, and then danced to conclude the evening.

Gourmandizing in Nineteenth Century Russia

from Dead Souls
by Nikolai Gogol
(*translated by Constance Garnett*)

"WELL, MY LOVE, shall we go in to dinner?" said Madame Sobakevitch to her husband.

"Please!" said Sobakevitch. Whereupon the two gentlemen, going up to the table which was laid with savories, duly drank a glass of vodka each; they took a preliminary snack as is done all over the vast expanse of Russia, throughout the towns and villages, that is, tasted various salt dishes and other stimulating dainties; then all proceeded to the dining-room; the hotess sailed in at their head like a goose swimming. The small table was laid for four . . .

"The cabbage soup is particularly good today," said Sobakevitch, taking spoonfuls of the soup and helping himself to an immense portion of a well-known delicacy which is served with cabbage soup and consists of sheep's stomach, stuffed with buckwheat, brains, and sheep's trotters. "You won't find a dish like this in town," he went on, addressing Tchitchikov, "the devil only knows what they give you there!"

"The governor keeps a good table, however," said Tchitchikov.

"But do you know what it is all made of? You won't eat it when you do know."

"I don't know how the dishes were cooked, I can't judge of that; but the pork chops and the stewed fish were excellent."

"You fancy so. You see I know what they buy at the market. That scoundrelly cook who has been trained in France buys a cat and skins it and sends it up to the table for a hare."

"Faugh, what unpleasant things you say!" said his wife.

"Well, my love! That's how they do things; it's not my fault, that's how they do things, all of them. All the refuse that our Alkulka throws, if I may be permitted to say so, into the rubbish pail, they put into the soup, yes, into the soup! In it goes!"

"You always talk about such things at table," his wife protested again.

"Well, my love," said Sobakevitch, "if I did the same myself, you might complain, but I tell you straight that I am not going to eat filth. If you sprinkle frogs with sugar I wouldn't put them into my mouth, and I wouldn't taste oysters, either: I know what oysters are like. Take some mutton," he went on, addressing Tchitchikov. "This is saddle of mutton with grain, not the fricassees that they make in gentlemen's kitchens out of mutton which has been lying about in the market-place for days. The French and German doctors have invented all that; I'd have them all hanged for it. They have invented a treatment too, the hunger cure! Because they have a thin-blooded German constitution, they fancy they can treat the Russian stomach too. No, it's all wrong, it's all their fancies, it's all . . ." Here Sobakevitch shook his head wrathfully. "They talk of enlightenment, enlightenment, and this enlightenment is . . . faugh! I might use another word for it but it would be improper at the dinner table. It is not like that in my house. If we have pork we put the whole pig on the table, if it's mutton, we bring in the whole sheep, if it's a goose, the whole goose! I had rather eat only two dishes, and eat my fill of them." Sobakevitch confirmed this in practice; he put half a saddle of mutton on his plate and ate it all, gnawing and sucking every little bone . . .

The saddle of mutton was followed by curd cheese-cakes, each one of which was much larger than a plate, then a turkey as big as a calf, stuffed with all sorts of good things: eggs, rice, kidneys, and goodness knows what. With this the dinner ended, but when they had risen from the table Tchitchikov felt as though he were two or three stones heavier. They went into the drawing-room, where they found a saucer of jam already awaiting them—not a pear, nor a plum, nor any kind of berry—and neither of the gentlemen touched it. The lady of the house went out of the room to put out some more on other saucers.

Taking advantage of her absence, Tchitchikov turned to Sobakevitch, who, lying in an easy-chair, was merely gasping after his ample repast and emitting from his throat undefinable sounds while he crossed himself and continually put his hand before his mouth. Tchitchikov addressed him as follows: "I should like to have a few words with you about a little matter of business."

"Here is some more jam," said the lady of the house, returning with a saucer, "It's very choice, made with honey!"

"We will have some of it later on," said Sobakevitch. "You go to your own room now, Pavel Ivanitch and I will take off our coats and have a little nap."

The lady began suggesting that she should send for feather beds and pillows, but her husband said, "There's no need, we can doze in our easy-chairs," and she withdrew . . .

LATER, Tchitchikov finds himself overeating again in the country home of Piotr Petrovitch, a fat man whose gourmandizing pursues his host even into bed after a day of spectacular stuffing.

At supper they over-ate themselves again. When Pavel Ivanovitch had retired to the room assigned to him, and had got into bed, he felt his stomach: "It's as tight as a drum!" he said; "no more could possibly get in." As luck would have it, his host's room was the other side of the wall; the wall was a thin one and everything that was said was audible. On the pretense of an early lunch he was giving the cook directions for a regular dinner, and what directions! It was enough to give a dead man an appetite. He licked and smacked his lips. There were continually such phrases as: "But roast it well, let it soak well." While the cook kept saying in a thin high voice: "Yes, sir, I can, I can do that too."

"And make a four-cornered fish pastry; in one corner put a sturgeon's cheeks and the jelly from its back, in another put buckwheat mush, mushrooms and onions and sweet roe, and brains and something else—you know . . ."

"Yes, sir, I can do it like that."

"And let it be just a little colored on one side, you know, and let it be a little less done on the other. And bake the underpart, you understand, that it may be all crumbling, all soaked in juice, so that it will melt in the mouth like snow."

"Confound him," thought Tchitchikov, turning over on the other side, "he won't let me sleep."

"Make me a haggis and put a piece of ice in the middle, so that it may swell up properly. And let the garnishing for the sturgeon be rich. Garnish it with crayfish and little fried fish, with a stuffing of little smelts, add fine mince, horse radish and mushrooms and turnips, and carrots and beans, and is there any other root?"

"I might put in kohlrabi and beetroot cut in stars," said the cook.

"Yes, put in kohlrabi, and beetroot, and I'll tell you what garnish to serve with the roast . . ."

"I shall never get to sleep," said Tchitchikov. Turning over on the other side, he buried his head in the pillow and pulled the quilt up over it, that he might hear nothing, but through the quilt he heard unceasingly: "And roast it well," and "Bake it thoroughly." He fell asleep over a turkey.

* * *

"Tell me, why Lettuce, which our grandsires last did eate,
Is now of late become to be first of meat?"

—GERARDE'S *Herbal*

An Elderly Canon Eats Well

from Gluttony

by Eugène Sue

SOON THE MAJOR-DOMO reappeared.

He walked with a solemn air, bearing on a tray a little chafing-dish of silver, the size of a plate, surmounted with its stew-pan. On the side of the tray was a small crystal flagon, filled with a limpid liquid, the color of burnt topaz.

Pablo, as he approached, several times held his nose to the edge of the stew-pan to inhale the appetizing exhalations which escaped from it; finally, he placed on the table the little chafing-dish, the flagon, and a small card.

"Pablo," asked the canon, pointing to the chafing-dish, surmounted with its pan, "what is that silver plate?"

"It belongs to M. Appetite, sir; under this pan is a dish with a double bottom, filled with boiling water, because this great man says the food must be eaten burning hot."

"And that flagon, Pablo?"

"Its use is marked on the card, sir, which informs you of all the dishes you are going to eat."

"Let me see this card," said the canon, and he read:

" 'Guinea fowl eggs fried in the fat of quails, relieved with a gravy of crabs.

" 'N. B. Eat burning hot, make only one mouthful of each egg, after having softened it well with the gravy.

" 'Masticate *pianissimo*.

" 'Drink after each egg two fingers of Madeira wine of 1807, which has made five voyages from Rio de Janeiro to Calcutta. (It is needless to say that certain wines are vastly improved by long voyages.)

" 'Drink this wine with meditation.

" 'It is impossible for me not to take the liberty to accompany each dish which I have the honor of serving Lord Dom Diégo with a flagon of wine appropriate to the particular character of the aforesaid dish.' "

The canon, whose agitation was increasing, lifted the top of the silver dish with a trembling hand.

Suddenly a delicious odor spread itself through the atmosphere. Pablo clasped his hands, dilating his wide nostrils, and looking at the dish with a greedy eye.

In the middle of the silver dish, half steeped in an unctuous, velvety gravy of a beautiful rosy hue, the major-domo saw four little round soft eggs, that seemed still to tremble with their smoking, golden frying.

The canon, struck like his major-domo with the delicious fragrance of the dish, literally ate it with his eyes, and for the first time in two months a sudden desire of appetite tickled his palate. Nevertheless, he still doubted, believing in the deceitful illusion of a false hunger. Taking in a spoon one of the little eggs, well impregnated with gravy, he shoveled it into his large mouth.

"Masticate *pianissimo,* my lord!" cried Pablo, who followed every motion of his master with a beating heart. "Masticate slowly, the magician said, and afterwards drink this, according to the directions."

And Pablo poured out two fingers of the Madeira wine of 1807, in a glass as thin as the peel of an onion, and presented it to Dom Diégo.

Oh, wonder! Oh, marvel! Oh, miracle! The second movement of the mastication *pianissimo* was hardly accomplished when the canon threw his head gently back, and, half shutting his eyes in a sort of ecstasy, crossed his two hands on his breast, still holding in one hand the spoon with which he had just served himself . . .

Each service was accompanied with an "order," as Pablo called it, and new flagons of wine, drawn, no doubt, from the cellar of this wonderful cook.

A collection of these culinary bulletins will give an idea of the varied delights enjoyed by Dom Diégo.

After the note which announced the Guinea fowl eggs, the following menu was served, in the order in which we present it:

"Trout from the lake of Geneva with Montpellier butter, preserved in ice.

"Envelope each mouthful of this exquisite fish, hermetically, in a layer of this highly spiced seasoning.

"Masticate *allegro*.

"Drink two glasses of this Bordeaux wine, Sauterne of 1834, which has made the voyage from the Indies three times.

"This wine should be *meditated*."

"A painter or a poet would have made an enchanting picture of this trout with Montpellier butter preserved in ice," said the canon to Pablo. "See there, this charming little trout, with flesh the color of a rose, and a head like mother-of-pearl, voluptuously lying on this bed of shining green, composed of fresh butter and virgin oil congealed by ice, to which tarragon, chive, parsley, and watercresses have given this bright emerald color! And what perfume! How the freshness of this seasoning contrasts with the pungency of the spices which relieve it! How delicious! And this wine of Sauterne! As the great man of the kitchen says, how admirably this ambrosia is suited to the character of this divine trout which gives me a growing appetite!"

After the trout came another dish, accompanied with this bulletin:

"Fillets of grouse with white Piedmont truffles, minced raw.

"Enclose each mouthful of grouse between two slices of truffle, and moisten the whole well with sauce à la Periguex, with which black truffles are mingled.

"Masticate *forte*, as the white truffles are raw.

"Drink two glasses of this wine of Château-Margaux 1834—it also has made a voyage from the Indies.

It is needless to say that all the prescriptions of the cook were followed literally by the canon, whose appetite, now a prodigious thing, seemed to increase in proportion as it was fed; finally, having exhausted his glass to the last drop, Dom Diègo, his ears scarlet, his eyes softly closed, and his cheeks flushed, commenced to feel the tepid moisture and light torpor of a happy and easy digestion. . . .

Dinner at the Buddenbrooks'

from Buddenbrooks
by Thomas Mann

THE COMPANY HAD for the most part seated themselves on the chairs and the sofa. They talked with the children or discussed the unseasonable cold and the new house. Herr Hoffstede admired a beautiful Sèvres inkstand, in the shape of a black and white hunting dog, that stood on the secretary. Doctor Grabow, a man of about the Consul's age, with a long mild face between thin whiskers, was looking at the table, set out with cakes and currant bread and salt-cellars in different shapes. This was the "bread and salt" that had been sent by friends for the house-warming; but the "bread" consisted of rich, heavy pastries, and the salt came in dishes of massive gold, that the senders might not seem to be mean in their gifts.

"There will be work for me here," said the Doctor, pointing to the sweetmeats and threatening the children with his glance . . .

The guests did not sit down, but stood about awaiting the principal event of the evening and passing the time in casual talk. At length, Johann Buddenbrook the older offered his arm to Madame Köppen and said in an elevated voice, "Well, *mesdames et messieurs,* if you are hungry . . ."

Mamsell Jungmann and the servant had opened the folding doors into the dining-room; and the company made its way with studied ease to table. One could be sure of a good square meal at the Buddenbrooks' . . .

"*Bon appetit!*" [Madame Buddenbrook] said, with her short, quick, hearty nod, flashing a glance down the whole length of the table till it reached the children at the bottom.

"Our best respects to you, Buddenbrook—I repeat, our best respects!" Herr Köppen's powerful voice drowned the general conversation as the maid-servant, in her heavy striped petticoat, her fat arms bare and a little white cap on the back of her head, passed the cabbage soup and toast, assisted by Mamsell Jungmann and the Frau Consul's maid from upstairs. The guests began to use their soup-spoons . . .

Madame Antoinette kept a sharp eye on the servants while they changed the gilt-edged Meissen plates; Mamsell Jungmann called orders through the speaking-tube into the kitchen, and the fish was brought in . . .

The plates were being changed again. An enormous brick-red boiled ham appeared, strewn with crumbs and served with a sour brown onion sauce, and so many vegetables that the company could have satisfied their appetites from that one vegetable-dish. Lebrecht Kröger undertook the carving and skilfully cut the succulent slices, with his elbows tightly elevated and his two long forefingers laid out along the back of the knife and fork. With the ham went the Frau Consul's celebrated "Russian jam," a pungent fruit conserve flavored with spirits. . . .

Herr Köppen had grown more and more crimson from eating, and puffed audibly as he spoke. Pastor Wunderlich had not changed color; he looked as pale, refined, and alert as ever, while drinking down glass after glass of wine.

The candles burned down slowly in their sockets. Now and then they flickered in a draught and dispersed a faint smell of wax over the table.

There they all sat, on heavy, high-backed chairs, consuming good heavy food from good heavy silver plate, drinking full-bodied wines and expressing their views freely on all subjects. When they began to talk shop, they slipped unconsciously more and more into dialect, and used the clumsy but comfortable idioms that seemed to embody to them the business efficiency and the easy well-being of their community. Sometimes they even used an over-drawn pronunciation by way of making fun of themselves and each other, and relished their clipped phrases and exaggerated vowels with the same heartiness as they did their food.

The ladies had not long followed the discussion. Madame Kröger gave them the cue by setting forth a tempting method of boiling carp in red wine. "You cut it into nice pieces, my dear, and put it in the saucepan, add some cloves, and onions, and a few rusks, a little sugar, and a spoonful of butter, and set it on the fire . . . But don't wash it, on any account. All the blood must remain in it." . . .

"Krishan, don't eat too much," the [older Buddenbrook] suddenly called out, in dialect. "Never mind about Tilda—it doesn't hurt her. She can put it away like a dozen harvest hands, that child!"

And truly it was amazing, the prowess of this scraggy child with the long, old-maidish face. Asked if she wanted more soup, she answered in a mock drawling voice: "Ye-es, ple-ase." She had two large helpings both of fish and ham, with piles of vegetables; and she bent short-sightedly over her plate, completely absorbed in the food, which she chewed ruminantly, in large mouthfuls. "Oh, Un-cle," she replied, with amiable simplicity, to the old man's gibe, which did not in the least disconcert her. She ate: whether it tasted good or not, whether they teased her or not, she smiled and kept on, heaping her plate with good things, with the instinctive, insensitive voracity of a poor relation—patient, persevering, hungry, and lean.

And now came, in two great cut-glass dishes, the "Pletten-pudding." It was made of layers of macaroons, raspberries, lady-fingers, and custard. At the same time, at the other end of the table, appeared the blazing plum-pudding which was the children's favorite sweet.

"Thomas, my son, come here a minute," said Johann Buddenbrook, taking his great bunch of keys from his trousers pocket. "In the second cellar to the right, the second bin, behind the red Bordeaux, two bottles—you understand?" Thomas, to whom such orders were familiar, ran off and soon came back with the two bottles, covered with dust and cobwebs; and the little dessert-glasses were filled with sweet, golden-yellow Malmsey from these unsightly receptacles. Now the moment came when Pastor Wunderlich rose, glass in hand, to propose a toast; and the company fell silent to listen. He spoke in the pleasant, conversational tone which he liked to use in the pulpit; his head a little on one side, a subtle, humorous smile on his pale face, gesturing easily with his free hand. "Come, my honest friends, let us honor ourselves by drinking a glass of this excellent liquor to the health of our host and hostess in their beautiful new home. Come, then—to the health of the Buddenbrook family, present and absent! May they live long and prosper!" . . .

The butter, cheese, and fruit had just been handed round; and the Frau Consul rose from her chair and unobtrusively followed the waitress from the room; for the Doctor, Mamsell Jungmann, and Christian were no longer in their places; and a smothered wail was proceeding from the hall. There in the dim light, little Christian was half lying, half crouching on the round settee that encircled the central pillar. He was uttering heart-breaking groans. Ida and the Doctor stood beside him.

"Oh dear, oh dear," said she, "the poor child is very bad!"

"I'm ill, Mamma, damned ill," whimpered Christian, his little deep-set eyes darting back and forth, and his big nose looking bigger than ever. The "damned" came out in a tone of utter despair; but the Frau Consul said: "If we use such words, God will punish us by making us suffer still more!"

Doctor Grabow felt the lad's pulse. His kindly face was longer and gentler.

"It's nothing much, Frau Consul," he reassured her. "A touch of indigestion." He prescribed in his best bedside manner: "Better put him to bed and give him a Dover powder—perhaps a cup of camomile tea, to bring out the perspiration . . . And a rigorous diet, you know, Frau Consul. A little pigeon, a little French bread . . ."

"I don't want any pigeon," bellowed Christian angrily. "I don't want to eat anything, ever any more. I'm ill, I tell you, damned ill!" The fervor with which he uttered the bad word seemed to bring him relief.

Doctor Grabow smiled to himself—a thoughtful, almost a melancholy smile. He would soon eat again, this young man. He would do as the rest of the world did—his father, and all their relatives and friends: he would lead a sedentary life and eat four good, rich, satisfying meals a day. Well, God bless us all! He, Friedrich Grabow, was not the man to upset the habits of these prosperous, comfortable tradesmen and their families. He would come when he was sent for, prescribe a few days' diet—a little pigeon, a slice of French bread—yes, yes, and assure the family that it was nothing serious this time. Young as he was, he had held the head of many an honest burgher who had eaten his last joint of smoked meat, his last stuffed turkey, and, whether overtaken unaware in his counting-house or after a brief illness in his solid old four-poster, had commended his soul to God. Then it was called paralysis, a "stroke," a sudden death. And he, Friedrich Grabow, could have predicted it, on all of these occasions when it was "nothing serious this time"—or perhaps at the times when he had not even been summoned, when there had only been a slight giddiness after luncheon. Well, God bless us all! He, Friedrich Grabow, was not the man to despise a roast turkey himself. That ham with onion sauce had been delicious, hang it! And the Pletten-pudding, when they were already stuffed full—macaroons, raspberries, custard . . . "A rigorous diet, Frau Consul, as I say. A little pigeon, a little French bread . . ."

They were rising from table.

Chapter Six

THE AMERICAN TABLE

HOME AGAIN, to the much maligned food of the United States. We call it a table here, because it has borrowed from the cuisine of every nation poured into the American melting pot, and developed its own distinctive dishes as well. Laid out on the national table one may find the best of the world in our great cities, and elsewhere those concoctions which are splendidly native.

It is no chauvinism to deny the common canard that American cooking, by and large, is exceeded in evil only by the British. True, there is bad cooking in small towns and in many homes in America, but the same could be said of any country. In the past decade or so the preparation of superior food has spread in this country, not only to most of the major cities, but seeping outward to unlikely whistle stops where once only fried meat and lumpy mashed potatoes could be found.

Nor is there any lack of a gastronomic tradition in America, as the following excerpts will show. We begin with the early nineteenth century, when good eating was confined to the homes of the rich, as exemplified by the Van Tassels, and to solid country homes, of the kind in which Geoffrey Crayon celebrated his Christmas dinner. These are described by Washington Irving, one of the earliest delineators of the American scene.

Then comes a classic example of American gourmandizing on the grand scale, and although this is a legendary episode, it may be said that lumberjacks ate prodigiously even without benefit of Paul Bunyan.

There is such eating in the novels of Thomas Wolfe, as there is a prodigality of everything else, that once more it is difficult to choose. Our selection is the gastronomic discovery made by Eugene Gant (young Wolfe, of course) in the upper-class Hudson River Valley home of a young friend. To a hungry and struggling young student from a poor family, it was like discovering the New World.

As a contrast to Eugene's overflowing wonder, we close with the matter-of-fact consumption of a matter-of-fact, strictly American meal by one of Jack Kerouac's beat characters. The meal may not be spectacular, but the appreciation of it is timeless.

Ichabod Crane Surveys Van Tassel Abundance

from The Legend of Sleepy Hollow
by Washington Irving

As Ichabod jogged slowly on his way, his eye, ever open to every symptom of culinary abundance, ranged with delight over the treasures of jolly autumn. On all sides he beheld vast stores of apples; some hanging in oppressive opulence on the trees; some gathered into baskets and barrels for the market; others heaped up in rich piles for the cider-press. Further on he beheld great fields of Indian corn, with its golden ears peeping from their leafy coverts, and holding out the promise of cakes and hasty pudding; and the yellow pumpkins lying beneath them, turning up their fair round bellies to the sun, and giving ample prospects of the most luxurious of pies; and anon he passed the fragrant buckwheat fields, breathing the odor of the bee-hive, and as he beheld them, soft anticipations stole over his mind of dainty slapjacks, well buttered, and garnished with honey or treacle, by the delicate little dimpled hand of Katrina Van Tassel . . .

Fain would I pause to dwell upon the world of charms that burst upon the enraptured gaze of my hero, as he entered the state parlor of Van Tassel's mansion. Not those of the bevy of buxom lasses, with their luxurious display of red and white; but the ample charms of a genuine Dutch country tea-table in the sumptuous time of autumn. Such heaped-up platters of cakes of various and almost indescribable kinds, known only to experienced Dutch housewives! There was the doughty dough-nut, the tenderer oly koek, and the crisp and crumbling kruller; sweet-cakes and short-cakes, ginger-cakes and honey-cakes, and the whole family of cakes. And then there were apple-pies and peach-pies and pumpkin-pies; besides slices of ham and smoked beef; and, moreover, delectable dishes of preserved plums, and peaches, and pears, and quinces; not to mention broiled shad and roasted chickens; together with bowls of milk and cream, all mingled higgledy-piggledy, pretty much as I have enumerated them, with the motherly teapot sending up its clouds of vapor from the midst—Heaven bless the mark! I want breath and time to discuss this banquet as it deserves, and am too eager to get on with my story. Happily, Ichabod Crane was not in so great a hurry as his historian, but did ample justice to every dainty.

He was a kind and thankful creature, whose heart dilated in proportion as his skin was filled with good cheer; and whose spirits rose with eating as some men's do with drink. He could not help, too, rolling his large eyes round him as he ate, and chuckling with the possibility that he might one day be lord of all this scene of almost unimaginable luxury and splendor. Then he thought, how soon he'd turn his back upon the old schoolhouse, snap his fingers in the face of Hans Van Ripper, and every other niggardly patron, and kick any itinerant pedagogue out of doors that should dare to call him comrade!

Geoffrey Crayon's Christmas Dinner

from The Sketch-Book

by Washington Irving

THE PARSON said grace, which was not a short familiar one, such as is commonly addressed to the Deity in these unceremonious days; but a long, courtly, well-worded one of the ancient school. There was now a pause, as if something was expected; when suddenly the butler entered the hall with some degree of bustle: he was attended by a servant on each side with a large wax-light, and bore a silver dish, on which was an enormous pig's-head, decorated with rosemary, with a lemon in its mouth, which was placed with great formality at the head of the table. The moment this pageant made its appearance, the harper struck up a flourish; at the conclusion of which the young Oxonian, on receiving a hint from the squire, gave, with an air of the most comic gravity, an old carol, the first verse of which was as follows:

> *Caput apri defero*
> *Reddens laudes Domino.*
> *The boar's head in hand bring I,*
> *With garlands gay and rosemary.*
> *I pray you all synge merrilly*
> *Qui estis in convivio.*

Though prepared to witness many of these little eccentricities, from being apprised of the peculiar hobby of mine host, yet, I confess, the parade with which so odd a dish was introduced somewhat perplexed me, until I gathered from the conversation of the squire and the parson, that it was meant to represent the bringing in of the boar's head; a dish formerly served up with much ceremony and the sound of minstrelsy and song, at great tables, on Christmas day. "I like the old custom," said the squire, "not merely because it is stately and pleasing in itself, but because it was observed at the college at Oxford at which I was educated. When I hear the old song chanted, it brings to mind the time when I was young and gamesome, and the noble old college hall, and my fellow students loitering about in their black gowns; many of whom, poor lads, are now in their graves!"

The parson, however, whose mind was not haunted by such associations, and who was always more taken up with the text than the sentiment, objected to the Oxonian's version of the carol: which he affirmed was different from that sung at college. He went on, with the dry perseverance of a commentator, to give the college reading, accompanied by sundry annotations; addressing himself at first to the company at large; but finding their attention gradually diverted to other talk and other objects, he lowered his tone as his number of auditors diminished, until he concluded his remarks in an under voice, to a fat-headed old gentleman next him, who was silently engaged in the discussion of a huge plateful of turkey.

The table was literally loaded with good cheer, and presented an epitome of country abundance, in this season of overflowing larders. A distinguished post was allotted to "ancient sirloin," as mine host termed it; being, as he added, "the standard of old English hospitality, and a joint of goodly presence, and full of expectation." There were several dishes quaintly decorated, and which had evidently something traditional in their embellishments; but about which, as I did not like to appear over-curious, I asked no questions.

I could not, however, but notice a pie, magnificently decorated with peacock's feathers, in imitation of the tail of that bird, which overshadowed a considerable tract of the table. This, the squire confessed with some little hesitation, was a pheasant pie, though a peacock pie was certainly the most authentical; but there had been such a mortality among the peacocks this season, that he could not prevail upon himself to have one killed.

The Great Black Duck Dinner

from Paul Bunyan

by James Stevens

ALL NIGHT FIRES roared in the ranges as preparations went on for the great dinner. The elevators brought a load of vegetables every few minutes from the deep bins, potatoes were pared and washed, kettles and roasting pans were made ready, and sauces and dressings were devised. The black ducks were scaled, plucked, and cleaned by the Preparations Department, and by morning the cranemen were bringing them by the hundreds to the Finishing Department, where the kettles and pans were waiting for them.

Most of the loggers stayed in their bunks this morning, and those who did not come to breakfast ate sparingly, saving their appetites. Time passed quietly in the camp. The loggers washed and mended their clothes and greased their boots, but they did not worry themselves with bedmaking. The other Sunday morning chores finished, they stretched out on their unmade bunks and smoked. They were silent and preoccupied, but now and again a breeze blowing from the direction of the cookhouse would cause them to sigh. What enchantment was in the air, so redolent with the aroma of roasting duck and stewing cabbages, so sharply sweet with the fragrance of hot ginger and cinnamon from the bakery where Cream Puff Fatty fashioned his creations! A logger who was shaving would take a deep breath of this incense, and the blood would trickle unnoticed from a slash in his cheek; another, in his bunk, would let his pipe slip from his hand and enjoy ardent inhalations, blissfully unaware of his burning shirt; yet another, engaged in greasing his boots, would halt his task and sit in motionless beatitude, his head thrown back, his eyes closed, quite unconscious of the grease that poured from a tilted can into a prized boot.

At half past eleven the hungriest of the loggers began to mass before the cookhouse door, and as the minutes passed the throng swiftly increased. At five minutes to noon all the bunkhouses were empty and the furthest fringe of the crowd was far up Onion River valley. The ground shook under a restless trampling, and the faces of the loggers were glowing and eager as they hearkened to the clatter and rumble inside the cookhouse, as four-horse teams hauled in loads of salt, pepper and sugar for the shakers and bowls. Then the loggers began to stamp and shout as they heard the flunkies, led by Galloping Kid on his white horse, rushing the platters and bowls of food to the tables. Tantalizing smells wafted forth from the steaming dishes. The loggers grew more restless and eager; they surged to and fro in a tidal movement; jests and glad oaths made a joyous clamor over the throng. This was softened into a universal sigh as the doors swung open and Hot Biscuit Slim, in spotless cap and apron, appeared wearing the impressive mien of a conquering general. He lifted an iron bar with a majestic gesture, paused for dramatic effect amid a breathless hush, and then struck a resounding note from the steel triangle that hung from the wall. At the sound a heaving torrent of men began to pour through the doors in a rush that was like the roaring plunge of water when the gate of a dam is lifted. The chief cook continued to pound out clanging rhythms until the last impatient logger was inside.

Then Hot Biscuit Slim re-entered the cookhouse. He was reminded of a forested plain veiled in thin fog as he surveyed the assemblage of darkly clad figures, wreathed with white and fragrant blooms of steam. His impression was made the more vivid when the loggers plunged their spoons into the deep bowls of oyster soup, for the ensuing sounds seemed like the soughing of wind in the woods. The chief cook marched to the kitchen with dignity and pride, glancing to right and left at the tables that held his masterwork. He asked for no praise or acclaim; the ecstasy that now transfigured the plainest face was a sufficient light of glory for him.

The soup bowls pushed aside, the loggers began to fill their plates, which were of such circumference that even a long-armed man could hardly reach across one. The black ducks, of course, received first attention. And great as the plates were, by the time one was heaped with a brown fried drumstick, a ladle of duck dumplings, several large fragments of duck fricassee, a slab of duck baked gumbo style, a rich portion of stewed duck, and a mound of crisp brown dressing, all immersed in golden duck gravy, a formidable space was covered. Yet there was room for tender leaves of odorous cabbage beaded and streaked with creamy sauce; for mashed potatoes which seemed like fluffs of snow beside the darkness of duck and gravy; for brittle and savory potato cakes, marvelously right as to texture and thickness; for stewed tomatoes of a sultry ruddiness, pungent and ticklish with mysterious spices; for a hot cob of corn as long as a man's forearm, golden with sirupy kernels as big as buns; for fat and juicy baked beans, plump peas, sunny applesauce, and buttered lettuce, not to mention various condiments. Squares of cornbread and hot biscuits were buttered and leaned against the plate; a pot-bellied coffee-pot was tilted over a gaping cup, into which it gushed an aromatic beverage of drowsy charm; a kingly pleasure was prepared. More than one logger swooned with delight this day when his plate was filled and, red-faced, hot-eyed, wet-lipped, he bent over it for the first mouthful with the joy of a lover claiming a first embrace.

In the kitchen the chief cook, the baker, and their helpers watched and listened. At first the volume of sounds that filled the vast room was like the roar and crash of an avalanche, as dishes were rattled and banged about. Then the duck bones crackled like the limbs of falling trees. At last came a steady sound of eating, a sound of seventy threshing machines devouring bundles of wheat. It persisted far beyond the usual length of time, and Hot Biscuit Slim brought out his field glasses and surveyed the tables. The loggers were still bent tensely over their plates, and their elbows rose and fell with an energetic movement as they scooped up the food with undiminished vigor.

"Still eatin' duck," marveled Hot Biscuit Slim.

"They won't be more'n able to smell my cream puffs," said the baker enviously.

The loggers ate on. They had now spent twice their usual length of time at the table. Each plate was in a dark shadow from tall rows of slick black duck bones and heaps of corn cobs. But—

"Still eatin' duck," reported Hot Biscuit Slim.

That no one might see his grief, Cream Puff Fatty moved to a dark corner. He was now certain that none of the loggers could have room for his pastries. They ate on. They had now spent three times their usual length of time at the table. The baker was sweating and weeping; he was soaked with despair. Then, suddenly:

"They're eatin' cream puffs!" cried Hot Biscuit Slim.

Cream Puff Fatty could not believe it, but a thrill of hope urged him to see for himself. True enough, the loggers were tackling the pastries at last. On each plate cream puffs the size of squashes lay in golden mounds. As the spoons struck them their creamy contents oozed forth from breaks and crevices. Stimulated by their rich flavor, the loggers ate on with renewed gusto. They had now stayed four times as long as usual at the table. Other enchantments still kept them in their seats: lemon pies with airy frostings, yellow pumpkin pies strewn with brown spice specks, cherry pies with cracks in their flaky crusts through which the red fruit winked, custard pies with russet freckles on their golden faces, fat apple pies all odorous with cinnamon, cool, snowy cream pies, peach cobblers, chocolate puddings, glittering cakes of many colors, slabs of gingerbread, sugar-powdered jelly rolls, doughnuts as large around as saucers and as thick through as cups, and so soft and toothsome that a morsel from one melted on the tongue like cream. So endearing were the flavors of these pastries that the loggers consumed them all.

Cream Puff Fatty and Hot Biscuit Slim solemnly shook hands. There was glory enough for both of them.

At last there were no sounds at the tables save those of heavy breathing. The loggers arose in a body and moved sluggishly and wordlessly from the cookhouse. They labored over the ground towards the bunkhouses as wearily as though they had just finished a day of deadening toil. Soon Onion River valley resounded with their snores and groans . . .

At supper time, when Hot Biscuit Slim rang the gong, Cream Puff Fatty stood by his side. This was to be the supreme test of their achievement. For five minutes the chief cook beat the triangle, and then a solitary logger appeared in the door of a bunkhouse. He stared at them dully for a moment and then staggered back into the darkness. This was indeed a triumph! Great as other feasts in the cookhouse had been, never before had all the loggers been unable to appear for supper. This was a historic day. Cream Puff Fatty and Hot Biscuit Slim embraced and mingled rapturous tears. It was their high moment. They would not have traded it for all the glory that was Greece and the grandeur that was Rome . . .

"The juice of leeks who fondly sips,
To kiss the fair must close his lips."

—Martial

Eugene Discovers a Kitchen

from Of Time and the River
by Thomas Wolfe

IT WAS SUCH a kitchen as he had never seen before—a kitchen such as he had never dreamed possible. In its space, its order, its astounding cleanliness, it had the beauty of a great machine—a machine of tremendous power, fabulous richness and complexity—which in its ordered magnificence, its vast readiness, had the clear and glittering precision of a geometric pattern. Even the stove—a vast hooded range as large as those in a great restaurant—glittered with the groomed perfection of a racing motor. There was, as well, an enormous electric stove that was polished like a silver ornament, the pots and pans were hung in gleaming rows, in vast but orderly profusion ranging from great copper kettles big enough to roast an ox to little pans and skillets just large enough to poach an egg, but all hung there in regimented order, instant readiness, shining like mirrors, scrubbed and polished into gleaming disks, the battered cleanliness of well-used copper, seasoned iron and heavy steel.

The great cupboards were crowded with huge stacks of gleaming china ware and crockery, enough to serve the needs of a hotel. And the long kitchen table, as well as the chairs and woodwork of the room, was white and shining as a surgeon's table: the sinks and drains were blocks of creamy porcelain, clean scrubbed copper, shining steel.

It would be impossible to describe in detail the lavish variety, the orderly complexity, the gleaming cleanliness of that great room, but the effect it wrought upon his senses was instant and overwhelming. It was one of the most beautiful, spacious, thrilling, and magnificently serviceable rooms that he had ever seen: everything in it was designed for use, and edged with instant readiness; there was not a single thing in the room that was not needed, and yet its total effect was to give one a feeling of power, space, comfort, rightness and abundant joy.

The pantry shelves were crowded to the ceiling with the growing treasure of a lavish victualling—an astounding variety and abundance of delicious foods, enough to stock a grocery store, or to supply an Arctic expedition—but the like of which he had never seen, or dreamed of, in a country house before.

Everything was there, from the familiar staples of a cook's necessities to every rare and toothsome dainty that the climates and the markets of the earth produce. There was food in cans, and food in tins, and food in crocks, and food in bottles. There were—in addition to such staples of the canning art as corn, tomatoes, beans and peas, pears, plums and peaches, such rarer relishes, as herrings, sardines, olives, pickles, mustard, relishes, anchovies. There were boxes of glacéd crystalline fruits from California, and little wickered jars of sharp-spiced ginger fruit from China: there were expensive jellies green as emerald, red as rubies, smoother than whipped cream, there were fine oils and vinegars in bottles, and jars of pungent relishes of every sort, and boxes of assorted spices. There was everything that one could think of, and everywhere there was evident the same scrubbed and gleaming cleanliness with which the kitchen shone, but here there was as well, that pungent, haunting, spicy odor that pervades the atmosphere of pantries—a haunting and nostalgic fusion of delicious smells whose exact quality it is impossible to define, but which has in it the odors of cinnamon, pepper, cheese, smoked ham, and cloves.

When they got into the kitchen they found Rosalind there: she was standing by the long white table drinking a glass of milk. Joel, in the swift and correct manner with which he gave instruction, at once eager, gentle and decisive, began to show his guest around.

"And look," he whispered with his soft, and yet incisive slowness, as he opened the heavy shining doors of the great refrigerator —"here's the icebox: if you find anything there you like, just help yourself—"

Food! Food, indeed! The great icebox was crowded with such an assortment of delicious foods as he had not seen in many years: just to look at it made the mouth begin to water, and aroused the pangs of a hunger so ravenous and insatiate that it was almost more painful than the pangs of bitter want. One was so torn with desire and greedy gluttony as he looked at the maddening plenty of that feast that his will was rendered almost impotent. Even as the eye glistened and the mouth began to water at the sight of a noble roast of beef, all crisp and crackly in its cold brown succulence, the attention was diverted to a plump broiled chicken, whose brown and crackly tenderness fairly seemed to beg for the sweet and savage pillage of the tooth. But now a pungent and exciting fragrance would assail the nostrils: It was the smoked pink slices of an Austrian ham—should it be brawny bully beef, now, or the juicy breast of a white tender pullet, or should it be the smoky pungency, the half-nostalgic savor of the Austrian ham? Or that noble dish of green lima beans, now already beautifully congealed in their pervading film of melted butter; or that dish of tender stewed young cucumbers; or those tomato slices, red and thick and ripe, and heavy as a chop; or that dish of cold asparagus, say; or that dish of corn; or, say, one of those musty fragrant, deep-ribbed cantaloupes, chilled to the heart, now, in all their pink-fleshed taste and ripeness; or a round thick slab cut from the red ripe heart of that great watermelon; or a bowl of those red raspberries, most luscious and most rich with sugar, and a bottle of that thick rich cream which filled one whole compartment of that treasure-chest of gluttony, or—

What shall it be now? What shall it be? A snack! A snack!—Before we prowl the meadows of the moon to-night, and soak our hearts in the moonlight's magic and the visions of our youth—what shall it be before we prowl the meadows of the moon? Oh, it shall be a snack, a snack—hah! hah!—it shall be nothing but a snack because—hah! hah!—you understand, we are not hungry and it is not well to eat too much before retiring—so we'll just investigate the icebox as we have done so oft at midnight in America—and we are the moon's man, boys—and all that it will be, I do assure you, will be something swift and quick and ready, something instant and felicitous, and quite delicate and dainty—just a snack!

I think—now let me see—h'm, now!—well, perhaps I'll have a slice or two of that pink Austrian ham that smells so sweet and pungent and looks so pretty and so delicate there in the crisp garlands of the parsley leaf!—and yes, perhaps, I'll have a slice of this roast beef, as well—h'm now!—yes, I think that's what I'm going to do—say a slice of red rare meat there at the centre—ah-h! there you are! yes, that's the stuff, that does quite nicely, thank you—with just a trifle of that crisp brown crackling there to oil the lips and make its passage easy, and a little of that cold but brown and oh—most—brawny gravy—and, yes, sir!—I think I *will*, now, that it occurs to me, a slice of that plump chicken—some white meat, thank you, at the breast—ah, there it is!—how sweetly doth the noble fowl submit to the swift and keen persuasion of the knife—and now, perhaps, just for our diet's healthy balance, a spoonful of those lima beans, as gay as April and as sweet as butter, a tomato slice or two, a speared forkful of those thin-sliced cucumbers—ah! what a delicate and toothsome pickle they do make—what sorcerer invented them, a little corn perhaps, a bottle of this milk, a pound of butter and that crusty loaf of bread—and even this moon-haunted wilderness were paradise enow—with just a snack—a snack—a snack—

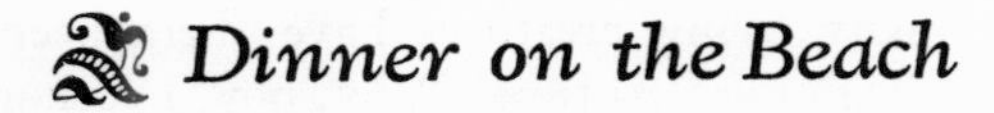

Dinner on the Beach

from The Dharma Bums

by Jack Kerouac

I BADE FAREWELL to the little bum of Saint Teresa at the crossing, where we jumped off, and went to sleep for the night in the sand in my blankets, far down the beach at the foot of a cliff where cops wouldn't see me and drive me away. I cooked hotdogs on freshly cut and sharpened sticks over the coals of a big wood fire, and heated a can of beans and a can of cheese macaroni in the redhot hollows, and drank my newly bought wine, and exulted in one of the most pleasant nights of my life. I waded in the water and dunked a little and stood looking up at the splendorous night sky, Avalokitesvara's ten-wondered universe of dark and diamonds. "Well, Ray," sez I, glad, "only a few miles to go. You've done it again." Happy. Just in my swim shorts, barefooted, wild-haired, in the red fire dark, singing, swigging wine, spitting, jumping, running—that's the way to live. All alone and free in the soft sands of the beach by the sigh of the sea out there, with the Ma-Wink fallopian virgin warm stars reflecting on the outer channel fluid belly waters. And if your cans are redhot and you can't hold them in your hands, just use good old railroad gloves, that's all. I let the food cool a little to enjoy more wine and my thoughts. I sat crosslegged in the sand and contemplated my life. Well, there, and what difference did it make? "What's going to happen to me up ahead?" Then the wine got to work on my taste buds and before long I had to pitch into those hotdogs, biting them right off the end of the stick spit, and chomp chomp, and dig down into the two tasty cans with an old pack spoon, spooning up rich bites of hot beans and pork, or of macaroni with sizzling hot sauce, and maybe a little sand thrown in. "And how many grains of sand are there on this beach." I think. "Why, as many grains of sand as there are stars in that sky!" (chomp chomp) and if so "How many human beings have there been, in fact how many living creatures have there been, since before the *less* part of beginningless time? Why, boy, I reckon you would have to calculate the number of grains of sand on this beach and on every star in the sky, in every one of the ten thousand great chilicosms, which would be a number of sand grains uncomputable by IBM and Burroughs too, why boy I don't rightly know" (swig of wine) "I don't rightly know but it must be a couple umpteen trillion sextillion infideled and busted up innumerable number of roses that sweet Saint Teresa and that fine little old man are now this minute showering your head, with lilies."

Then, meal done, wiping my lips with my red bandana, I washed up the dishes in the salt sea, kicked a few clods of sand, wandered around, wiped them, put them away, stuck the old spoon back in the salty pack, and lay down curled in my blanket for a night's good and just rest.

DO YOU WISH to cross that ridiculously disappointing ocean called the Atlantic and try an American dinner? Come with me to the Criterion and instruct the American chef to prepare the dinner on the lines shown below:

Chicken Okra Clam Broth
Salt Cod and Hash Oyster Fritters
Mixed Turkey and Corn
Stuffed Red Peppers
Terrapin Maryland Chipped Beef
Scalloped Sweet Potatoes Cole Slaw
Graham Pudding
New England Indian Pudding
Temperance Punch

This program calls for little explanation. The okra cooked with the chicken gives it a peculiar and quite delicious flavor. The clam is a dulcet combination of the oyster, the mussel, and the scallop.

—FRANK SCHLOESSER, *The Greedy Book* (1906).

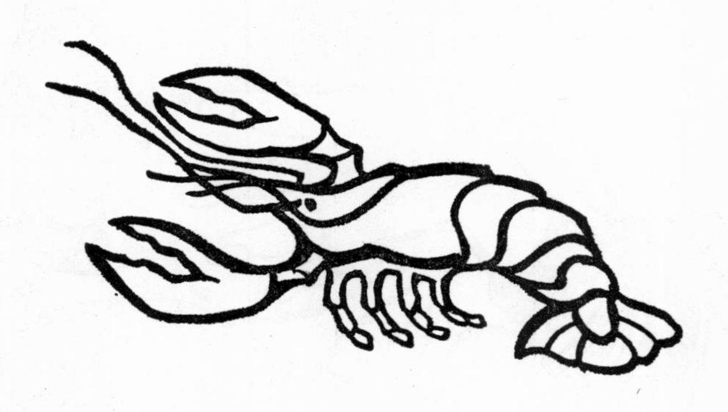

PART 2

CUSTOMS AND MANNERS

Chapter Seven

FOOD AS HISTORY

THERE IS MORE to dining than what delights pass the lips, as everyone knows, and in this part of our collection we have assembled some of the writing about the preparation of food and the curious complexity of customs and manners which have come to surround its serving.

The literature in this field is, of course, voluminous, from which it would be entirely possible to extract a book twice as large as this one. Admittedly what we have mined from the lode consists of those illuminations which we found entertaining and informative, rather than a cross-section or even a studiously representative presentation.

We begin with a few excerpts from gastronomic history. As Abraham Hayward, the amiable nineteenth-century English lawyer and essayist remarks in the opening piece: "The history of gastronomy is that of manners, if not of morals . . ." Hayward himself demonstrates this thesis in the excerpt drawn from his most notable essay, "The Art of Dining," and the English historian Charles Martyn gives us a further revelation of the past in his discussion of the Ancients.

Then comes the first of several selections in our volume from the work of John Cordy Jeaffreson, a nineteenth century English writer still regarded as one of the two or three outstanding authorities on the history of food.

The chapter closes with the work of lesser known writers whose names are far less important than the insights they give us here into the customs of other times and places.

Gastronomy from Homer to Carême

from The Art of Dining
by Abraham Hayward

THE HISTORY OF gastronomy is that of manners, if not of morals; and the learned are aware that its literature is both instructive and amusing; for it is replete with curious traits of character and comparative views of society at different periods, as well as with striking anecdotes of remarkable men and women, whose destinies have been strangely influenced by their epicurean tastes and habits . . .

It is sagaciously remarked by Madame Dacier, that Homer makes no mention of boiled meat in any of his works; and in all the entertainments described by him, as in the dinner given by Achilles to the royal messengers in the ninth Iliad, the *pièce de résistance* undoubtedly is a broil; from which it is plausibly, if somewhat hastily, inferred that the Greeks had not then discovered the mode of making vessels to bear fire.

This discovery is supposed to have reached them from Egypt, and they rapidly turned it to the best possible account. The Athenians, in particular, seemed to have as much excelled the rest of Greece in gastronomy, as the French, the modern nation most nearly resembling them, excel the rest of Europe in this respect. The best proof of this assertion is to be found in the circumstance that the learned have agreed to rank amongst the most valuable of the lost works of antiquity, a didactic poem on gastronomy, by Archestratus, the intimate friend of one of the sons of Pericles. "This great writer," says Athenaeus, "had traversed earth and sea to render himself acquainted with the best things which they produced. He did not, during his travels, inquire concerning the manners of nations, as to which it is useless to inform ourselves, since it is impossible to change them; but he entered the laboratories where the delicacies of the table were prepared, and he held intercourse with none but those who could advance his pleasures. His poem is a treasure of science, every verse a precept."

These terms of exalted praise must be taken with a few grains of salt, for, considering the imperfect state of the physical sciences at the time, it may well be doubted whether Archestratus succeeded in producing so complete a treasure of precepts as his admirers have supposed. . . . Besides, it is highly probable that all which was really valuable in the cookery of the Greeks was carried off, along with the other arts to which ordinary opinion assigns a yet higher value, to Rome. As, indeed, we know that the Romans sent a deputation to Athens for the laws of Solon, and were in the constant habit of repairing thither to study in the schools, it would be ludicrous to suppose that they neglected the *cuisine;* and there can be little or no doubt whatever that when, at a somewhat later period, the Grecian philosophers, poets, and rhetoricians flocked to Rome as the metropolis of civilization, the cooks of Athens accompanied them. Yet concentrating, as the Roman banquets must have done, all the gastronomic genius and resources of the world, they were much more remarkable for profusion and costliness than for taste.... Neither have we much respect for epicures who could select so awkward and uncomfortable a position as a reclining one. It is quite startling to think how they must have slobbered their long beards and togas, in conveying food from the table to their mouths without forks—for forks are clearly a modern discovery, none having been found in the ruins of Herculaneum—and it is difficult to conceive how they could manage to drink at all, unless they sat up as the goblet was passed to them....

The period comprising the fall of the Roman empire and the greater portion of the middle ages was one of unmitigated darkness for the fine arts. Charlemagne, as appears from his Capitularies, took a warm personal interest in the management of his table; and the Normans, two or three centuries later, are said to have prided themselves on their superior taste and discrimination in this respect. ... But the revival of cookery, like that of learning, is due to Italy. We are unable to fix the precise time when it there began to be cultivated with success, but it met with the most enlightened encouragement from the merchant-princes of Florence, and the French received the first rudiments of the science from the professors who accompanied Catherine de Medici to Paris....

History, which has only become philosophical within the last century, and took little note of manners until Voltaire had demonstrated the importance of commemorating them, affords no authentic materials for filling up the period which intervened between the arrival of Catherine de Medici and the accession of Louis XIV, under whom cookery made prodigious advances, being one while employed to give a zest to his glories, and then again to console him in their decline. The name of his celebrated *maître d'hôtel,* Béchamel —a name surely destined to immortality by his sauce, as that of Herschel by his star, or that of Baffin by his bay—affords guarantee and proof enough of the discriminating elegance with which the royal table was served....

To turn for a moment to England—the state of cookery under

Charles II is sufficiently indicated by the names of Chiffinch and Chaubert, to whose taste and skill the author of Waverly has borne ample testimony by his description of the dinner prepared for Smith, Ganlesse, and Peveril of the Peak, at the little Derbyshire inn:

"We could bring no chauffettes with any convenience; and even Chaubert is nothing, unless his dishes are tasted in the very moment of projection. Come, uncover, and let us see what he has done for us. Hum! ha! ay—squab pigeons—wild-fowl—young chickens—venison cutlets—and a space in the center, wet, alas! by a gentle tear from Chaubert's eye, where should have been the *soupe aux écrevisses. . . .*"—Peveril, vol. ii, p. 165

Decisive evidence of the palmy condition of the art in the seventeenth century is afforded by "The Accomplisht Cook" of Robert May, the first edition of which appeared in 1665. . . .

He speaks rather contemptuously of the French *cuisine*, but acknowledges himself "not a little beholding to the Italian and Spanish treatises; though, without my fosterage and bringing up under the generosities and bounties of my noble patrons and masters, I could never have arrived to this experience." This fosterage was certainly remarkable. From "a short narrative of some passages of the Author's Life," modestly prefaced to the book, we learn that, having attained to some perfection under his father, one of the ablest cooks of his time, the old Lady Dormer sent him over to France, where he continued five years, in the family of a noble peer and first president of Paris. On his return he was bound apprentice to "Mr. Arthur Hollingsworth, in Newgate Market, one of the ablest workmen in London, cook to the Grocers' Hall and Star Chamber. His apprenticeship being out, the Lady Dormer sent for him to be her cook, under his father (who then served that honorable lady), where there were four cooks more; such noble houses were then (about 1610) kept, the glory of that and the shame of this present age. Then were those days wherein were practiced the triumphs and trophies of cookery." One of these triumphs is the construction of a ship of confectionery, with guns charged with actual powder, and a castle of pies, containing live frogs and birds. . . .

Fortunately there were men of taste on both sides of the Channel, who made art minister to other purposes than vanity, and amongst these the Regent Duke of Orleans most signally distinguished himself. His *petits soupers* conferred a celebrity on the scene of them, which it still preserves, sufficiently to justify the reply of the Frenchman, who, on being asked by a stranger in a remote part of Europe if he could tell him the direction of Paris, made answer, "*Monsieur, ce chemin-là vous conduira au Palais Royal.*" There is a vague tradition that the *chef* of the Regent was pre-eminent in a *dinde aux truffes*. . . .

Louis XV, amidst his other luxuries, was not unmindful of that which, it has been sagaciously observed, harmonizes with all other pleasures, and remains to console us for their loss. . . .

It was to please Louis XV that the Duchesse de Mailly invented the *gigot à la Mailly*. Louis XVI is said to have been somewhat neglectful of his table, which may have been one amongst the many causes of his fall; for, as Johnson observes, a man who is careless about his table will generally be found careless in other matters. Louis XVIII (whom we mention now to obviate the necessity of returning to the dynasty) was a gastronome of the first water, and had the Duc d'Escars for his grand *maître d'hôtel*—a man whose fortunes were hardly on a par with his desserts. . . .

The Revolution bade fair at its commencement to bring back a long night of barbarism upon art; and the destruction of the pre-existing races of amphitryons and diners-out was actually the most efficiently accomplished by it. We allude not merely to the nobility, with their appendages the chevaliers and abbés, but to the financiers, who employed their ill-got fortunes so gloriously. . . .

At some compensation, again, for the injurious influence of the Revolution in its first stages upon cookery, it is right to mention that it contributed to emancipate the *cuisine* from prejudice, and added largely to its resources. *Pièces de résistance,* says Lady Morgan on Carême's authority, came in with the National Convention,—potatoes were dressed *au naturel* in the Reign of Terror—and it was under the Directory that tea-drinking commenced in France. . . .

The first restaurateur in Paris was *Champ d'Oiseau, Rue des Poulies,* who commenced business in 1770. In 1789 the number of restaurateurs had increased to a hundred; in 1804 to five or six hundred; and it now considerably exceeds a thousand . . . at the commencement of the nineteenth century the culinary genius of France had become permanently fixed in the restaurants, and when the allied monarchs arrived in Paris in 1814 they were absolutely compelled to contract with a restaurateur (Véry) for the supply of their table, at the moderate sum of 3000 francs a day, exclusive of wine.

About this time, however, a reactionary movement took place. Many of the best cooks were again formed and retained in private establishments. The illustrious strangers who repaired to Paris after the peace vied with the native amphitryons, royal and noble, in munificent patronage of the art; and the ten or fifteen years immediately subsequent to the Restoration may be specified as the epoch during which French cookery had reached its culminating point.

If the new Pantheon or Valhalla were set apart for eminent cooks, the following, who matured or laid the foundations of their fame during the first quarter of this century, would have been held entitled to niches, pedestals, or inscriptions within its hallowed precincts:—Robert (inventor of the sauce), Rechaud, Merillion; Benaud, the *chef* of Cambacérès; Farci, *chef de la Bouche Impériale;* Boucheseche, Chevalier, Louis Esbras, Plumeret, and Paul Véry, who formed the famous culinary brigade of Talleyrand; Legacque, cook to Marshal Duroc, and the founder of a *restaurant* which, under the Empire, became celebrated for its *parties fines;* Joubert, many years cook to M. Lafitte, and afterwards to Prince Esterhazy; Baleine and Borel, of the renowned Rocher; Tailleur; the brothers Véry; Robin, afterwards in the service of the late Lord Stair; Beauvilliers, Carême, etc. . . .

Beauvilliers was a remarkable man in many ways, and we are fortunately enabled to furnish a few materials for his future biographer. He commenced the practice of his profession on about 1782, in the Rue Richelieu, No. 2, which we record for the instruction of those who love to trace the historic sites of a metropolis. His reputation grew slowly, and did not arrive at its full height until the beginning of the present century, but it was never known to retrograde, and in 1814 and 1815 he fairly rivalled Véry in the favor of "*nos amis les ennemis.*" . . . "Beauvilliers," says the author of the *Physiologie du Gout,* "made, unmade, and remade his fortune several times, nor is it exactly known in which of these phases he was surprised by death; but he had so many means of getting rid of his money, that no great prize could have devolved upon his heirs."

Shortly before his exit he discharged the debt which, according to Lord Bacon, every man owes to his profession, by the publication of his *Art du Cuisinier,* in two volumes octavo. He died a few months before Napoleon.

Carême, like his great rival, is an author, and an intrepid one, for in the preface to his *Maître d'Hôtel Français,* he says, "I have proved incontestably that all the books, down to the present time, on our *cuisine,* are full of errors"; and he then proceeds to give evidence of his own superior breeding, with his natural and acquired qualifications for the art. We have to thank himself and Lady Morgan, who prides herself on a personal acquaintance with him, for most of the leading particulars of his life.

How the Ancients Cooked and Ate

from Foods and Culinary Utensils of the Ancients
compiled from standard historical works
by Charles Martyn

NATURE SEEMS, indeed, to have blessed her first children with an abundance of the good things of life!

It does not appear that the flesh of domestic animals was eaten to any great extent, and the inference is that it was beyond the means of most persons, for when warriors, upon an expedition, were able to obtain it at the expense of others, they freely indulged their appetites. After their victories they killed and cut up sheep and oxen, and roasted the joints over the embers of a wood fire. Sometimes they boiled the joints or the whole body in a huge pot or cauldron, over a dead wood fire—on which, also, pieces of the flesh were fried.

Amongst the upper classes mutton appears to have been the favorite meat. Chickens were also considered a great delicacy.

As the races of those days, with the exception probably of a few people closely confined in the cities, were great hunters, a plentiful supply of game was usually obtainable—venison, antelopes' flesh, hares, partridges, etc. The flesh of the wild boar was also eaten, but there is no evidence to prove that the animal was domesticated with the intention of using it for food.

According to Herodotus, some of the Babylonian tribes ate nothing but fish, dried in the sun, pounded in a mortar until the fibres would pass through a fine cloth, and kneaded into a sort of bread and baked. At first a prejudice against this species of food seems to have existed, but later it was held in much esteem. The supply of both fresh and salt water fish was practically unlimited.

Locusts were also eaten with great gusto.

The culinary arrangements and operations are not yet very clearly defined by the chroniclers.

The fireplace, built presumably of well-burned bricks, was open at the top, about two feet in height, and occasionally covering an area of many square feet. Whether it was of square or cylindrical shape does not appear. Over the top was set or suspended a large bronze cauldron.

These cauldrons were sometimes of great value. They were usually circular in shape, flat or nearly flat at the bottom, without feet, and furnished at the rim with ears or rings to receive an arched handle or a hooked chain. . . .

Roasting was perhaps the most common mode of preparing meat, but it was also broiled, slices being cut from the divided joints and transfixed with wooden spits. . . .

The cook's knife, closely resembling the modern two-bladed dagger, was usually made of bronze, often thickly gilded, with a much ornamented hilt carved from the hard black wood of the Syrian terebinth. Some, however, were fashioned with bone, partly covered with metal and adorned with pins and studs of gold. . . .

Among the kitchen utensils was a jug with a long neck, an angular handle, and a painted bottom. It was usually suspended from a nail or hook.

There was also a plentiful and varied supply of vases, large and small, pitchers for holding water and other liquids, bowls, cups, pans, small bottles, ladles, jars and funnels—some of pottery and others of bronze, some of simple form and other elaborately patterned. The funnels were generally shaped like the wine strainers of today. . . .

The plates and dishes were of stone, alabaster or bronze. The dishes were generally made with handles, either fixed or movable, by which they could be carried or hung on pegs when not in use, and the red unglazed basins bore inscriptions, in cursive character, running round the interior in many lines to the bottom.

The cups, especially those used for wine, were very beautiful. The lower part was often modeled in the form of a lion's head from which the cup itself rose in a graceful outward curve. Many of them were of gold and silver.

To Assyria is due the birth of the "culinary art" and its gradual growth to a state closely bordering on perfection. . . .

The recorded history of ancient Egypt which was, according to Herodotus, known as Thebes, commences with the reign of Menes, or Menas, who is supposed to have been its first king. He ascended the throne about 2320 B.C.

The growth of civilization among the early Egyptians was much more rapid than among the people of any contemporary nation. Even in the days of Abraham and Joseph they had attained to as high a degree of social culture as during the most glorious periods of their career. In art and science their advancement was especially marked.

In her infancy, Egypt contented herself with the pursuits of agriculture, the chase, and, as the habits of the people became more settled, the rearing of cattle.

The domestic oxen were usually of the hump-backed variety. But not only were the ordinary domestic animals tamed and reared, but also animals such as gazelles and oryxes.

Sheep, though, do not appear to have been generally eaten; in some parts it was, indeed, unlawful to devour them.

Goats were kept, presumably for their milk, and kids were occasionally allowed to browse on the vines in order to impart to their flesh a more delicate flavor.

Pigs were generally looked upon as unclean, and therefore unfit for food. The chroniclers show them as used for food at only one festival. Those represented on the monuments were ugly in the extreme, with long legs and necks, rough hair, and a crest of bristles running down the back.

Beef and goose were more generally eaten than any other kind of animal food. The flesh of the cow was, though, never consumed on account of its supposedly sacred character.

The animals chiefly hunted were the gazelle, wild goat, auk, wild ox, stag, wild sheep, hare, porcupine and even the hyena. The wild boar is not represented on the monuments, but it probably thrived in ancient Egypt, for the country was admirably suited to its habits, as is proved by its tenancy there at the present date.

In lower Egypt, people were in the habit of drying and salting birds of various kinds, such as geese, teal, quail, duck and some of smaller size.

Pigeons were also very plentiful and were much liked, and many of the wading tribe, as for instance the ardea, were so highly esteemed as to have been considered choice offerings for the gods.

The greatest favorite, however, was the Vulpanser, known to us as the "Egyptian goose," which, with some others of the same genus, was caught alive and tamed. They were also taken in a wild state to the poulterers' shops to be displayed for immediate sale, and when not so disposed of were then often salted and potted in earthenware jars.

According to Diodorus, the eggs of domestic birds were hatched by the use of artificial heat furnished by manure.

Of the wild birds, the "sic sac," a small plover, was often mentioned.

The river of Egypt was noted for the excellent quality of its fish (eaten both fresh and salted or dried), many varieties of which seem to have been peculiar to it. "The Israelites remembered with regret the fish which they did eat in Egypt freely."

The kinds most highly regarded were the oxyrhynchus, lepidotus and lotus. . . .

Other varieties much liked were: The oulti, to modern palates the best of all; the nefareh or Nile salmon, which occasionally attained the weight of one hundred pounds; the sagbosa, a kind of herring;

a species of mullet, the shall, shilbeh byad, kilbel bahr, (the Nile dogfish) a species of carp, eels, and turtles of the soft-shelled variety.

Eels were, though, considered unwholesome in summer.

Crocodiles were considered sacred in the neighborhood of Lake Moeris and of Thebes, but were eaten by the natives of the southern frontier. . . .

In the early ages, before men had acquired the art of smelting ore, many of the culinary utensils of the Egyptians were either of stone or earthenware.

Knives were made of flint or stone, and were of two kinds, one broad and flat, the other narrow and pointed.

The skins of the goat and gazelle were fashioned into vessels for the carrying of water, and pans, dishes and vases for kitchen purposes were made of a red ware—sometimes of a light or yellow tint, sometimes of a brilliant and polished appearance.

The Egyptians were acquainted with the use of glass at least as early as the reign of Sesortasen II (more than 3800 years ago), and made for it bottles and other utensils. Some of the former were made from two thicknesses of glass, enclosing between them bands of gold, alternating with a set of blue, green or other color. . . .

Bronze cauldrons of various sizes were used for boiling. They were placed over the fire on metal stands or tripods or supported on stones. Some of the smaller vessels, used for stewing meats, were heated over pans of charcoal. They resembled almost exactly the *magoor* of modern Egypt.

The mortars used for the pounding of spices were made of hard stone and the pestles of metal.

Most of the bowls, ewers, jugs, buckets, basins, vases and ladles used in the kitchen were made of bronze alloyed with tin and iron. . . .

Simpula, or ladles, were commonly made of bronze (often gilded), with the curved summit of the handle, which served to suspend the ladle at the side of the tureen or other vessel, terminating in the likeness of a goose's head (a favorite Egyptian ornament).

Small strainers or collanders of bronze were also used, though for kitchen purposes they were made of strong papyrus stalks or rushes.

The spoons were of various forms and made from ivory, wood

and divers metals. In some the handle ended in a hook, by which when required they were suspended on nails. The handles of others were made to represent men, women or animals. Many were ornamented with lotus flowers. . . .

Though the Egyptians, except when impelled by the desire for extravagant display, partook sparingly of all but one or two meats, they were fond of a great variety of cakes and dainty confections. The more elaborate forms of pastry were mixed with fruits and spirits, and shaped to represent animals, birds and human beings.

The plainer rolls were generally mixed and shaped by hand and sprinkled with seeds before baking. At other times, though, they were prepared from a thinner mixture, first well kneaded in a large wooden bowl (the feet often being used for this purpose), and then carried in vases to the chief pastry cook, who formed it into a sort of macaroni upon a metal pan over the fire, stirring the mixture with a wooden spatula, whilst an assistant stood ready with two pointed sticks to remove it when sufficiently cooked. . . .

When the country was in the zenith of her power and magnificence, the drinking goblets were of gold, silver, glass, porcelain, alabaster and bronze. They varied also in form, some plain in appearance, others beautifully engraved and studded with precious stones. Heads of animals often adorned the handles, the eyes frequently composed of various gems. Many were without handles, while others were so shaped as to more properly come under the name of beakers and saucers. The beakers were frequently made of alabaster with a round base, which prevented their maintaining an upright position without additional support; and when empty they were turned downwards upon their rims. The saucers, which were of glazed pottery, were ornamented with lotus and fish carved or molded on their concave surface.

Many of the vases have never yet been surpassed in daintiness of ornamentation. The most remarkable were those fashioned from porcelain which was made of a fine sand or grit, loosely fused and covered with a thick silicious glaze of a blue, green, white, purple or yellow color. The blue tints obtained have never been equalled in modern times. . . .

The hospitality of the early Grecians was unbounded. The high moral and social standard of the masses of the people rendered it possible to extend greater courtesy towards strangers than would have been deemed prudent in later days. Every stranger or traveler who knocked at the door of a residence was sure of a welcome. No questions were asked him until he had been generously entertained in every feasible manner, for he stood under the protection of Zeus Xenios, guardian of the guest.

This lavish friendliness was probably caused by, or was perhaps itself the cause of, the scarcity of hostelries of reputable character. A spirit of compassion also existed, as it was then considered an ill fortune that made one journey far from home.

As the centuries of increasing wealth and power relaxed the rigidity of the morals of these ancient inhabitants of Greece, the love of luxury gradually supplanted the absorbing desire for intellectual enjoyment which had at first raised them so far above the people of the neighboring territories. Gluttonous devotion to the table, in conjunction with numerous vices, undermined the physical as well as the moral constitution, and the country which had astounded the ages with the valor of its sons, which had proved invulnerable to numerous martial forces, succumbed to the influence of sensual tastes and passions, suggested by the idleness of worldly success. And as their worship of their palates grew, the trained cook obtained an even greater influence until his position became one of extreme importance, and was so recorded by the poets and dramatists of the time.

Little difference, in fact, was there between the habits of the latter day Greeks and the Romans in the days of their great wealth, for Grecian luxuries and Grecian habits were the models that Rome took as its models. . . .

The food of the early Romans resembled to a great extent that of the Greek heroes (their national dish was pulmentarium, a porridge made of pulse). . . . It should, however, be mentioned that Greece never attained such enormous wealth as Rome, and that even in her greatest recklessness she was more refined. Goethe said that in the days of their highest civilization the Romans remained parvenus; that they did not know how to live, that they wasted their riches in tasteless extravagance and vulgar ostentation—but it must be remembered that, whereas the civilization of the nineteenth century is industrial, that of Rome was militant, and to that should be attributed the fact that some of the simplest means of comfort were then unknown.

Many moderns are inclined to doubt the assertions made concerning the countless riches and marvelous expenditures of those days. They read with skepticism the writings of Juvenal, Seneca and the elder Pliny. But, though in some cases exaggeration was doubtless resorted to, sufficient proof remains to convince the observing mind that the wealth of the Roman far surpasses the wildest dreams of the richest man of the present day. The ruins of the Colosseum and of the baths of Caracalla, two structures raised solely for pleasure, impress us with their stupendous magnificence, and even the twentieth century has failed to equal the palaces of the nobles.

Moreover, it must be remembered that the wealthy Roman owned many mansions. Each of the larger ones was a miniature city, sheltering a small army of slaves. The buildings were surrounded by parks, vineyards, woods and artificial lakes. . . .

All Italy was covered with the country residences of the patricians. They were found in numbers on the coast of Campania, the Sabine hills and the lakes of the North.

The most esteemed members of the household staff were the coqui (cooks) and the pistores (fancy bakers). They often amassed large fortunes from their salaries and the many presents they received. All the other servants (who were usually slaves) were under the jurisdiction of a headman, an *atriensis*.

The first meal was light, consisting ordinarily of bread and wine with honey, dates, olives or cheese. At the prandium (their *déjeuner à la fourchette,* which took the place of their noon dinner of former days), meats, vegetables, fruits, bread and wine were provided. After the second meal, the meridiato (or in modern language, the siesta) was enjoyed, as it is in the Italy of this century—although, unlike the sleepy town we know, business Rome then never slept. . . .

The cena, the principal meal, commenced at three, four or five o'clock in the afternoon. Seldom less than four hours were spent at table. Pliny the elder, who was considered a very abstemious man, sat down to his meal at four o'clock, and remained there "until it began to grow dark in summer and soon after night in winter," at least three hours. The amount of food consumed would be incredible were it not for the explanation recorded by Seneca, "*Edunt ut vomat: vomat ut edunt.*"

The dinner menu given below was of a very ordinary affair.

Gustus

Sorrel
Lettuce
Pickled Cabbage and Gherkins
Radishes, Mushrooms, etc.
Oysters
Sardines
Eggs

First Course

Conger Eels
Oysters
Two kinds of Mussels
Thrushes on Asparagus
Fat Fowls
Ragout of Oysters and other Shellfish with black and white Maroons

Second Course

Shellfish and other Marine Products
Beccaficos
Haunches of Venison
Wild Boar
Pastry of Beccaficos and other Birds

Third Course

Sow's Udder
Boar's Head
Fricassee of Fish
Fricassee of Sow's Udders
Various kinds of ducks
Roast Fowl
Hares
Sausages
Roast Pig
Peacocks

Fourth Course

Pastry in wonderfully elaborate forms and colors
Pirentine bread

Fifth Course

Fruits and wines

The "gustus," or appetizer, was also variously known as the "gustatio." A favorite drink served with it was a mulsum of Hymetian honey and Falernian wine.

Toothpicks made from the leaves of the mastich pistachio were in common use.

All the dishes were carved at the sideboards by expert carvers who were trained in schools by practice on jointed models.

Salt was much used in the flavoring of dishes and also to mingle with sacrifices.

Fowls were fattened in the dark. Ducks and geese were fed on figs and dates. Pigs were cooked in fifty different ways. Boars were cooked whole; peacocks with their tails. Sausages were imported from Gaul.

Vitellius and Apicius feasted on the tongues of flamingoes, and Elagabalus on their brains.

The greater the waste at a dinner, the more absurd the extravagance, the more successful it was deemed. . . .

In order to lengthen the time, jugglers, rope-dancers, buffoons and actors were introduced between courses. Beautiful Andalusian girls charmed the diners with their voluptuous dances. Even gladiators were engaged. Games of chance concluded the entertainment when the condition of the revelers permitted. . . .

At the table, the somber togas were exchanged for gay-colored garments, and the shoes for sandals. . . .

The tables first used were of quadrangular shape—three sides being decorated for the guests and the fourth left vacant to facilitate the movements of the attendants. They, however, were soon supplanted by small tables of marble, bronze or citrus. These and a large sideboard supported an amount of heavy gold and silver utensils.

The diners reclined on costly sofas, inlaid with tortoise shells and jewels, and the lower parts decked with embroidered gold. The pillows were stuffed with wool and covered with gorgeous purple. The cushions which supported the elbows were covered with silk stuffs, often marked to designate the places of the various guests.

Three people occupied each sofa. The lowest place on the middle sofa was the seat of honor.

The room or hall was illuminated by lamps and candles, set on individual and very expensive stands or massed in candelabras of great magnificence. The oils and fats used for illumination were diluted with substances which under the influence of heat gave forth odors of great fragrance.

Each guest brought his own napkin.

Ivory-handled knives were manufactured, but seldom used, as the reclining position rendered the spoons more convenient. . . .

Much care was devoted by the wealthy to their private stores of wines. They were sealed in jars or bottles of baked clay, with labels attached bearing the year of the consulship during which they were made. Some old wines were very expensive. That of Campania was considered the best. The Caecuban Falernian was very good. He was pitied who was forced to drink the Vatican!

Greek wines were popular and were found in many Roman cellars.

In winter, wine was heated with water, honey and spices in a caldarium, a vessel fitted with a small charcoal furnace, closely resembling the Russian samovar.

Being unable to sensibly decrease their riches by ordinary methods, many novel ideas were put in use, often at great expense.

Nero constructed in his golden house a vaulted ceiling which turned continually on its axis.

At a banquet given by Otho, tubes of gold and silver suddenly protruded from various parts of the hall and sprinkled perfumes on the assembly. . . .

A weird dinner was once given by the Emperor Domitian. He invited a number of senators and knights to dine with him at a late hour. When they arrived they found that the banquet room had been draped in somber black. At each seat had been placed a tombstone bearing the inscription of a diner and naked black slaves danced weird dances and served up funeral viands on black dishes. When the company had been dismissed, its members found that all their slaves had disappeared and unknown bearers carried them to their homes. Each found on his return a message and a souvenir awaiting him—a silver tombstone bearing his name.

The Gluttony of Rome

from A Book About the Table
by John Cordy Jeaffreson

When it perished, after a long decay, the Roman Empire bequeathed two precious legacies to mankind—its laws and its cookery. The societies that reformed themselves on Theodosian principles, on emerging from the disorder and violence of universal anarchy, followed the culinary precepts which Rome had taught and illustrated in her period of highest luxury. Social convulsions had never caused a general neglect of those rules. To suppose that the Apician code fell out of sight and practice during the struggles which preceded and followed the empire's dissolution, is to surpass in imaginative error the historians who long maintained that the medieval civilians were indebted for their system to the accidental discovery of a copy of Justinian's pandects.

Political agitations lessen neither the appetite nor the need for food. The people of a falling State must have their pottage. Public calamity may occupy the mind, but it cannot satisfy the belly. War and flight only sharpen the desire for meat and drink. The fasting soldier cannot fight; the hungry fugitive falls behind his comrades. It is the same with private sorrow. The death of a virtuous citizen is an occasion for offering a funeral banquet to his mourners. Whilst Rome lay gasping on her death-bed, spits turned before her kitchen-fires. When she was dead, and her heirs were struggling desperately for one or another of the disevered portions of her estate, the spits went on turning, and her cooks, the slaves of precedent, prepared their sauces, and seasoned their dishes, by the rules of Apicius, even as our English cooks followed the directions of Mrs. Glasse and Mrs. Rundell on the eve of the battle of Waterloo, and as they would obey the orders of Acton and Ude, if the Germans were marching on London, or Mr. Odger were First President of the British Republic. . . .

But though we owe a vast debt of gratitude to Rome for her culinary benefactions, we need not shut our eyes to the imperfections and barbaric grossness of her cuisine. . . .

The discomforts and gastronomic outrages of an Augustan supper are so notorious, that no epicure of modern London would care to accept an invitation to a feast served after the manner of the ancients. . . . Under the most favorable circumstances, a Roman dinner must have been a sloppy affair, even to nicely circumspect feeders. Consumed hastily, in an hour of vexatious and untoward incidents, it must have been less advantageous to the eater than to his tailor. . . .

The familiar stories of their gross and fantastic enjoyments would of themselves demonstrate that the voluptuaries of ancient Rome were incapable of the finer delights of the table. Whether we regard the Augustan spendthrifts, or the later *bon-vivants* of the Eastern and Western empires, it may be asserted that the Roman sensualist was devoid of nice perceptions. Always a glutton, he was never an epicure in the modern sense of the term. The dishes with which he gorged himself appealed to the fancy rather than the palate; and his imagination preferred grotesque, and even repulsive, ideas to pleasant and cheerful associations. Vedium Pollio, who could not relish a lamprey unless he could imagine it to have been fattened on human flesh, was a type of the many Roman gourmands whose appetite was quickened by cruel fancies. Like the Australian digger, who ate bank-note sandwiches, the Roman gastronomer delighted to eat and drink money. If he could not obtain, or was too amiable to desire, dishes seasoned with human agony, he required patellae of inordinate cost, and relished them in proportion to the amount of labor expended in their preparation.

Five thousand pounds of money were expended on the pie which made Aesop, the player, famous amongst wasteful feeders, and was believed by the purchaser to have been made of birds that could imitate human voices. Clodius, the son of this preposterous connoisseur of bird-pies, peppered his drink with powdered pearls, and had no gust for the daintiest dish, unless his cook could assure him that a precious stone was one of it ingredients. . . . Sheer wastefulness, that squandered on the whimsical humors of a single person the money which, with discriminating expenditure, might have brought felicity to a thousand intelligent epicures, reached its climax in the kitchens of the Apicius of Augustan Rome, who surpassed all the money-eaters of his time in bootless prodigality. The strongest passion of this gourmandizing fool was for ragouts of half-a-hundred more or less incongruous elements; and when he had weakened his intellect, and destroyed a naturally fine digestion by gastronomic absurdities, he put a violent end to his excesses with a cup of poison. Having squandered on his belly, in the course of a few years, something more than a million and a half of money (English), he killed himself, rather than prolong existence on the wretched eighty or hundred thousand pounds that still remained in his exchequer.

Gallo-Romans in the Fifth Century

from the work of Monsieur de la Bedollière

THE GALLO-ROMAN lunches lightly, on raisins in honey, a piece of bread dipped in wine; he dines at midday, near the end of the fifth hour; he sups at the ninth hour, and he sometimes takes a light collation before going to bed. He is naturally a great eater, and the normal satisfaction of his appetite would pass elsewhere for gluttony.

It is generally in the evening that elaborate feasts are given. The table, adorned with incrustations, is round, covered with a linen cloth. The cushioned chairs or divans that follow its contours are in the shape of a half-circle, or else of a Greek letter; they are upholstered with cloth; they are named according to the number of guests, and to parasites whose presence is tolerated by the master of the house without being desired. A few Gauls, disdainful of Roman indolence, substitute for the cushioned chairs, benches, stools or wooden seats, covered with rugs.

The maître d'hôtel announces that the supper is served. The

guests wash their hands, which they do again after the first serving. They pick up special robes and slippers which they will leave at the base of the sigma. They spread the napkins which they have brought in, the host not furnishing any; then they range themselves around the table. The slaves bring an abundance of roasted or boiled meats, which are carved with promptness and dexterity by special carvers. The repast always begins with heated wine mixed with honey; it is the absinthe of the Vth century. A platter (repositorium) placed in the center of the table, receives in succession fresh eggs, quarters of beef, of mutton, of pig, of goat, the whole seasoned with the yolk of eggs, pepper, pickles, caraway seeds, saffron, poppy seeds, benjamin, honey, salt from the mines or obtained from boiling seawater. If the masters of the household are hunters, they will serve to their guests the meat of the boar with a garniture of cooked apples, that of the deer, the roebuck, the hedgehog, the hare, the crane, the blackbird, the stork, the heron, the crow, and even of the urus, that wild buffalo whose horns become at once a cup and a trophy. The barnyard will provide hens, peacocks, geese with fat livers; the vegetable garden: broadbeans, asparagus, candied elecampane, chick peas and salads of beets and lupine; the woods: mushrooms and truffles. The tench, the shad, the pike, are disdained; the eel is preferred, as is the perch, the salmon, all flavored with caraway seeds, salt and vinegar.

The inhabitants of the seashore favor the mullet, the tunny, the gurnet, oysters fattened in vast ponds, left to be bathed by the tides, specially those of Marseille, of Collioure, of the Evreux and Medoc coasts. For dessert, hot or cold tarts, soft cheese, broiled snails, medlars, chestnuts, figs, Gaul peaches, fresh or dry raisins, are served. At the end of the repast, hot mulse liqueur returns in the guise of coffee, and the tricliniarques distribute the tooth-pick quills, of wood, or of silver.

That all senses might be catered to at once, the hall and the sigma are strewn with laurel leaves, ivy, green vine leaves; masters and servants are crowned with flowers; garlands of flowers hang from the handles of the canthares; large baskets placed as much on the table as on l'abaque or dresser, bearing bouquets of cytious, saffron, privet, amelle, marigolds, rosemary, whose perfume mix with those of the aromatics of Araby crackling in tripods.

The English Dinner Table of the 14th and 15th Centuries

from The Boke of Nurture
by John Russell

A MENU FOR "a dynere of flesche" as published in John Russell's *Boke of Nurture* describes in detail the English dinner table of the fourteenth and fifteenth centuries.

The Furst Course

Furst set for the mustard and brawne of boore, the wild swyne,
Such potage as the cooke hath made of yerbis, spice, and wyne,
Beeff, moton, stewed feysawnd, Swan with the Chawdwyn,
Capourn, pigge, vensoun bake, leche lombard, fruture viaunt fyne;
And than a Sotelte:
Maydon mary that holy virgyne,
And Gabrielle gretynge hur with an ave.

The Second Course

Two potages, blanger mangere, and also jely,
For a standard, vensoun rost, kyd, fawne, or cony,
Bustard, stork, crane, pecok in hakille ryally,
Heiron-sew or betowre, with serve with bred yf that drynk be by;
Partriche, wodcok, plovere, egret, rabettes sowhere;
Gret briddes, larkes, gentille breme de mere,
Doucettes, payn puff, with leche Joly Ambere,
Fretour powche, a sotelte folowynge in fere,
The course for to fullfylle,
An angelle goodly kan appere,
And syngynge with a mery chere,
Unto iii sheperdes uppon an hille.

The III$^{d.}$ Course

Creme of almondes, and mameny, the iii course in coost,
Curlew, brew, snytes, quales, sparrows, martonettes rost,
Perche in gely, crevise deive douz, pty perneis with the moost,
Quynces bake, leche dugard, Fruture sage, y speke of cost,
And soteltes for the soleyne:
That lady that conseuyd by the holy gost,
Hym that distroyed the fendes boost,
Presented plesauntly by the kynges of coleyn.
Afftur this, delicatis mo.
Blaunderelle, or pepyns, with carawey in confite,
Wafurs to ete, ypocras to drynk with delite.
Now this fest is fynysched, voyd the able quyte,
Go we to the fysche fest while we haue respite,
And than with goddes grace the fest wille be do.

TWO VIEWS OF THE CHAFING DISH

IT MAY BE that the revival of chafing dish cookery in recent years is another sign and symbol of the renaissance of home entertainment at table, which suffered a decline after the turn of the century. No doubt the revival is rooted in economics—more money, more leisure—but it is also the result of an increased interest in the preparation of food, notwithstanding that we live in the quick-freeze, instant era.

For the chafing dish, simple though it may be in some respects, is also a symbol of culinary elegance, and has been so for many centuries, as our excerpts show. Its graceful lines and cheerful flame below are soothing to the eye, and its cover conceals a variety of delights. Sometimes the blue-yellow flare of the flambé is an added enchantment.

The Chafing Dish in Civilization

from The Chafing Dish

by H. M. Kinsley

THE CHAFING DISH has played no small part in the civilization of the world. In tracing its history it is interesting to note that it has always appeared when nations had ceased to war and had turned their attention to the science of good living and the art of enjoyment. It has ever been associated with the graces and amenities of life. Indeed, its appearance has seemed to signalize a nation's progress and to be significant of general good cheer and success.

Athenaeus, the Greek philosopher, asserted that "nothing has so powerfully contributed to instill piety into the souls of men as good cookery." That the Chafing Dish is a paramount instrument of good cookery no one will deny. That piety received an impetus from it is easily inferred from the fact that a Chafing Dish was a familiar adjunct on the altars in old French churches. Glowing with lighted charcoal in winter, it was a beacon of comfort to the faithful priests.

Its use, however, was not limited to chancels. More than two thousand years ago the Chafing Dish fulfilled its true office as the promoter of man's palatable pleasures at the tables of the wealthy Greeks and Romans. When it first appeared Seneca said of it, "Daintiness gave birth to this useful invention in order that no viand should be chilled and that everything should be hot enough to please the most pampered palate. The kitchen follows the supper."

The Chafing Dishes of the ancient epicures were exquisite in workmanship and beautiful in design. . . .

"Each of these elegant utensils," says Soyer, who has written exhaustively of the lives and customs of the Greeks and Romans, "was supported by three geese. It measured seven inches from the extremity of one of the bird's heads to the opposite edge of the circumference. The tray is fifteen lines or an inch and a quarter deep, and the feet raise it about two inches above the plane. The three geese have their wings spread and terminate by neats' feet. The heads raised on the breasts form graceful handles. These Chafing Dishes arranged systematically on the sigma produce a delightful effect. . . ."

Cicero undoubtedly referred to the Chafing Dish in making one of his most telling points in his first public law case. He was engaged to defend Sextus Roscius, who was accused of murdering his father, against Sylla, who sold the estates of Roscius for a trifling sum to his favorite slave, Chrysogonus. In making a summary of the wealth of this slave and an exposition of his luxurious living, Cicero says: "A house filled with Corinthian and Delvan vessels, among which was that celebrated stove which he so lately bought at so great a price that passers-by who heard the money being counted out, thought a farm was being sold." This was the anthepsa to which Cicero referred, and is described as "a kind of saucepan of Corinthian brass of considerable value, and made with such art that its contents cook instantly and almost without fire. This simple and ingenious vessel possessed a double bottom, the uppermost one holds the light delicacies destined for the dessert and the fire is underneath. . . ."

Silver gridirons with Syrian plums and pomegranate seeds beneath them to simulate fire were a feature of the table at a supper of the Roman Lentulus. Not only did the Chafing Dish adorn the tables at royal banquets and contribute to the gastronomic enjoyments of the rich, but it was in high favor then as now, among the representatives of the histrionic art. Pliny relates that the tragic actor Aesopus had a dish worth 1,000 sestercii. No doubt then, as at the present time, the actor enjoyed his hot midnight meal filled with grateful appreciation of the Chafing Dish, which has inspired a modern playwright to make it the subject of an ode.

In the middle ages, when strife and anarchy reigned, this utensil of polite life fell into disuse. But in the fifteenth century when learning received an impetus and the life of queen and of laymen became more elegant and comfortable, the Chafing Dish is heard of again. Lord Francis Bacon in a treatise on "Physiological Remains," used the silver Chafing Dish as a standard of comparison for durability in metals. He charges experimenters "to make proof of the incorporation of silver and tin in equal, or with two parts silver and one part tin and to observe whether it will endure the ordinary fire which belongeth to Chafing Dishes, posnets and such other silver vessels."

The Chafing Dish is a cosmopolitan vessel. It belongs to all nations. It was no less appreciated by the French than the English.

But during the political turmoils and wars in France the Chafing Dish, like other comforts and enjoyments of good living was relegated to the shelf. . . .

The Chafing Dish, ever identified with the progressive phase of life, appeared in America in 1720. The colonists, having overcome the difficulties incidental upon the making of a new country, began to appreciate and to desire the luxuries and adornments of refined living. The father of a rich bride of the day, who desired to give his daughter "a truly elegant outfit," in the list of household furnishings he ordered from England, included "6 small brass Chafing Dishes, 4 shillings apiece." From which fact may be inferred that the hospitable hostesses of that time were wont to give Chafing Dish parties, as do the entertainers of this enlightened century.

This period of early prosperity was followed by wars and times of such arduous toil and financial stringency that entertaining almost became a lost art.

But now that the nation prospers and life in America shows a fuller expression of beauty, refinement and artistic development, and there is time to consider the ethics of good cookery, the Chafing Dish has become as necessary a feature of the elegantly equipped modern household as it was of the ancient Greeks and Romans. . . .

The mastery of the Chafing Dish is one of the undisputed arts where a man and woman may share equal privileges and triumphs. A man may prove his skill in cooking with it without detracting from his dignity and a woman can scarcely manipulate it without adding to her charm.

The heroes of Homer prepared their repasts with their own hands and prided themselves on their culinary accomplishments. Ulysses surpassed in lighting a fire and laying a cloth; Patroclus drew wine and Achilles turned the spit. It is, therefore, not only classic, but the highest honor a host can confer upon a guest to prepare food for him with his own hands.

The Chafing Dish not only makes possible the sincerest expression of the most perfect hospitality, but it seems the true symbol of good fellowship. It develops a spirit of camaraderie. Even a pessimist would be inclined to judge his neighbor by his excellencies and not by his defects, as succulent odors whet the appetite and carry the sweet assurance of coming gustatory joys.

Verily, "a good dish sharpens the wit and softens the heart." Who can measure the beneficent influence of exquisite savors! The Chafing Dish is the culinary censer.

The Magic Utensil

from The Chafing Dish Supper

by Christine Terhune Herrick

THE CHAFING DISH began its career in the hands of the bachelors.

With them it was a substitute for a hearthstone, and supplemented by cosy bachelor apartments and a good club, measurably consoled them for the domestic joys most of them neither missed nor desired.

Assisted by the chafing dish, they could—and often did—not only "welcome cheerful evening in," but also see it out in a blaze of glory. Even now, when the chafing dish has become an ordinary sight on family tables, it is still haloed with a suggestion of revelry and midnight feasts that endears it to the hearts of that large class who, amid the proprieties of Philistia, secretly long for the joys of Bohemia.

For the chafing dish has ceased to be the peculiar possession of the dweller in tents. The most sedate householder now owns one, which is often expensive enough to exonerate its proprietor from any suspicion of Bohemianism. A solid silver chafing dish should be as good a guarantee of purse and position in these days as was a gig in Carlyle's time, and when the cooking of a dinner *entree* in the aforesaid dish is personally conducted by an irreproachable butler, the acme of elegance and incongruity has surely been reached.

Never, perhaps, is a chafing dish more out of place than under such circumstances. Its very presence is a plea for unconventionality, for a license that is incompatible with the stern etiquette of the feast of ceremony. . . .

No; the chafing dish is most happily in evidence at the midnight supper, the Sunday night tea, and the summer luncheon. There it provides a delightful substitute for the regulation cooking common on such occasions.

For a long time the man or woman—it was usually a man—who achieved a successful product in the chafing dish was regarded by the uninitiated as hardly second to a magician of the Middle Ages. But we have changed all that! The dish that has for so long been a valued standby to the few who appreciated its possibilities and knew how to make the most of them, has leaped into sudden popularity. Classes of women, of men, of women and men, are organized for the study of chafing dish cookery. Clubs are formed where the only refreshments served are those prepared in the chafing dish. Books have been written in which recipes for chafing dish compounds are given with more or less accuracy. Even the very poor are learning that by the help of a chafing dish they can prepare hot food in the middle of the day without cooking themselves as well as the dinner over a blazing fire in a wood or coal stove. . . .

Like every other branch of cookery, that conducted in the chafing dish demands due study. But when certain points have been mastered, when one has learned the degree of heat required for different dishes, and has become familiar enough with the appearance of her work to know when it is progressing favorably, she need fear no contretemps so long as she follows rules and uses her judgment. . . .

There are a few people who possess so little appreciation of cookery as an art that they are bored by the sight of the workings of a chafing dish. These persons are, happily, in a small minority. Nearly everyone feels a keen interest in watching the preparation of the dish that is soon to gratify his palate, and the hostess who presides over a chafing dish is usually flattered or fluttered by finding herself the center of observation. Unless she is an exceptionally skillful cook, and has a clear and steady head, she will show wisdom if she tries no experiments on a large audience, and reserves her efforts with unfamiliar dishes for a time when she has but a few spectators.

As an aid in making appetizing dishes of left-overs, the housekeeper will find the chafing dish especially useful. . . . Most useful is it, too, when unexpected company makes necessary an addition to the meal that was just enough for the family before the unlooked-for guest arrived. Then is the time when the hostess flies for the magic utensil, and with eggs, or cheese, or sardines, or a can of lobster or salmon, prepares a delicious *entrée* that supplies all former deficiencies.

Chapter Eight

THE TABLE AND ITS GUESTS

AS EVERY HOSTESS knows, the setting for food becomes an important part of its serving, an ingredient of the hospitality we extend to those who compliment us by dining at our table. It is all very well for the pragmatist to contend that splendid food could be eaten off bare boards with no loss, but the hosts and hostesses of civilized societies have always tried, some with simplicity and others with ostentation, to make the table itself an extension of the epicure's art.

Some of the folklore that has come to surround the table is offered here, along with a few notes about the delicate relationship between guests and those who entertain them. We begin with "Directions for a Grand Table," in the eighteenth century manner, which Elizabeth Raffald wrote in 1787 "for the use and ease of Ladies, Housekeepers, Cooks, Etc." in the London of her day. It was, she noted in her lengthy subtitle, "Written purely from PRACTICE."

Turning to hospitality, we have Jane Austen's Miss C. Lutterell, whose fretful and impatient letter discloses the gastronomic frustrations attendant upon her sister's broken engagement.

The final excerpt in the first series is a description of that famous "frog pye" so often quoted from May's seventeenth century classic, "The Accomplisht Cook." Probably it belongs elsewhere. We have placed it here simply because it is the ultimate extravagance in table setting.

Directions for a Grand Table

from The Experienced English Housekeeper
by Elizabeth Raffald

JANUARY BEING A month when entertainments are most used, and most wanted, from that motive I have drawn my dinner at that season of the year, and hope it will be of service to my worthy friends; not that I have the least pretention to confine any Lady to such a particular number of dishes, but to choose out of them what number they please; being all in season, and most of them to be got without much difficulty; as I from long experience can tell what a troublesome task it is to make a bill of fare to be in propriety, and not to have two things of the same kind; and being desirous of rendering it easy for the future, have made it my study to set out the dinner in as elegant a manner as lies in my power, and in the modern taste; but finding I could not express myself to be understood by young housekeepers in placing the dishes upon the table, obliged me to have two copper-plates, as I am very unwilling to leave even the weakest capacity in the dark, being my greatest study to render my whole work both plain and easy. As to French cooks, and old-experienced house-keepers, they have no occasion for my assistance, it is not from them I look for any applause. I have not engraved a copper-plate for a third course, or a cold collation, for that generally consists of things extravagant; but I have endeavored to set out a desert of sweetmeats, which the industrious house-keeper may lay up in summer at a small expense, and, when added to what little fruit is then in season, will make a pretty appearance after the cloth is drawn, and be entertaining to the company. Before you draw your cloth, have all your sweetmeats and fruit dishes up in China dishes or fruit-baskets, and as many dishes as you have in one course, so many baskets or plates your desert must have; and as my bill of fare is twenty-five to each course, so must your desert be of the same number, and set out in the same manner, and as ice is very often plentiful at that time, it will be easy to make five different ices for the middle, either to be served upon a frame or without, with four plates of dried fruit round them, apricots, green-gages, grapes, and pears—the four outward corners, pistacho nuts, prunellas, oranges, and olives—the four squares, nonpareils, pears, walnuts, and filberts—the two in the centre, betwist the top and bottom, chestnuts and Portugal plums—for six long dishes, pine-apples, French plums, and the four brandy-fruits, which are peaches, nectarines, apricots, and cherries.

We may live without friends; we may live without books;
But civilized man cannot live without cooks.

—Owen Meredith

A Wedding Dinner Postponed

from Lesley Castle

by Jane Austen

(Miss C. Lutterell to Miss M. Lesley)
Glenford, February 12th

I HAVE A thousand excuses to beg for having so long delayed thanking you my dear Peggy for your agreeable Letter, which believe me I should not have deferred doing, had not every moment of my time during the last five weeks been so fully employed in the necessary arrangements for my sister's wedding... And now what provokes me more than anything else is that the Match is broke off, and all my Labor thrown away. Imagine how great the Disappointment must be to me, when you consider that after having labored both by Night and by Day, in order to get the Wedding dinner ready by the time appointed, after having roasted Beef, Broiled Mutton, and Stewed Soup enough to last the new-married Couple through the Honey-moon, I had the mortification of finding that I had been Roasting, Broiling and Stewing both the Meat and Myself to no purpose. Indeed, my dear Friend, I never remember suffering any vexation equal to what I experienced on last Monday when my sister came running to me in the store-room with her face as White as a Whipt Syllabub, and told me that Henry had been thrown from his Horse, had fractured his Scull and was pronounced by his surgeon to be in the most eminent Danger. "Good God! (said I) you don't say so? Why what in name of Heaven will become of all the Victuals! We shall never be able to eat it while it is good. However, we'll call in the Surgeon to help us. I shall be able to manage the Sirloin myself, my Mother will eat the soup, and You and the Doctor must finish the rest." Here I was interrupted, by seeing my poor Sister fall down to all appearance Lifeless upon one of the Chests, where we keep our table linen. I immediately called my Mother and the Maids, and at last we brought her to herself again . . . we laid her upon the Bed, and she continued for some Hours in the most dreadful Convulsions. My Mother and I continued in the room with her, and when any intervals of tolerable Composure in Eloisa would allow us, we joined in heartfelt lamentations on the dreadful Waste in our provisions which the Event must occasion, and in concerting some plan for getting rid of them. We agreed that the best thing we could do was to begin eating them immediately, and accordingly we ordered up the cold Ham and Fowls, and instantly began our Devouring Plan on them with great Alacrity. We would have persuaded Eloisa to have taken a wing of Chicken, but she would not be persuaded . . . We endeavored to rouse her by every means in our power, but to no purpose. I talked to her of Henry. "Dear Eloisa (said I) there's no occasion for your crying so much about such a trifle. (For I was willing to make light of it in order to comfort her.) I beg you would not mind it—You see it does not vex me in the least; though perhaps *I* may suffer most from it after all; for I shall not only be obliged to eat up all the Victuals I have dressed already, but must if Henry should recover (which however is not very likely) dress as much for you again; or should he die (as I suppose he will) I shall still have to prepare a Dinner for you whenever you marry any one else —Yet I daresay he'll die soon, and then his pain will be over and you will be easy, whereas my Trouble will last much longer, for work as hard as I may, I am certain that the pantry cannot be cleared in less than a fortnight."

"A maxim, too, that must not be forgot,
Whatever be your dinner, "serve it hot,"
Your fine ragouts, like epigrams, require
A little salt,—but to be full of fire."

—The Banquet

Good Housekeeping in 1665

from Robert May's The Accomplisht Cook

THESE WERE THE DAYS wherein were practiced the triumphs and trophies of cookery. One of these triumphs is the construction of a ship of confectionary, with guns charged with actual powder, and a castle of pies containing live frogs and birds. After the firing of the guns the ladies are advised to "take the eggshells full of sweet waters and throw them at each other. All dangers being seemingly over, by this time you may suppose they will desire to see what is in the pyes; where, lifting first the lid off one pye, out skip some frogs, which makes the ladies to skip and shreek; next after, the other pye, whence come out the birds, who, by a natural instinct, flying in the light will put out the candles; so that, what with the flying birds and skipping frogs, the one above, the other beneath, will cause much delight and pleasure to the whole company: at length the candles are lighted and a banquet brought in, the musick sounds and everyone with much delight and content rehearses their actions in the former passages." These were the delights of the nobility before good housekeeping left England.

* * *

In democratic America, especially in these days of indiscriminate dining, it is easy to forget that in other countries and other centuries the guests at table were as carefully considered and debated over as the food itself.

A curious book of 1653, "The Accomplished Lady Rich's Closet of Rarities; or, Ingenious Gentlewoman's Delightful Companion," lays down strict rules of conduct for the lady dining at home or abroad.

John Cordy Jeaffreson then provides us with a glimpse of

one of the many discriminations suffered by women. The long prohibition of women from table in the course of history, and their later banning from the society of epicures in many places, may account for the almost total lack of celebrated female gastronomes. There is no reason, of course, why a lady's taste buds should be any less sensitive to *haute cuisine*, or to the subtle pleasures of wine—still, the great names among epicureans and master chefs are, without exception, male.

Literary men have always been noteworthy for their appreciation of good food, and in an excerpt from a contemporary book, "The English at Table," a British writer, John Hampson, tells us of some of them.

Three Views of the Sexes as Guests

A Gentlewoman at Table

from The Accomplished Lady Rich's Closet of Rarities;

or, Ingenious Gentlewoman's Delightful Companion (1653)

A GENTLEWOMAN, being at table abroad or at home, must observe to keep her body straight, and lean not by any means with her elbow, nor by ravenous gesture discover a voracious appetite. Talk not when you have meat in your mouth, and do not smack like a pig, nor venture to eat spoon-meat so hot that the tears stand in your eyes; which is as unseemly as the gentlewoman who pretended to have as little a stomach as she had a mouth, and therefore would not swallow her peas by spoonsful, but took them one by one, and cut them into two before she could eat them. It is very uncomely to drink so large a draught that your breath is almost gone, and are forced to blow strongly to recover yourself; throwing down your liquor as into a funnel, is an action fitter for a juggler than a gentlewoman. Thus much for our observations in general. If I am defective in particulars, your own prudence, discretion, and curious observations will supply. In carving at your own table, distribute the best pieces first; and it will appear very comely and decent to use a fork; so touch no meat without it.

Women at Table

from A Book About the Table
by John Cordy Jeaffreson

GRIMOD DE LA REYNIÈRE held that women were out of place in the company of feasting epicures, whose attention should not be diverted from beautiful things *on* to lovely creatures *at* the table. After coffee, the fair sex might resume their rights, which fell into abeyance during a grand meal. But fine gentleman though he was, M. de la Reynière was a vulgarian at table, who did not blush to declare that ceremonious politeness should be banished from the festal board. . . .

While Brillat-Savarin wished woman to participate in the finer pleasure of the table, in order that she should enhance and preserve her beauty, Louis Eustache Ude, whilom chef to Louis XVI and the Earl of Sefton, urged that the young ladies of noble houses should be brought at early age to their parent's tables, for the education of their palates, and for the development of gastronomic taste. Even more than from the English fog, which depressed his spirits, and from the prejudices of the English physicians, who held his art in contempt bordering on abhorrence, Ude suffered from the coldness and indifference which the women of our aristocracy exhibited to his special pursuit. Alike in *gourmandise* and *friandise,* he found them deficient in sensibility and enthusiasm. "The ladies of England," he wrote towards the close of his beneficent career, "are unfavorably disposed to our art; yet I find no difficulty in assigning the cause of it. It is particularly the case with them (and indeed it is so in some measure with our own sex) that they are not introduced to their parents' table till their palates have been completely benumbed by the strict diet observed in the nursery and boarding schools."

Literary Men of Taste

from The English at Table

by John Hampson

IN SPITE OF Charles Lamb's passion for pork, so ardently stressed in a letter to Coleridge, most of the literary men's taste seems to have been for "a large cold bottle and a small hot bird." Who can forget Hazlitt's descriptions of reading, while he ate chicken or pheasant, and drank sherry or coffee? He was knowledgeable about food and inns. But here we must thrust through the galazy (leaving Keats to enjoy his claret; and Byron, with his complaint of the ladies, who "always had the wings of the chicken") since Thomas Love Peacock towers over them all on the subject. Not only did he write poems about food, but his novels are stuffed with meals; the people who eat them have much to say on the subject of delicious wines and foods. No other English novelist has ever written so well or so much for the gourmet as he. At much the same time another English eccentric was preoccupied by the various problems of the table. Dr. William Kitchiner not only learned to cook for himself, but wrote learnedly for the benefit of others; producing his famous *Cook's Oracle,* which is the forerunner of the cookery book of our own time with its precise directions as to quantities and method. Creevey has many amusing glimpses at the great at table; nor does he hesitate to blame the careless: at one house the dinner "was damnable in cookery, comfort and everything else" while at another "no roast beef on the side-table but only a suckling pig," a third gave him "excellent and plentiful dinners . . . a table with a barrel of oysters and hot pheasant, etc., wheeled into the drawing room every night at half-past-ten."

In 1827 London prices included "Chickens are 15/—a couple . . . cock's combs 22/—a pound, and it takes a pound and a half to make a dish." Lord Cowper tells how William IV "ate very heartily of turtle, accompanying it with punch, sherry, and champagne." Dinner always lasted a long time: "the king must have drunk a couple of bottles of claret before we left the table." A dinner at a fashionable club cost no less than *"a pund."*

Thomas Walker published his *Art of Dining* in 1835. One of his dinners for eight people consisted of turtle soup with punch to drink, his guests were next given whitebait and champagne, then grouse and claret. The sweet was of apple fritters served with jelly. Thackeray's passion for whitebait of the Greenwich variety led him to write: "It has an almost angelic delicacy of flavor: it is as fresh as the recollections of childhood—it wants a Correggio's pencil to describe it with sufficient tenderness." The Whitebait Dinner, a Cabinet-ministerial celebration, was held in Greenwich in August, at the termination of a parliamentary session, a practice begun towards the end of the eighteenth century; which, after it lapsed, was revived by Disraeli, another gourmet. His banquets in fiction are too arch and solemn, but he prettily suggests that eggs when served with bacon resemble "tufts of primroses" and describes dinner as "that royal meal." Sydney Smith rhymed the pleasures of the table, telling his readers how to make salads and to roast legs of mutton: his "idea of heaven, is eating *foies gras* to the sound of trumpets," while roast pheasant and bread sauce are "a pure and elevated pleasure." The more solemn though still arch Tennyson could write of a picnic meal:

"Brought out a dusky loaf that smelt of home,
And, half cut down, a pasty costly made,
Where quail and pigeon, lark and leveret, lay
Like fossils of the rock, with golden yolks
Imbedded and injellied."

While to Dickens we owe: "poverty and oysters always seem to go together." So did "pickled salmon," which Mr. Pickwick thought "very remarkable facts." The engraver Bewick says the poor ate "course bread, oatmeal porridge, and milk" which was only varied on Sundays by a stew containing a little meat with "cabbage or other succulent vegetables." As a boy, he relates, he never paid more than three halfpence a pound for salmon which was plentiful. Benson Hill published in 1841 his *Epicure's Almanack,* an interesting sign of the period. So many new discoveries were being made, one expert predicted that soon the proper preparation of food would convey immortality on the eaters, at which the poet Crabbe ejaculated "God forbid!" Mrs. Gaskell's Mr. Holbrook had the pudding served before the meat: since his father's dictum had been "no broth, no ball; no ball, no beef." Many are the details of country dishes and customs in *Cranford* and her other writings, while Charlotte Brontë gives us details of the healthy appetites of curates, and Jane Austen left the opinion: "An egg boiled very softly is not unwholesome." Miss Acton produced an excellent book of recipes; but it was left to the young Mrs. Beeton to produce a monumental general work on cookery in 1863. Her recipes are more reliable than the notes which accompany them; for generally her historic data is hopelessly unsound. However, we can get much from her pages even today, and her work is a gold mine still for those interested in food and eating. Who, one wonders, last prepared "Sudden Death," a dish of broiled fowl very popular at the smart Thames-side hotels? Her "delicately clean saucepan" is an indication of her sterling quality; one could quote and quote from her thousand-page volume, for she well deserved the niche she has won for herself in our culinary history. But in spite of a general plenty, with new sources of practical information, with easier method of preparation, the general standard among the well-to-do was stereotyped, the idea of a correct dinner table was still fashionable; so that the frequent diner-out began at last complaining of the dullness and similarity of the dishes offered by the average hostess, with turbot, mutton, and boiled chickens going strong after forty years on fashionable tables.

Among the noted epicures of the age must be mentioned Abraham Hayward, who wrote a book on the art of dining. He gives sound and sensible advice about cookery and tells some amusing anecdotes about the great, one of which concerns an Earl of Dudley, who was most lavish with entertainments on the grand scale, and who, while at a dinner party given by Prince Esterhazy, kept muttering audibly "God bless my soul! No apple pie!"

* * *

ETIQUETTE from age to age is a fascinating subject worthy of its own history, although nobody seems to have written one. There are numerous books, however, in which the etiquette of a given place or period is set forth. These guides have been popular in America from early in the nineteenth century until the present day, when Emily Post's name has become a part of the language.

Rather than examine the successive evolution of table manners at length, we have chosen four brief samples somewhat off the beaten path. One is John Jeaffreson's brief history of forks and spoons. Another is Thomas Coryate's observations on the early seventeenth-century use of forks in Italy. Coryate, an English traveler, published in 1611 his impressions of a 1,975-mile journey through Paris, Lyons, Turin, Venice, Zurich and Strasbourg, under the title, "Coryate's Crudities: Hastily gobled up in Five Moneths' Travels."

Before a short lesson in etiquette from the redoubtable Johnson, we come to the notes of another traveler, Charles Dickens, whose impressions of America, traveling from West to East on his first visit, when he was still unknown here, indicate something of the distaste for Americans and their ways which he was never able to overcome.

Fingers Before Forks

from A Book About the Table
by John Cordy Jeaffreson

"FINGERS WERE MADE before forks," says the familiar adage that had its origin in the warm disdain with which our ancestors of the seventeenth century repudiated the Italian tablefork as a fantastic and even impious contrivance. The ancient people of the world fingered their cooked meat, and it was only at a quite recent date that the modern peoples adopted the pronged tool by which we convey food to the mouth without soiling the hand.

Products of necessity, the first culinary forks were devised for the benefit of artistes bent on withdrawing sodden flesh from a boiling cauldron. The Greek *creqgra*—a staff, fitted at the lower end with a hook, or with prongs that bore a distant resemblance to human fingers—was a rude pot-fork, which, though greatly serviceable to cooks, would have been of no convenience to a reclining gourmand. Possessing several varieties of this kitchen tool, the Romans, notwithstanding their care for the caprice as well as for the comfort of epicurean feasters, never produced a table fork, though it was more needed by the ancient, whose recumbent posture deprived him of the use of one arm, than by the mediaevalist who, sitting at meat, could serve his mouth with both hands. . . . Had the luxurious Romans been users of forks, some specimens of the implement would certainly have been found in the ruins of Herculaneum and Pompeii.

But though they fed themselves with their fingers, it must not be imagined that the mediaevalists were altogether fork-less. Forty years since, a fork of Anglo-Saxon manufacture was discovered in Wiltshire, under circumstances which leave no room for doubt that it was made at least as early as the later part of the ninth century.

. . . And from that period to the close of the Tudor time, there is evidence that our ancestors had a few forks, long before they were commonly placed on the English table, and regarded as necessary articles of furniture. . . .

Whilst the spoon was the only implement used in feeding the mouth, entertainers were not required to provide the guest with one. Whether he came for a month or a day, to a series of banquets or a single repast every guest always brought his spoon in his pocket. Never traveling without the implement, which was as universal a piece of personal equipment as a watch is at the present time, the modish man of olden England no sooner found himself seated at a strange board than, taking his spoon-case from its place of concealment, he exhibited the spoon, which had usually been given him by one of his baptismal sponsors. It was the same with women and children. When everyone used a spoon, and hosts seldom thought of providing spoons, the spoon was a piece of portable property that went wherever its owner went. . . .

Spoons were made of several materials. In the rich or fairly prosperous circles they were usually of silver, which was sometimes gilt. But for folk of the poorer sort, spoons were made of tinned iron, horn, wood, and other cheap stuff. . . .

To say of a man, "He was born with a silver spoon in his mouth," was equivalent to calling him a prosperous fellow, whose good fortunes commenced at his very birth, when he had a sponsor rich enough to give him a silver spoon. . . . To remark of a man that "he had always fed himself with the wooden spoon," implied that he was a person of no account, who at any banquet would of course sit "below the salt" with inferior company, and fill himself with the poorer fare, as became a guest armed only with a spoon of wood.

Crowd not your table, let your number be
Not more than seven, and never less than three.

—DR. KING'S *Art of Cookery*

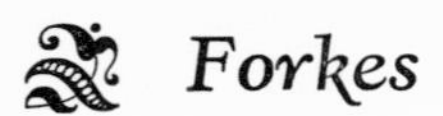

Forkes

from Crudities
by Thomas Coryate

HERE I will mention a thing that might have been spoken of before in the discourse of the first Italian towne. I observed a custome in all those Italian cities and townes through which I passed, that is not used in any other country that I saw in my travels, neither do I thinke that any other nation of Christendome doth use it, but only Italy. The Italians, and also most strangers that are commonrant in Italy, do alwaies at their meates use a little forke when they cut their meat. For while with their knife which they hold in one hand, they cut the meate out of the dish, they fasten their forke, which they hold in the other hand, upon the same dish; so that whatsoever he be that sitteth in the company of any others at meals, should unadvisedly touch the dishes of meate with his fingers from which all at the table doe cut, he will give occasion of offence unto the company, as having transgressed the lawes of good manners, insomuch that for his error he shalle be at least brow-beaten if not reprehended in wordes. This form of feeding, I understand, is generally used in all places of Italy; their forkes being for the most of yron or steels, and some silver, but those are used only by gentlemen. The reason of their curiosity is, because the Italian cannot by any means indure to have his dish touched with fingers, seeing that all men's fingers are not alike cleane. Hereupon I myselfe thought good to imitate the Italian fashion by this forked cutting of meate, not only while I was in Italy, but also in Germany, and oftentimes in England since I came home, being once quipped for that frequent using of my forke by a certain learned gentleman, a familiar friend of mine, one Mr. Lawrence Whitaker, who in his merry humour doubted not to call me *Furcifer* only for using a forke at feeding, but for no other cause.

Habits of the Americans

from American Notes
by Charles Dickens

WE ARE TO BE on board the Messenger three days; arriving at Cincinnati (barring accidents) on Monday morning. There are three meals a day. Breakfast at seven, dinner at half-past twelve, supper about six. At each, there are a great many small dishes and plates upon the table, with very little in them; so that although there is every appearance of a mighty "spread," there is seldom really more than a joint: except for those who fancy slices of beet-root, shreds of dried beef, complicated entanglements of yellow pickle; maize, Indian corn, applesauce, and pumpkin.

Some people fancy all these little dainties together (and sweet preserves besides), by way of relish to their roast pig. They are generally those dyspeptic ladies and gentlemen who eat unheard-of quantities of hot corn bread (almost as good for the digestion as a kneaded pin-cushion), for breakfast, and for supper. Those who do not observe this custom, and who help themselves several times instead, usually suck their knives and forks meditatively, until they have decided what to take next: then pull them out of their mouths: put them in the dish; help themselves; and fall to work again. At dinner, there is nothing to drink upon the table, but great jugs full of cold water. Nobody says anything, at any meal, to anybody. All the passengers are very dismal, and seem to have tremendous secrets weighing on their minds. There is no conversation, no laughter, no cheerfulness, no sociality, except in spitting; and that is done in silent fellowship round the stove, when the meal is over. Every man sits down, dull and languid; swallows his fare as if breakfasts, dinners, and suppers, were necessities of nature never to be coupled with recreation or enjoyment; and having bolted his food in a gloomy silence, bolts himself, in the same state.

But for these animal observances, you might suppose the whole male portion of the company to be the melancholy ghosts of departed bookkeepers, who had fallen dead at the desk: such is their weary air of business and calculation. Undertakers on duty would be sprightly beside them; and a collation of funeral-baked meats, in comparison with these meals, would be a sparkling festivity.

He [Johnson] honored me with his company at dinner on the 16th of October, at my lodgings in Old Bond Street, with Sir Joshua Reynolds, Mr. Garrick, Dr. Goldsmith, Mr. Murphy, Mr. Bickerstaff, and Mr. Thomas Davies. Garrick played round him with a fond vivacity, taking hold of the breasts of his coat, and, looking up in his face with a lively archness, complimented him on the good health he seemed to enjoy; while the sage, shaking his head beheld him with a gentle complacency. One of the company not being come at the appointed hour, I proposed, as usual, upon such occasions, to order dinner to be served; adding, "Ought six people to be kept waiting for one?" "Why, yes," answered Johnson, with a delicate humanity, "if the one will suffer more by your sitting down, than the six will do by waiting."

—James Boswell
The Life of Samuel Johnson

Chapter Nine

COOKS AND COOKBOOKS

SO AT LAST to the kitchen, whence cometh all good things, and to the cookbooks in which are collected the treasures of countless chefs, professional and amateur.

Dick Humbelbergius Secundus, who gives us a quick glimpse of a Roman cook, is an imaginary translator of Apicius, of whom more later. Dr. William Kitchiner, the English eccentric described a few pages before by John Hampson, gives cooks a few words of friendly advice. Dr. John Doran, the English journalist and stage historian, provides us with a survey of the French kitchen and some of its glories, followed by a dissertation on the ancient cook. "Soup Untasted" is an anecdote from Disraeli's "Tancred," one of the novels he wrote in his later years.

The chapter also includes an excerpt from a recently published facsimile edition of "American Cookery," by Amelia Simmons, the first American cookbook, published in Hartford, Connecticut, in 1796. The author's "Advice to Young Ladies Expecting to Cook," suggests that the older adults of 1796 were as reluctant to give way to changing times and the oncoming generation as adults have always been.

Picture of a Cook

from Apician Morsels
by Dick Humbelbergius Secundus

THE ASIATICS WERE so intemperate and luxurious in their feeding, that they were known by the surname of gluttons, then called *Asotae*. Pliny informs us, that after the conquest of Asia, foreign luxury first entered into Rome, and that then the Roman people began to make sumptuous banquets. Then was a cook a most useful slave among the ancients, and began to be much esteemed and valued; all bespattered with broths, and begrimmed with the soot of his pots, his platters, dishes, pestles and mortars, he was welcomed out of the kitchen into the schools: and that which before was accounted but a vile and nauseous slavery, was afterwards honored as an art; the chief object of which was only to forage everywhere for provocatives of appetite, and to study all manner of dainties to satisfy a most profound gluttony.

Not long the flood had left the face of earth,
And lost mankind received a second birth,
Ere luxury rose, with sickness in her train,
And all the frightful family of pain:
Nature's spare wants forsook the homely board,
With mad profusion to see each table stor'd!
Invention labor'd to debauch the treat,
And whet the jaded appetite to eat:
Intoxicating wines henceforth began
T' inflame the blood, not cheer the heart of man.

Friendly Advice to Cooks

from The Cook's Oracle

by William Kitchiner

ON YOUR FIRST coming into a family, lose no time in immediately getting into the good graces of your fellow-servants, that you may learn from them the customs of the Kitchen, and the various rules and orders of the House.

Take care to be on good terms with the servant who waits at table:—make use of him as your Sentinel, to inform you how your work has pleased in the parlor; by his report you may be enabled in some measure to rectify any mistake; but request the favor of an early interview with your Master or Mistress,—depend as little as possible on second-hand opinions. Judge of your Employers from your own observations, and their behavior to you—not from any idle reports from the other Servants, who, if your Master or Mistress inadvertently drop a word in your praise, will immediately take alarm, and, fearing your being more in favor than themselves, will seldom stick at trifles to prevent it, by pretending to take a prodigious liking to you, and poisoning your mind in such a manner as to destroy all your confidence, etc. in your Employers, and if they do not immediately succeed in worrying you away—will take care that you have no comfort while you stay:—Be most cautious of those who profess most: not only, beware of believing such honey-tongued folks, but beware as much, of betraying your suspicions of them—for that will set fire to the train at once, and of a doubtful Friend, make a determined Enemy.

If you are a good Cook, and strictly do your duty—you will soon become a favorite domestic—but never boast of the approbation of your Employers, for in proportion as they think you rise in their estimation—you will excite all the tricks, that Envy, Hatred, Malice, and all Uncharitableness, can suggest to your fellow-servants;—every one of whom, if less sober, honest, or industrious, or less favored than Yourself,—will be your Enemy.

While we warn you against making others your Enemy, take care that you do not Yourself become your own and greatest Enemy —"Favorites are never in greater danger of falling, than when in the greatest favor" which often begets a careless inattention to the commands of their Employers, and insolent overbearance to their equals, a gradual neglect of duty, and a corresponding forfeiture of that Regard—which can only be preserved by the means which created it.

"Those arts by which at first you gain it,
You still must practice to maintain it."

If your Employers are so pleased with your conduct as to treat you as a friend rather than a servant—do not let their kindness excite your self-conceit, so as to make you for a moment forget you are one. Condescension, even to a proverb, produces Contempt in inconsiderate minds, and to such, the very means which Benevolence takes to cherish attention to duty, becomes the cause of the evil it is intended to prevent . . .

Let your Character be remarkable for Industry and Moderation —your Manners and Deportment, for modesty and humility—your

Dress distinguished for simplicity, frugality, and neatness. A dressy servant is a disgrace to a house—and renders her employers as ridiculous as she does herself. If you outshine your companions in finery, you will inevitably excite their Envy, and make them your enemies. . . .

Giving away any thing without consent or privity of your Master or Mistress, is a liberty you must not take;—Charity and compassion for the wants of our fellow-creatures are very amiable virtues, but they are not to be indulged at the expense of your own Honesty, and other people's property.

When you find that there is anything to spare, and that it is in danger of being spoiled by being kept too long,—it is very commendable in you to ask leave to dispose of it while it is fit for Christians to eat: If such permission is refused, the sin does not lie at your door. But you must on no account bestow the least morsel in contradiction to the will of those to whom it belongs. . . .

Saucy Answers are highly aggravating, and answer no good purpose. Let your master or mistress scold ever so much, or be ever so unreasonable; as "a soft answer turneth away wrath"—"so will Silence—be the best a Servant can make." . . .

Be extremely cautious of Seasoning High,—leave it to the Eaters to add the piquante condiments, according to their own palate and fancy: . . .

Tastes are as different as faces; and without a most attentive observation of the directions given by her Employers, the most experienced Cook will never be esteemed a profound Palatician. . . .

However, delicately sensitive nature may have formed the organs of Taste,—it is only during those few happy movements that they are perfectly awake, and in perfect good humor—(Alas! how very seldom they are!) that the most accomplished and experienced Cook has a chance of working with any degree of certainty without the auxiliary tests of the balance and measures: by the help of these, when you are once right, it is your own fault if you are ever otherwise. . . .

To taste any thing in perfection, the Tongue must be moistened, or the substance applied to it contain moisture—the nervous papillae which constitute this sense are aroused to still more lively sensibility by Salt—Sugar—Aromatics, etc.

If the Palate becomes dull by repeated tasting, one of the best ways of refreshing it—is to masticate an Apple, or to wash your mouth well with milk.

The Incessant Exercise of Tasting, which a Cook is obliged to submit to during the Education of her Tongue, frequently impairs the very faculty she is trying to improve. " 'Tis true—'tis pity—and pity 'tis" (says a *grand gourmand*), " 'tis true,—her too anxious perseverance to penetrate the mysteries of Palatics may diminish the tact, exhaust the powder, and destroy the Index, without which all her labor is in vain."

Therefore a sagacious Cook, instead of idly and wantonly wasting the excitability of her Palate—on the sensibility of which her reputation and fortune depends, when she has ascertained the relative strength of the flavor of the various ingredients she employs, will call in the Balance and the Measure to do the ordinary business, and endeavor to preserve her Organ of Taste with the utmost care, that it may be a faithful Oracle to refer to on grand occasions, and new Compositions,—of these an ingenious Cook may form as endless a variety, as a Musician with his seven notes, or a Painter with his colors.

Benefactors of Mankind

from Table Traits

by Dr. John Doran

THE GLORY OF the French kitchen rose with that of the *Grand Monarque,* and Vatel and Louis XIV were contemporaries. . . .

The cooks "looked up" in the nights and suppers of the Regency, and the days and dinners of Louis XV. It would be difficult to say whether under the Regent, or under the King, the culinary art and its professors most flourished. I am inclined, however, to think that, during the tranquil and voluptuous period of the reign of Louis XV, the cooks of France rose to that importance from which they have never descended. They became a recognized and esteemed class in society whose spoiled children they were; and in return, it was very like spoiled children that they behaved. But how could it be otherwise, when the noble, the brave, and the fair girded aprons to their loins, and stood over stew-pans, with the air of alchymists over alembics? It is to the nobility and other distinguished persons in high life, yet not noble, in France, that gastronomy owes many a dish, whose very name betrays to ecstasy. And here are a few of these droll benefactors of mankind.

The Marquis de Bechamel immortalized his name, in the reign of Louis XIV, by his invention of cream-sauce, for turbot and cod. Madame de Maintenon imagined the "cutlets in curlpapers" which go by her name, and which her ingenuity created in order to guard the sacred stomach of the Grand Monarque from the grease which he could not digest. The "*Chartreuse à la Mauconseil*" is the work, and the most innocent one, of the free and easy Marchioness of that name. A woman more free and easy still, the Duchess of Villeroy, (Maréchale de Luxembourg,) produced, in her hours of reflection, the dish known as *poulets à la Villeroy*. They were eaten with bread *à la Régent*, of which the author was the *roué* Duke of Orleans. His too "well-beloved" daughter, the Duchess of Berry, had a gastronomic turn of mind, like her illustrious father. She was an epicurean lady, who tasted of all the pleasures of life without moderation, whose device was, "Short and sweet," and who was contented to die young, seeing that she had exhausted all enjoyment, and had achieved a renown, that should embalm her name forever, as the inventor of the *filets de lapereau*. The *gigot à la Mailly* was the result of much study, on the part of the first mistress of Louis XV, to rid herself of a sister who was a rival. Madame de Pompadour, another of the same King's "ladies," testified her gratitude for the present which the Monarch made her of the Chateau de Bellevue, by the production of the *filets de volaille à la Bellevue*. The Queen of Louis was more devout, but not less epicurean, than his mistresses; and the *petites bouchées à la Reine*, if they were not of her creating, were named in honor of Maria Leczinzka. Louis himself had a contempt for female cooks; but Madame Du Barry had one so well-trained, that with a charming dinner of *coulis de faisans, croustades de la foie de lottes, salmis de bécassine, pain de volaille à la suprême, poularde au cresson, écrevisses au vin de Sauterne, bisquets de pêches au Noyau,* and *crème de cerneaux,* the King was so overcome with ecstasy, that, after recovering from the temporary disgust he experienced at hearing that it was the handywork of a woman, he consented to ennoble her by conferring upon her the *cordon bleu,*—which phrase, from that time, has been accepted as signifying a skilled female cook.

* * *

THE ANCIENT COOK

It is an incontestable fact that he who lives soberly does not depend upon his cook for the pleasure which he derives from his repast. Nevertheless, the cook is one of the most important of personages; and even appetite, without him, would not be of the value that it is at present. A great *artiste* knows his vocation. When the cook of Louis XVIII was reproached by His Majesty's Physician with ruining the royal health by savory juices, the dignitary of the kitchen sententiously remarked that it was the office of the cook to supply His Majesty with pleasant dishes, and that it was the duty of the doctor to enable the King to digest them. . . .

From old times the cook has had a proper sense of the solemn importance of his wonderful art. The *Coquus Gloriosus,* in a fragment of Philemon, shows us what these artists were in the very olden time. He swears by Minerva that he is delighted at his success, and that he cooked a fish so exquisitely that it returned him admiring and grateful looks from the frying-pan! . . .

Posidippus shows us a classical master-cook instructing his pupils. Leucon is the name of the teacher; the first truth he impresses on his young friend is that the most precious sauce for the purpose of a cook is impudence. "Boast away," he says, "and never be tired of it." For, as he logically remarks, "if there be many a Captain under whose dragoon-embossed cuirass lies a poor hare, why should not we, who kill hares, pass for better than we are, like the Captains? A modest Cook must be looked on," he says, "as a contradiction in nature. If he be hired out to cook a dinner in another man's house, he will only get considered in proportion to his impudence and overbearing conduct. If he be quiet and modest, he will be held as a pitiful cook."

The earthly paradise of the early cooks was, unquestionably, among the Sybarites,—the people to whom the crumpling of a rose under the side on which they lay, gave exquisite pain. They were as self-luxurious as though the world was made for them alone, and they and the world were intended to last forever. . . .

Athenaeus, borrowing, if I remember rightly, from one of the authors whose works were in that Alexandrian library, the destruction of which by the Caliph Omar, Dr. Cumming tells us in his "Finger of God," is a circumstance at which he is rather glad than sorry,—Athenaeus mentions the visit of a Sybarite to Sparta, where he was invited to one of the public dinners, at which the citizens ate very black broth, in common, out of wooden bowls. Having tasted the national diet, he feebly uttered the Sybarite expression for "Stap my vitals!" and convulsively remarked that "he no longer wondered why the Lacedaemonians sought death in battle, seeing that such a fate was preferable to life with such broth!"

Certainly the public repasts of the Sybarites were of another quality. The giver of such repasts was enrolled among the benefactors of their country, and the cook who had distinguished himself was invested with a golden crown, and an opera ticket; that is, free admission to those public games where hired dancers voluptuously perverted time and the human form divine.

I am afraid that all cooks in remote ages enjoyed but an indifferent reputation, and thoroughly deserved what they enjoyed. The comic Dionysius introduces one of the succulent brotherhood, impressing upon a young apprentice the propriety of stealing in houses where they were hired to cook dinners. . . .

And yet Athenaeus asserts that nothing has so powerfully contributed to instill piety into the souls of men, as good cookery! His proof is that when men devoured each other, they were beasts,—which is a self-evident proposition; but when they took to cooked meats, and were particular with regard to these, why, then alone they began to live cleanly,—which is a proposition by no means self-evident. . . .

If Sybaris was the paradise of cooks, Lacedaemon was their purgatory. They were blamed if men grew fat on their diet, and plump children were legally condemned to get spare again upon their gruel. The Romans, again, restored the cook to his proper place in society. He might still be a slave, and so were greater men than he; but he was the confidant of his master, and there were not a few who would have exchanged their liberty for such a post and chains. . . .

Then came the age when, if men had not appetites of nature's making, they were made for them by the cooks; and the latter, in return, were crowned with flowers by the guests who had eaten largely, and had no fears of indigestion. The inventor of a new dish had a patent for its exclusive preparation for a year. But ere that time it had probably been forgotten in something more novel discovered by a Sicilian rival; for the Greeks looked on Sicily as the Parisians of the last century used to look on Languedoc,—as the only place on earth where cooks were born and bred, and were worth the paying. . . .

In Sicily, the goddess of good cheer, Adephagia, had her especial altars, and thence, perhaps, the estimation in which the Sicilian cooks were held, who prayed to her for inspiration. Her ministers were paid salaries as rich as the sauces they invented. . . .

The best-fed cook on record is the happy mortal to whom his master Antony gave a city, because he had cooked a repast which had called forth encomium from that dreadful jade, Cleopatra.

But money was the last thing thought of by the wearied epicures of Rome, especially when what they gave belonged to somebody else. When Lucullus spent £1,000 sterling on a snug dinner for three,—himself, Caesar, and Pompey,—he doubtless spent his creditors' money; at least, extravagant people generally do. Claudius dined often with six hundred guests, and the Roman people paid the cooks. The dinners of Vitellius cost that sacrilegious feeder upwards of £3,000 each, but the bills were discharged by a levy on the public pocket. . . .

The cooks of such epicures must necessarily, however, have been as despotic in the kitchen as their lord was in the saloon. . . . The stewards possessed no little power; but when the fires were lighted, and the dinner had to be thought of, the head cook was the kitchen Jupiter; and when he spoke, obedience, silence, and trembling followed upon his word.

From his raised platform, the *Archimagirus,* as he was called, could overlook all the preparations, and with his tremendous spoon of office he could break the heads of his least skillful disciples, and taste the sauce seething in the remotest saucepans. . . .

I conclude with a remark that I hope will be gratifying to all culinary artists who respect themselves and their calling, and who are anxious to prove their vocation is of ancient and honorable descent. Cadmus, who introduced letters into Greece, had formerly been cook to the King of Sidon. Thus learning ascended to us from the kitchen; and to the ex-cook of the King of Sidon we perhaps owe all the epics that have ever been written. By this genealogy, even "Paradise Lost" may be traced to the patties of Cadmus. But cooks in England may boast of a *noblesse de cuisine,* which dates from the Norman Conquest. When William, who wooed his wife Matilda by knocking her down, had established himself in England, he gave a banquet, at which his cook, Tezelin, served a new white soup of such exquisite flavor, that William sent for the artist, and inquired its name. "I call it *Dillegrout,*" said Tezelin. "A scurvy name for so good a soup," said the Conqueror; "but let that pass. We make you Lord of the Manor of Addington!" Thus modern cooks may boast of a descent from the landed aristocracy of the Conquest! Some of their masters cannot do as much; and, this, perhaps, accounts for the pride of the one, and the simplicity of the other.

* * *

Aromatic herbs and aphrodisiac recipes judiciously used in the preparation of meals, renew weakened organisms; they bring back to life exhausted feelings, and permit man to enjoy for a long time "those endowments of strength so dear."

—The Squire of Baudricourt

Advice to Young Ladies Expecting to Cook

from American Cookery
by Amelia Simmons

AS THIS TREATISE is calculated for the improvement of the rising generation of *Females* in America, the Lady of fashion and fortune will not be displeased, if many hints are suggested for the more general and universal knowledge of those females in this country, who by the loss of their parents, or other unfortunate circumstances, are reduced to the necessity of going into families in the line of domestics, or taking refuge with their friends or relations, and doing those things which are really essential to the perfecting them as good wives, and useful members of society. The orphan, tho' left to the care of virtuous guardians, will find it essentially necessary to have an opinion and determination of her own. The world, and the fashion thereof, is so variable, that old people cannot accommodate themselves to the various changes and fashions which daily occur; *they* will adhere to the fashion of *their* day, and will not surrender their attachments to the good old way—while the young and gay bend and conform readily to the taste of the times, and fancy of the hour. By having an opinion and determination, I would not be understood to mean an obstinate perseverance in trifles, which borders on obstinacy—by no means, but only an adherence to those roles and maxims which have stood the test of ages, and will forever establish the *female character,* a virtuous character—altho' they conform to the ruling taste of the age in cookery, dress, language, manners, etc.

It must ever remain a check upon the poor solitary orphan, that while those females who have parents, or brothers, or riches, to defend their indiscretions, that the orphan must depend solely upon *character.* How immensely important, therefore, that every action, every word, every thought, be regulated by the strictest purity, and that every movement meet the approbation of the good wife.

The candor of the American Ladies is solicitously intreated by the Authoress, as she is circumscribed in her knowledge, this being an original work in this country. Should any future editions appear, she hopes to render it more valuable.

Soup Untasted

from Tancred

by Benjamin Disraeli

WHO CAN COMBINE gout with new combinations? 'Tis yourself, Leander." . . . "What you learned from me came at least from a good school. It is something to have served under Napoleon," added Prevost, with the grand air of the Imperial Kitchen. "Had it not been for Waterloo I should have had the Cross. But the Bourbons and the Cooks of the Empire never could understand each other. They brought over an immigrant chef who did not comprehend the taste of the age. He wished to bring everything back to the time of the *oeil de boeuf*. When Napoleon passed my soup of Austerlitz untasted I knew the old family was doomed."

The custom of saying grace at meals had, probably, its origin in the early times of the world, and the hunter-state of man, when dinners were precarious things, and a full meal was something more than a common blessing; when a belly-full was a windfall, and looked like a special providence. In the shouts and triumphant songs with which, after a season of sharp abstinence, a lucky booty of deer's or goat's flesh would naturally be ushered home, existed, perhaps, the germ of the modern grace.

—Charles Lamb, *Essays of Elia*

I regard the discovery of a dish as a far more interesting event than the discovery of a star, for we have always stars enough, but we can never have too many dishes; and I shall not regard the sciences as sufficiently honored or adequately represented amongst us, until I see a cook in the first class of the Institute.

—M. Henrion de Pensey

Chapter Ten

THE CUISINE DE L'AMOUR

Of food as an aphrodisiac, let it be said at once, and regretfully, that the anthologists of this volume do not believe in it. And don't be so precipitate in muttering, "But no one does." It is firmly rooted in the folk beliefs of nearly every nation, including the pragmatic Americans of the twentieth century, many of whom are convinced that oysters, eggs, and a dozen other foods are stimulators of virility. The advice given to incipient bridegrooms on this point is traditional in America, and more than half-believed by most of those who give it, one may assume.

Ancient beliefs survive in parts of the world. Honey as an aphrodisiac is used today in some portions of Asia, and apples are still highly regarded in other parts of that continent. In the Western world we no longer believe, at least in more sophisticated societies, that sexual appetite can be stimulated by way of the stomach, but the fact that we *have* believed in it is evident in the hardy persistence of the old saw, "The way to a man's heart is through his stomach." Practically, of course, good dining is a damper to carnality. Anticipation of good dining is an appetite in itself, a refined appetite, it is true, but not conducive to coexistence with lust, an explicit word which seems to have gone out of fashion. When a superb meal is finished, or even a passably good one, the urge is to repose rather than passion, except in the very young, on whom sexual appetite is wasted as much as their youth.

Nevertheless, the extensive literature on food and love persists, as it has for centuries, in marrying these disparate appetites, and it would be a poor food anthology indeed which did not include some examples.

We begin with an historical note drawn from a book on the subject compiled privately for The Gourmets' Company of New Orleans, in 1942.

A short trip back to Apuleius discloses the ideal marriage of cuisine with amour, after which, no doubt to the astonishment of some who may be unfamiliar with it, we have Robert Burton's description of an aphrodisiac diet, from "The Anatomy of Melancholy." There follows a dissertation on love potions, a discussion of courtesans and cookery, and the chapter concludes with "The Song of Solomon," which theologians have never really been able to explain away in purely spiritual terms.

Hunger and Love

from Cuisine de l'Amour
compiled by Charles F. Heartman

THE PHILOSOPHER and the physiologist have agreed upon one fact; that hunger and love are the driving forces in the universe. Since the dawn of mankind no incident has taken place in the history of the world without either of them or both together being responsible for it. . . . There are, of course, many kinds of love and hunger, all springing from the same mysterious instinct, yet all requiring attention. While in the process of satisfying hunger, mankind has built a physical world and during the process of searching for fulfillment in love, has created a spiritual world: the arts, literature, music, and speculative flights into inventive imagination.

Sometimes the twins have even worked when interfered with, one might say as negative forces; although when thus engaged it has rarely been of a constructive character. The human race, as such, is of little value when it is not employing the two driving forces, for instance, when sickness or old age interrupt the natural function of creative energy. It is curious how little human beings in the prime of life occupy their minds analytically with the performance of their bodies. Everything is taken for granted, quite often Dionysiacally enjoyed but seldom appreciated. This matter-of-fact attitude undergoes a considerable change when a different aspect presents itself. If a weakened lover's embrace suddenly recognizes the ghastly fact of diminishing energies and points to a dreaded interval of impotence and sterility, then the pleasures which have been accepted as evidence of an unalterable course are suddenly magnified into an important necessity hardly believable. And a frantic search begins for a remedy.

For more than two hundred generations mankind has gone

through the same experiences, looking in advanced age for the Fountain of Youth, the Elixir of Life, the recapture of the power of adolescence, and forever has the search been in vain. In all these efforts to thwart the disappearance of creative powers, a mysterious instinct has compelled the individual to connect the correction of impaired conditions with the stomach; with food and drink. Hippocrates knew what went into the stomach would make the individual. The Chinese Emperor Shennung, in his Medical Herbal, three thousand years before Christ, spoke learnedly of internally taken medicines. When Marco Polo roamed at the end of the thirteenth century in foreign lands, he described vividly the ginseng, which is certainly the mandrake of the Bible. Parallel with this school of thought and experience traveled superstition and hoodooism, belief in charms and maledictions . . . the search for rejuvenation has been an everlasting, never-ending effort.

It was natural that the great Oriental handbooks of love: The Kama Sutra of Vatsyayana, and the Ananga-Ranga should give considerable space to the subject as did the Sheik Nefzaoui. Forberg became the scavenger of the classics, all restating an endless variety of ways and means toward the same goal. The search goes on in the present day, but so far has been in vain.

The Preparation of Venus

from The Golden Asse

by Lucius Apuleius

WHEN I was within the house I found my dear and sweet Fotis mincing of meat and making pottage for her master and mistresse, the Cupboard was all set with wines, and I thought I smelled the savor of some dainty meats: she had about her middle a white and clean apron, and shee was girded about her body under the paps with a swathell of red silke, and shee stirred the pot and turned the meat with her faire and white hands, in such sort that with stirring and turning the same, her loynes and hips did likewise move and shake, which was in my mind a comely sight to see . . . wherewithall I rose up and went into my chamber, where I found all things finely prepared . . . The table was all covered with those meats that were left at supper, the cups were filled halfe full with water, to temper and delay the wines, the flaggon stood ready prepared, and there lacked nothing that was necessary for the preparation of Venus. And when I was entring the bed, behold my Fotis (who had brought her mistresse to bed) came in and gave me roses and floures which shee had in her apron, and some shee threw about the bed, and kissed mee sweetly, and tied a garland about my head, and bespred the chamber with the residue. Which when shee had done, shee took a cup of wine and delaied it with hot water, and profered it me to drinke; and before I had drunk off all shee pulled it from my mouth, and then gave it me againe, and in this manner we emptied the pot twice or thrice together.

THE HORSE OF PARNASSUS

If with water you fill up your glasses,
You'll never write anything wise
But wine is the horse of Parnassus,
That carries a bard to the skies.

—Athenaeus, *The Deipnosophists*

An Aphrodisiac Diet

from The Anatomy of Melancholy
by Robert Burton

A RARE THING TO see a young man or woman that lives idly and fares well, of what condition soever not to be in love. Alcibiades was still dallying with wanton young women, immoderate in his expenses, effeminate in his apparel, ever in love, but why? he was over-delicate in his diet, too frequent and excessive in banquets. Lust and security domineer together, as St. Hierome averreth. All which the Wife of Bath in Chaucer freely justifies:

> For all to sicker, as cold engendreth hail,
> A liquorish tongue must have a liquorish tail.

Especially if they shall further it by choice diet, as many times those Sybarites and Phaeaces do, feed liberally, and by their good will eat nothing but lascivious meats. (First and foremost, strong wine, vegetables, beans, roots of all kinds, well seasoned and with plenty of pepper, garden radishes, lettuces, rocket, grapes, leeks, onions, pine-nuts, sweet almonds, electuaries, syrups, juices, snails, shell-fish, fish tastefully cooked, poultry, testicles of animals, eggs, various sauces, soft beds and couches, etc. Also . . . more delicate dishes, mulled wine, choice fruits, scents, cakes, essences more tasty than wine, and all the products of the kitchen, the chemist's shop, or any other factory.)

Love Potions

from The Magic of Herbs
by Mrs. C. F. Leyel

ALL THROUGH THE ages the baser forms of magic have been used for the purpose of foretelling, divining and inspiring the affections between the sexes, and the success of every fortune-teller has and always will depend upon her ability to exploit successfully her powers to satisfy human craving for this kind of knowledge. . . .

Love philtres and aphrodisiacs were known and used among the Greeks and Romans to such an extent that at one time the law interfered and inflicted a heavy penalty on the users. They seem always to have been of two kinds. A love philtre was usually a concoction of herbs which, through its magical attributes or combined with them, induced a feeling of love towards a particular person, like the poet's "philtre divin herbes" which gave birth to the love between Tristram and Iseult; whereas an aphrodicias or *poculum amatorium* was composed of ingredients which conduced to a state of amorousness.

The Greek writers tell us that the aphrodisiacs of the Greek and Roman courtesans were made of pepper, myrrh, and equal quantities of two scents called Cyprus and Egyptian, and that the cups from which these potions were drunk were made of scented earthenware. According to Pliny the glands of animals were commonly used, especially those of the pig, the stag, the horse, and the hyena. . . .

Shakespeare attributes Othello's power over Desdemona to

> conjuration and mighty magic
> Thou has practis'd on her with foul charms,
> Abus'd her delicate youth with drugs or minerals
> That weaken motion.

The roots of the sea holly had a reputation as a love tonic amongst Englishmen of Queen Elizabeth's day, and a confection of these eryngo roots mixed with sugar became popular under the name of "Kissing comfits."...

Rowlands in one of his plays gives a recipe for making powder of turtle-dove to stir love in the heart of her who drinks it:

> ... Take me a turtle dove
> And in an oven let her lie and bake
> So dry that you may powder of her make;
> Which, being put into a cup of wine,
> The wench that drink'st it will to love incline.

During the Renaissance,... books were published containing recipes with curious and often revolting ingredients for inspiring amorous passions. The blood of a red-haired person, the obscene parts of animals, the hearts and tongues of toads and vipers, and the blood of a bat, were not unusual components. A very common ingredient was hippomanes (the thin membrane sometimes found covering the head of a newly born colt).

> Then hippomanes for shepherds call it so
> Distil as venom from their parts below,
> Hippomanes that wicked stepdames pluck
> Mingling with herbs that bring bad luck.

Hoffmann's water of magnanimity, which achieved such fame in the seventeenth century, was said to contain winged ants macerated in alcohol....

The references in plays of the seventeenth and eighteenth centuries are probably to cantharides.

> Strait to the 'pothecary's shop I went
> And in love powder all my money spent;
> Behap what will, next Sunday after prayers
> When to the ale house Lubberkin repairs,
> Then flies into his mug I'll throw
> And soon the swain with fervent love shall glow.
>
> —GAY

There are many stories in history . . . of the terrible effects of this drug, often ending in death.

The aphrodisiac properties are seldom induced unless the dose is big enough to endanger life. . . .

In most of the cases related in history the drug was administered by vindictive, mischievous or unscrupulous people, as in the story quoted by Ramsey (1663) of the courtesan who prepared a magnificent supper for an infatuated young man at which every dish was flavored with cantharides, from the results of which he died the following day. . . .

Madame de Pompadour, who resorted to a tincture of cantharides when she thought she was losing the love of Louis XV, was rescued by the Duchesse de Brancas, who, finding the bottle and recognizing the smell of the contents, threw it up the chimney, leaving the king's mistress to her less harmful diet of *chocolat à triple vanille* and celery soup, a *régimen un peu échauffant,* which the king's mistress had prescribed for herself to correct her naturally cold temperament. . . .

Alcohol sweetened with sugar is a common French restorative, and, it is said, was first invented to increase the ardor of the aged King Louis XIV. It is still a custom in some countries to give a bride and bridegroom cakes moistened with sugar and alcohol on their wedding night.

Truffles were also praised by the French for their venereal properties, and Brillat-Savarin, to prove the truth of this reputation, quotes the story of the virtuous French lady who, on her own account, nearly succumbed to the entreaties of the handsome and witty "Verseuil," and attributed her "dangerous predisposition" to the truffles fowl from Perigueux on which they had both dined.

Herbal philtres were usually aided in their success by magic, though the herbs employed in them, such as vervain, jasmin, coriander, cyclamen, purslain, maidenhair, valerian, navelwort, wild poppy, anemone, crocus, male fern, periwinkle, pansy, lettuce, carrot, and endive, were all considered of an erotic nature and were often combined with cantharides medicinally.

The carrot was so much used in Greece as a love medicine that it was called "Philtron," and another plant they used for the same purpose and called "Storgethron" is identified with our house leek.

The same virtues were attributed to the myrtle, and a water made from the flowers and leaves has been resorted to in every country....

The myrtle was used in the composition prepared for the most intimate toilet of Venus, and probably from its association with the Goddess has always been regarded as a love tonic....

Mandragora, henbane, dragon's blood, and stayrion, particularly the last, were all credited with lustful properties. The mandrake is mentioned in the Old Testament as a cure for sterility, and the belief is endorsed by the Doctrines of Signatures, which sees in its form a resemblance to the human body. The Chinese, for the same reason and for the same purpose, use ginseng root....

Circe made use of the mandragora in her love potions, and in Persia the mandrake is recommended to secure a husband's love, but if eaten with pickles it is said to drive the eater off his head.

In Persia newly married couples are given sheep's trotters steeped in vinegar on their bridal night....

Amongst the Hindus the jasmin, the lotus and the asoka plant are used to provoke venery, and the Sicilians claim that if a plant called the "Pizz a ugurdu" is given surreptitiously it will inspire the warmest feelings in the coldest person. This is identified with the "Vorax" of the Greeks and the "Provinsa" of Albertus Magnus, who describes it as the most powerful of all herbs for promoting love.

Famous Courtesans and the Art of Cookery

from Cuisine de l'Amour

compiled by Charles F. Heartman

THE FAMOUS COURTESANS of antiquity bequeathed to us famous traditions concerning the art of cookery, wherein they had, at times, discovered the multiple secrets of their dominance.

At the death of Caesar, Cleopatra, who reigned alone, fearing for her crown then menaced by Anthony the triumvir, had recourse, to better seduce him, to such voluptuousness as her table provided.

Plutarch makes use of the voyage of the queen on her way to meet Anthony to give us a recital worthy of a fairy tale: the galley shone with gold; its sails were of silk and purple. Cleopatra, herself, clothed like the Venus Anadyomene emerging from the waves, lay stretched out under a tent of goldcloth. Her ladies-in-waiting represented Nymphs and Graces, while children disguised as Cupids frolicked in the midst of that pagan paradise.

"It is Venus come to find Bacchus!" exclaimed Anthony's soldiers, and Bacchus-Anthony rushed to meet Venus-Cleopatra and threw himself at her feet, frantically in love . . . there is no doubt that it was due to the resources provided by especially emphasized cookery, to the so-called aphrodisiac concoctions it afforded, that Cleopatra owed the greater part of her power of seduction. The feasts she gave in honor of Anthony awoke within him the most passionate desires; for her Anthony may, perhaps, have lost a world empire, for he came to forget that Augustus was forging ahead, climbing, one at a time, the steps that led to the throne.

When Louis XIV came to feel the first signs of old age, Madame de Maintenon boiled for him a cordial made up of distilled spirits, sugar, orange water, and other perfumes. . . .

The du Barry, most expert in the art of libertinage, had secured complete dominance over the mind of Louis XV; through her knowledge of the pleasures of love, she kept her royal lover plunged into a state of intoxication of the senses bordering on depravity. Upon arrival in Paris, the famous courtesan had been placed in a convent under the protection of a friar named Lange; next in the house of a sieur Labille, a fashionable dressmaker, in the rue Saint-Honoré; finally she became woman companion to a *dame de la Garde,* widow of a former general, living at Madame de La Verrière. In her salon assembled *libertins gentils-hommes* giving free rein to debauchery without end. Her debut in gallant life dates from her entrance into that school of corruption.

Pensioner of the Gourdan, she had learned from that famous procuress the mysterious secrets of certain culinary recipes whose effects, it is said, helped to sharpen the phrenetic sensualism of the monarch.

Love for Delights

from The Song of Solomon

HOW FAIR AND how pleasant art thou, O love, for delights!

This thy stature is like to a palm tree, and thy breasts to clusters of grapes.

I said, I will go up to the palm tree, I will take hold of the boughs thereof: now also thy breasts shall be as clusters of the vine, and the smell of thy nose like apples;

And the roof of thy mouth like the best wine for my beloved, that goeth down sweetly, causing the lips of those that are asleep to speak.

I am my beloved's, and his desire is toward me.

Come, my beloved, let us go forth into the field; let us lodge in the villages.

Let us get up early to the vineyards; let us see if the vine flourish, whether the tender grape appear, and the pomegranates bud forth: there will I give thee my loves.

The mandrakes give a smell, and at our gates are all manner of pleasant fruits, new and old, which I have laid up for thee, O my beloved.

Chapter Eleven

A MENU OF SPECIFICS

WHEN IT COMES to considering a few of the specifics that go on our literary table, we choose to omit the preliminary courses in this section (they will be dealt with later) and get down at once to the main dish, meat. Vegetarians notwithstanding, it is the most satisfying item on the menu, and has been served up lovingly by any number of writers, a few of whom are represented here in these six views.

The first view is Biblical, and while the story of Jacob and Esau and their father is not, strictly speaking, a tale of gastronomy, still it illustrates an aspect of the "customs and manners" which have been the meat of this section. We leap then to nineteenth century England and a discussion of that traditional dish, English roast beef.

We are aware that Lamb's "Dissertation upon Roast Pig" is a tale often told, but so good, we insist, that it has not been told enough. There is always the chance, too, that a new generation of improperly taught readers may be discovering it for the first time. Perhaps not quite as well known is Lamb's letter to Coleridge, which follows the essay, in which Elia further extols the virtues of the pig.

Three short and early comments on the goose lead the way to a final view of meat, an anecdote about ham from Hayward's "The Art of Dining."

SIX VIEWS OF MEAT

Rebekah's Savory Meat

from Genesis XXVII, The Holy Bible

AND IT CAME to pass, that when Isaac was old, and his eyes were dim, so that he could not see, he called Esau his eldest son, and said unto him, Behold, here am I.

And he said, Behold now, I am old, I know not the day of my death:

Now therefore take, I pray thee, thy weapons, thy quiver and thy bow, and go out to the field, take me some venison;

And make me savory meat, such as I love, and bring it to me, that I may eat; that my soul may bless thee before I die.

And Rebekah heard when Isaac spake to Esau his son. And Esau went to the field to hunt for venison, and to bring it.

And Rebekah spake unto Jacob her son, saying, Behold, I heard thy father speak unto Esau thy brother, saying,

Bring me venison, and make me savory meat, that I may eat, and bless thee before the Lord before my death.

Now therefore, my son, obey my voice according to that which I command thee.

Go now to the flock, and fetch me from thence two good kids of the goats; and I will make them savory meat for thy father, such as he loveth:

And thou shalt bring it to thy father, that he may eat, and that he may bless thee before his death.

And Jacob said to Rebekah his mother, Behold, Esau my brother is a hairy man, and I am a smooth man:

My father peradventure will feel me, and I shall seem to him as a deceiver; and I shall bring a curse upon me, and not a blessing.

And his mother said unto him, Upon me be thy curse, my son: only obey my voice, and go fetch me them.

And he went, and fetched, and brought them to his mother: and his mother made savory meat, such as his father loved.

And Rebekah took goodly raiment of her eldest son Esau, which were with her in the house, and put them upon Jacob her younger son:

And she put the skins of the kids of the goats upon his hands, and upon the smooth of his neck:

And she gave the savory meat and the bread, which she had prepared, into the hand of her son Jacob.

And he came unto his father, and said, my father: and he said, Here am I; who art thou, my son?

And Jacob said unto his father, I am Esau thy first-born; I have done according as thou badest me: arise, I pray thee, sit and eat of my venison, that thy soul may bless me.

And Isaac said unto his son, How is it thou hast found it so quickly, my son? And he said, Because the Lord thy God brought it to me.

And Isaac said unto Jacob, Come near, I pray thee, that I may feel thee, my son, whether thou be my very son Esau or not.

And Jacob went near unto Isaac his father; and he felt him, and said, The voice is Jacob's voice, but the hands are the hands of Esau.

And he discerned him not, because his hands were hairy, as his brother Esau's hands: so he blessed him.

And he said, Art thou my very son Esau? And he said, I am.

And he said, Bring it near to me, and I will eat of my son's venison, that my soul may bless thee. And he brought it near to him, and he did eat: and he brought him wine, and he drank.

Roast Beef of Old England and the Boar's Head

from Our Viands

by Anne Walbank Buckland

ON THOUSANDS of tables at Christmas-tide the roast beef of Old England smokes with appetizing odor. From the lordly baron which always graces the Queen's table, and the goodly sirloin of aristocratic renown, to the humble but far from despicable aitch-bone, all is toothsome, wholesome, and highly esteemed alike by high and low, rich and poor. The wretched inmates of gaol and work-house look forward to the feast of roast beef and plum-pudding, which is almost sure to be given by the charitable for their delectation at Christmas, and in almost every parish the same substantial fare is provided for the poorer parishioners. At the tables of the rich, it is true, the time-honored sirloin is now relegated to a subordinate position, its place being usurped by the turkey, which has superseded also the stately peacock, formerly at this season, adorned with all its feathers, introduced with something approaching to religious ceremony, as was also the great boar's head, with its chaplet of rosemary and a lemon between the teeth; but then, as now, the loin of beef, knighted in due form by Charles II, was always the *pièce de résistance,* and from time immemorial the double loin, known as the *baron,* has always been a royal dish, and one specially selected is always sent from Windsor to Osborne to grace the Queen's dinner table, being accompanied by that other famous Christmas dish, a boar's head, sent of late from Germany.

In olden times great rejoicings were generally accompanied by an ox roasted whole, huge fires and monster spits being required for the purpose; and once history relates that an ox was thus roasted whole on the Thames. This was during the great frost in 1715-16, when the river was frozen over for several weeks. This somewhat barbarous mode of rejoicing is now almost obsolete, yet during the severe frost of the winter of 1890, in which the Thames was again frozen over in places, we heard of sheep being roasted whole on the river at Christmas; but in these days of refinement people in general prefer having their portion of meat to cook in their own way, instead of each slicing a half-cooked morsel from a burning carcase.

The practice of cutting meat from the spit seems to have been common before the invention of forks, and many old Saxon drawings show the cooks, or servers, kneeling by the king's table, holding spits from which the monarch cuts a portion with a huge knife; nor must the cook's useful drudge be forgotten, who, as late as 1800, when smokejacks came into fashion, had the chief share in roasting the meat in large establishments—we mean the "turnspit," a bandy-legged dog, somewhat resembling the modern dachshund—who was set to turn the spit by means of a wheel, somewhat after the fashion of a squirrel in a cage, and was probably beaten and sorely worried by the cooks whenever the jack stopped. There are many stories told of these useful dogs, who knew their proper turn, and would not be persuaded to work out of it; and if one of their companions got out of the way when it was his day for turning the spit, the one unjustly set to work has been known to find the truant and kill him. The poor turnspits must have hated Christmas, with its huge joints of roast beef, its peacocks and game, all entailing hard work upon the poor kitchen drudges.

Beef was known and appreciated from the very earliest times, the wild cattle having been hunted and slaughtered long before they were domesticated, and the skulls of many, of a species now extinct, are found all broken in the same way, evidently by a blow with a very heavy stone hammer. . . .

There is evidently something of a sacrificial origin in the eating of beef at Christmas, for it has undoubtedly a reference to the birth of Christ in the cow-shed, in remembrance of which event, the old superstition says, all oxen kneel in adoration at twelve o'clock on Christmas Eve. . . .

At present it must be allowed that as an article of food beef is better understood and more appreciated among English people than on the Continent, where the tasteless pieces of beef which have been used to make the bouillon are invariably served with sauce of various kinds, and the *bifsteak,* so called in honor of the famous English dish, is often a piece of very coarse buffalo, or of some tough old ox which has fulfilled his term of days at the yoke. Beefsteak, or to speak more correctly, rumpsteak, is only to be had in perfection in London, for it would seem as though country butchers had not learnt the secret of the proper cut. A rumpsteak grilled in a London eating-house is not to be surpassed as a savory dish, and may be eaten with fried onions or oyster sauce, according to taste. It often surprises colonists that they cannot obtain here the piece especially prized by them, and known in South Africa as *the hump,* but either our oxen are destitute of that appendage, or our butchers cut the carcase differently. . . .

Since the introduction of *diner à la Russe,* the great joints which formerly appeared on our dinner, supper, and breakfast tables have almost disappeared. We no longer see, except in cooks' shops, the great salted rump, formerly a famous breakfast dish; and the baron is reserved for the Queen's table, whilst the sirloin no longer appears entire, but is cut into several pieces to suit the requirements of the household. Doubtless, we lose much of the juices and flavor of the meat in these small joints, but the national taste has become of late more assimilated to that of the French, and prefers made dishes to the simple cut-and-come-again joints of our ancestors. It would appear that at Christmas in the olden days the great boar's head, eaten with mustard, held the first place; then came the peacock in his plumes, and geese, capons, "pheasants drenched with ambergrease," and pies of carps' tongues.

Of these savory dishes many have disappeared from the modern menu, whilst some are retained in the form of survival, and amongst the latter is the boar's head, which, in its ancient and natural form, is no longer seen amongst us except at the Queen's table, and perhaps on that of some other princes and potentates, but the ancient dish is still imitated by our cooks in forcemeat, and at almost every supper at Christmastide holds a conspicuous place, brown and glazed, with long, curved, white tusks of some composition, lemon in mouth, and buttered adornment, altogether a travesty of that great cruel beast, the pursuit of which has in all ages been deemed such noble sport, which formed the standing dish of Scandinavian heroes, in the Valhalla to which they aspired, and of which the ancient Romans were so fond, that it is related of Anthony that eight wild boars were usually roasted for his supper, not that they were all served and consumed at once, but they were held in various stages of preparation, that one might be ready whenever called for. The mode of dressing this boar appears to have been to roast it stuffed with game and poultry. Horace writes of—

> A Lucanian boar of tender kind,
> Caught, says our host, in a soft southern wind;
> Around him lay whatever could excite,
> With pungent force, the jaded appetite;
> Rapes, lettuce, radishes, anchovy brine,
> With skerrets, and the lees of coan wine.

The modern Romans still love the flesh of the wild boar, and I have eaten it in Italy served up with a sauce, the chief ingredients of which were raisins and the kernels of pine cones, but the flesh of the Roman wild boar is lean and hard, and can scarcely rival that of the domestic porker, well fatted, and served with apple sauce in the old English style. But in various parts of Europe the wild boar still affords excellent sport, and heads from these sometimes find their way to England. . . .

It would appear from "The Book of Days" that in olden times the boar's head garnished with bay and rosemary, and heralded by trumpets, was borne to the king's table on a dish of gold or silver by the server, followed by a long procession of nobles, knights, and ladies. The same book gives the origin of the custom of serving this ancient dish at Queen's College, Oxford, to a variation of the old carol. This arose from the presence of mind of a student of the college, who, when studying Aristotle in Shotover Forest, encountered a wild boar, which rushed at him openmouthed, whereup the scholar thrust the book down the creature's throat, thus "choking the savage with the sage." The carol used in serving the boar's head ran—

> *"Caput apri defero*
> *Reddens laudes Domino."*
> The boar's head in hand bring I
> With garlands gay and rosemary;
> I pray you all sing merrily
> *Qui estis in convivio.*
>
> The boar's head, I understand,
> Is the chief service of this land;
> Look wherever it be found,
> *Servite cum cantico.*
>
> Be glad, both more and less,
> For this hath ordained our steward,
> To cheer you all this Christmas—
> The boar's head and mustard!
> *"Caput apri defero*
> *Reddens laudes Domino."*

> ... Here's flowers for you;
> Hot lavender, mints savory, marjoram;
> The marigold, that goes to bed wi' the sun
> And with him rises weeping: these are flowers
> Of middle summer, and I think they are given
> To men of middle age ...

—SHAKESPEARE, *The Winter's Tale*

A *Dissertation upon Roast Pig*

from The Essays of Elia

by Charles Lamb

MANKIND, SAYS A Chinese manuscript, which my friend M. was obliging enough to read and explain to me, for the first seventy thousand ages ate their meat raw, clawing or biting it from the living animal, just as they do in Abyssinia to this day. This period is not obscurely hinted at by their great Confucius in the second chapter of his "Mundane Mutations," where he designates a kind of golden age by the term Cho-fang, literally the Cooks' Holiday. The manuscript goes on to say, that the art of roasting, or rather broiling (which I take to be the elder-brother) was accidentally discovered in the manner following. The swineherd, Ho-ti, having gone out into the woods one morning, as his manner was, to collect mast for his hogs, left his cottage in the care of his eldest son, Bo-bo, a great lubberly boy, who being fond of playing with fire, as younkers of his age commonly are, let some sparks escape into a bundle of straw, which kindling quickly, spread the conflagration over every part of their poor mansion, till it was reduced to ashes. Together with the cottage (a sorry antediluvian make-shift of a building, you may think it), what was of much more importance, a fine litter of new-farrowed pigs, no less than nine in number, perished. China pigs have been esteemed a luxury all over the east, from the remotest periods that we read of. Bo-bo was in the utmost consternation, as you may think, not so much for the sake of the tenement, which his father and he could easily build up again with a few dry branches, and the labor of an hour or two, at any time, as for the loss of the pigs. While he was thinking what he should say to his father, and wringing his hands over the smoking remnants of one of those untimely sufferers, an odor assailed his nostrils, unlike any scent which he had before experienced. What could it proceed from?

—not from the burnt cottage—he had smelt that smell before—indeed this was by no means the first accident of the kind which had occurred through the negligence of this unlucky young fire-brand. Much less did it resemble that of any known herb, weed, or flower. A premonitory moistening at the same time overflowed his nether lip. He knew not what to think. He next stooped down to feel the pig, if there were any signs of life in it. He burnt his fingers, and to cool them he applied them in his booby fashion to his mouth. Some of the crumbs of the scorched skin had come away with his fingers, and for the first time in his life (in the world's life indeed, for before him no man had known it) he tasted—*crackling!* Again he felt and fumbled at the pig. It did not burn him so much now; still he licked his fingers from a sort of habit. The truth at length broke into his slow understanding that it was the pig that smelt so, and the pig that tasted so delicious; and surrendering himself up to the new-born pleasure, he fell to tearing up whole handfuls of the scorched skin with the flesh next it, and was cramming it down his throat in his beastly fashion, when his sire entered amid the smoking rafters, armed with retributory cudgel, and finding how affairs stood, began to rain blows upon the young rogue's shoulders, as thick as hail-stones, which Bo-bo heeded not any more than if they had been flies. The tickling pleasure, which he experienced in his lower regions, had rendered him quite callous to any inconveniences he might feel in those remote quarters. His father might lay on, but he could not beat him from his pig, till he had fairly made an end of it, when, becoming a little more sensible of his situation, something like the following dialogue ensued.

"You graceless whelp, what have you got there devouring? Is it not enough that you have burnt me down three houses with your dog's tricks, and be hanged to you! but you must be eating fire, and I know not what—what have you got there, I say?"

"O father, the pig, the pig! do come and taste how nice the burnt pig eats."

The ears of Ho-ti tingled with horror. He cursed his son, and he cursed himself, that ever he should beget a son that should eat burnt pig.

Bo-bo, whose scent was wonderfully sharpened since morning, soon raked out another pig, and fairly rending it asunder, thrust the lesser half by main force into the hands of Ho-ti, still shouting out "Eat, eat, eat the burnt pig, father; only taste—O Lord!"—with such-like barbarous ejaculations, cramming all the while as if he would choke.

Ho-ti trembled in every joint while he grasped the abominable thing, wavering whether he should not put his son to death for an unnatural young monster, when the crackling scorching his fingers, as it had done his son's, and applying the same remedy to them, he in his turn tasted some of its flavor, which, make what sour mouths he would for pretense, proved not altogether displeasing to him. In conclusion (for the manuscript here is a little tedious), both father and son fairly set down to the mess, and never left off till they had dispatched all that remained of the litter.

Bo-bo was strictly enjoined not to let the secret escape, for the neighbors would certainly have stoned them for a couple of abominable wretches, who could think of improving upon the good meat which God had sent them. Nevertheless, strange stories got about. It was observed that Ho-ti's cottage was burnt down now more frequently than ever. Nothing but fires from this time forward. Some of them would break out in broad day, others in the night-time. As often as the sow farrowed, so sure was the house of Ho-ti to be in a blaze; and Ho-ti himself, which was the more remarkable, instead of chastising his son, seemed to grow more indulgent to him than ever. At length they were watched, the terrible mystery discovered, and father and son summoned to take their trial at Pekin, than an inconsiderable assize town. Evidence was given, the obnoxious food itself produced in court, and verdict about to be pronounced, then the foreman of the jury begged that some of the burnt pig of which the culprits stood accused, might be handed into the box. He handled it, and they all handled it; and burning their fingers, as Bo-bo and his father had done before them, and nature prompting to each of them the same remedy, against the face of all the facts, and the clearest charge which judge had ever given—to the surprise of the whole court, townsfolk, strangers, reporters, and all present—without leaving the box, or any manner of consultation whatever, they brought in a simultaneous verdict of Not Guilty.

The judge, who was a shrewd fellow, winked at the manifest iniquity of the decision: and when the court was dismissed, went privily, and bought up all the pigs that could be had for love or money. In a few days his Lordship's town-house was observed to be on fire. The thing took wing, and now there was nothing to be seen but fire in every direction. Fuel and pigs grew enormously dear all over the district. The insurance-offices one and all shut up shop. People built slighter and slighter every day, until it was feared that the very science of architecture would in no long time be lost to the world. Thus this custom of firing houses continued, till in process of time, says my manuscript, a sage arose, like our Locke, who made a discovery, that the flesh of swine, or indeed of any other animal, might be cooked (*burnt*, as they called it) without the necessity of consuming a whole house to dress it. Then first began the rude form of a gridiron. Roasting by the string or spit came in a century or two later, I forget in whose dynasty. By such slow degrees, concludes the manuscript, do the most useful, and seemingly the most obvious arts, make their way among mankind.

Without placing too implicit faith in the account above given, it must be agreed, that if a worthy pretext for so dangerous an experiment as setting houses on fire (especially in these days) could be assigned in favor of any culinary object, that pretext and excuse might be found in ROAST PIG.

Of all the delicacies in the whole *mundus edibilis*, I will maintain it to be the most delicate—*princeps obsoniorum*.

I speak not of your grown porkers—things between pig and pork—those hobbydehoys—but a young and tender suckling—under a moon old—guiltless as yet of the sty—with no original speck of the *amor immunditiae*, the hereditary failing of the first parent, yet manifest—his voice as yet not broken, but something between a childish treble and a grumble—the mild forerunner, or *praeludium* of a grunt.

He must be roasted. I am not ignorant that our ancestors ate them seethed, or boiled—but what a sacrifice of the exterior tegument!

There is no flavor comparable, I will contend, to that of the crisp, tawny, well-watched, not overroasted, *crackling*, as it is well called—the very teeth are invited to their share of the pleasure at this banquet in overcoming the coy, brittle resistance—with the adhesive oleaginous—oh call it not fat! but an indefinable sweetness growing up to it—the tender blossoming of fat—fat cropped in the bud—taken in the shoot—in the first innocence—the cream and quintessence of the child-pig's yet pure food—the lean, no lean, but a kind of animal manna—or rather, fat and lean (if it must be so) so blended and running into each other, that both together make but one ambrosian result, or common substance.

Behold him, while he is "doing"—it seemeth rather a refreshing warmth than a scorching heat that he is so passive to. How equably he twirleth round the string!—Now he is just done. To see the extreme sensibility of that tender age! he hath wept out his pretty eyes—radiant jellies—shooting stars.

See him in the dish, his second cradle, how meek he lieth!—wouldst thou have had this innocent grow up to the grossness and indocility which too often accompany maturer swinehood? Ten to one he would have proved a glutton, a sloven, an obstinate disagreeable animal—wallowing in all manner of filthy conversation—from these sins he is happily snatched away—

> Ere sin could blight or sorrow fade,
> Death came with timely care.

His memory is odoriferous—no clown curseth, while his stomach half rejecteth, the rank bacon—no coal heaver bolteth him in reeking sausages—he hath a fair sepulchre in the grateful stomach of the judicious epicure—and for such a tomb might be content to die.

He is the best of sapors. Pineapple is great. She is indeed almost too transcendent—a delight if not sinful, yet so like to sinning that really a tender-conscienced person would do well to pause—too ravishing for mortal taste, she woundeth and excoriateth the lips that approach her—like lovers' kisses, she biteth—she is a pleasure bordering on pain from the fierceness and insanity of her relish—but she stoppeth at the palate—she meddleth not with the appetite—and the coarsest hunger might barter her consistently for a mutton chop.

Pig—let me speak his praise—is no less provocative of the appetite, than he is satisfactory to the criticalness of the censorious palate. The strong man may batten on him, and the weakling refuseth not his mild juices.

Unlike to mankind's mixed characters, a bundle of virtues and vices, inexplicably intertwisted, and not to be unraveled without hazard, he is—good throughout. No part of him is better or worse than another. He helpeth, as far as his little means extend, all around. He is the least envious of banquets. He is all neighbors' fare.

I am one of those who freely and ungrudgingly impart a share of the good things of this life which fall to their lot (few as mine are in this kind) to a friend. I protest I take as great an interest in my friend's pleasures, his relishes, and proper satisfactions, as in mine own. "Presents," I often say, "endear Absents." Hares, pheasants, partridges, snipes, barn-door chickens (those "tame villatic fowl"), capons, plovers, brawn, barrels of oysters, I dispense as freely as I receive them. I love to taste them, as it were, upon the tongue of my friend. But a stop must be put somewhere. One would not, like Lear, "give everything." I make my stand upon pig. Methinks it is an ingratitude to the Giver of all good flavors, to extra-domiciliate, or send out of the house, slightingly (under pretext of friendship, or I know not what), a blessing so particularly adapted, predestined, I may say, to my individual palate. It argues an insensibility.

I remember a touch of conscience in this kind at school. My good old aunt, who never parted from me at the end of a holiday without stuffing a sweetmeat, or some nice thing into my pocket, had dismissed me one evening with a smoking plum-cake, fresh from the oven. In my way to school (it was over London bridge) a gray-headed old beggar saluted me (I have no doubt, at this time of day, that he was a counterfeit). I had no pence to console him with, and in the vanity of self-denial, and the very coxcombry of charity, schoolboy-like, I made him a present of—the whole cake! I walked on a little buoyed up, as one is on such occasions, with a sweet soothing of self-satisfaction; but before I had got to the end of the bridge, my better feelings returned, and I burst into tears, thinking how ungrateful I had been to my good aunt, to go and give her good gift away to a stranger that I had never seen before, and who might be a bad man for aught I knew; and then I thought of the pleasure my aunt would be taking in thinking that I—I myself and not another—would eat her nice cake—and what should I say to her the next time I saw her—how naughty I was to part with her pretty present!—and the odor of that spicy cake came back upon my recollection, and the pleasure and the curiosity I had taken in seeing her make it, and her joy when she had sent it to the oven, and how disappointed she would feel that I had never had a bit of it in my mouth at last—and I blamed my impertinent spirit of alms-giving, and out-of-place hypocrisy of goodness; and above all, I wished never to see the face again of that insidious, good-for-nothing, old gray impostor.

Our ancestors were nice in their method of sacrificing these tender victims. We read of pigs whipt to death with something of a shock, as we hear of any other obsolete custom. The age of discipline is gone by, or it would be curious to inquire (in a philosophical light merely) what effect this process might have towards intenerating and dulcifying a substance, naturally so mild and dulcet as the flesh of young pigs. It looks like refining a violet. Yet we should be cautious, while we condemn the inhumanity, how we censure the wisdom of the practice. It might impart a gusto.

I remember an hypothesis, argued upon by the young students, when I was at St. Omer's, and maintained with much leering and pleasantry on both sides, "Whether, supposing that the flavor of a pig who obtained his death by whipping (*per flagellationem extremam*) superadded a pleasure upon the palate of a man more intense than any possible suffering we can conceive in the animal, is man justified in using that method of putting the animal to death?" I forget the decision.

His sauce should be considered. Decidedly a few breadcrumbs, done up with his liver and brains, and a dish of mild sage. But banish, dear Mrs. Cook, I beseech you, the whole onion tribe. Barbecue your whole hogs to your palate, steep them in shalots, stuff them out with plantations of the rank and guilty garlic; you cannot poison them or make them stronger than they are—but consider he is a weakling—a flower.

Virtues of the Pig

from a letter to Coleridge by Charles Lamb

Dear C.—It gives me great satisfaction to hear that the pig turned out so well—they are interesting creatures at a certain age—what a pity such buds should blow out into the maturity of rank bacon! You had all some of the crackling and brain sauce—did you remember to rub it with butter and gently dredge it a little just before the crisis? Did the eyes come away kindly with no Oedipeaan avulsion? Was the crackling the color of the ripe pomegranate? Had you no complement of boiled neck of mutton before it, to blunt the edge of delicate desire? Did you flesh maiden teeth in it? Not that I sent the pig . . . To confess an honest truth, a pig is one of those things I could never think of sending away. Teals, widgeons, snipes, barndoor fowl, ducks, geese—your tame villatic things—Welsh mutton, collars of brawn, sturgeons, fresh or pickled, your potted char, Swiss cheeses, French pies, early grapes, muscadines, I impart as freely unto my friends as to myself. They are but self-extended . . . But pigs are pigs, and I myself therein am nearest to myself. . . .

Yours (short of pig) to command in everything.

C. L.

BREAKFAST

"Braikfastis for my lorde and my ladye. Furst a loof of brede in trenchers, two manchets, one quart of bere, a quart of wine, half a chyne of muton, ells a chyne of beif boyled."

—Northumberland Household Book (1512)

Celebrations of the Goose

YEA, POLL THYSELF and prevent others, and give the bailiff or like officer, now a capon, now a pig, now a goose, and so to thy landlord likewise, or if thou have a great farm, now a lamb, now a calf.

—TYNDALE'S Exposition

So stubble geese, at Michaelmas, are seen
upon the spit, next May produces green.

—KING'S *Art of Cookery*

Yet my wife would persuade (as I am a sinner)
To have a fat goose on St. Michael for dinner,
And then all the year round, I pray you would mind it,
I shall not want money—oh! grant I may find it!
Now several there are that believe this is true,
Yet the reason of this is desired from you.

We think you're so far from the having of more.
That the price of the goose you have less than before:
The custom came up from the tenants presenting
Their landlords with geese, to incline their relenting
On following payments.

—A writer for *British Apollo,* 1709

An Essence of Ham

from The Art of Dining
by Abraham Hayward

THE PRINCE DE SOUBISE (immortalized by the sauce named after him) rejoiced in an excellent cook—a man of true science, with princely notions of expenditure. His master one day announced to him his intention to give a supper, and demanded a *menu*. The *chef* presented one with an estimate; and the first article on which the prince cast his eyes was this,—*fifty hams*. "Eh! what!" said he "why, Bertrand, you must be out of your senses! are you going to feast my whole regiment?" "No, Monseigneur! only one ham will appear upon the table; the rest are not the less necessary for my *espagnoles*, my *blonds*, my *garnitures*, my—" "Bertrand, you are plundering me, and this article shall not pass." "Oh, my lord," replied the indignant artist, "You do not understand our resources: give the word, and these fifty hams which confound you, I will put them all into a glass bottle no bigger than my thumb." What answer could be made? The prince nodded, and the article passed.

FROM MEAT we turn, it may be with relief on the part of some satiated readers, to various side issues of the cuisine, no less important because they are not major dishes.

To begin, there is H. E. Jacob's fascinating comment on the rivalry of grasses, which preceded the grains that gave life to man. This is an excerpt from a modern classic in the history of food, "Six Thousand Years of Bread."

From Henry Phillips' definitive "History of Cultivated Vegetables," published in two volumes in London, 1822, we excerpt his knowledgeable essay on herbs, which is followed quite naturally by a small bouquet of herbal delights, from St. Matthew to Theophrastus to John Evelyn.

Then John Jeaffreson reappears with an historical and informative comment about the mushroom and truffle, and the portion ends with another Johnson anecdote, this one about oranges.

This Bouillabaisse a noble dish is—
  A sort of soup, or broth, or brew,
Or hotchpotch of all sorts of fishes,
  That Greenwich never could outdo:
Green herbs, red peppers, mussels, saffron,
  Soles, onions, garlic, roach, and dace:
All these you eat at Terré's tavern
  In that one dish of Bouillabaisse.

—from "The Ballad of Bouillabaisse"
by W. M. Thackeray

The Rivalry of Grasses

from Six Thousand Years of Bread
by H. E. Jacob

THE STORY OF the rivalry of grasses is one of the most tantalizing of the unwritten chapters in the history of human civilization. All grain was once grass. The grains favored by civilization were grasses whose seed pleased the taste of primitive man. But early man's crop of grass seeds was often pilfered before it could be harvested, not only by insects but by the force that propagated the waving meadows of grass—the wind. The wind shook the flowering heads of wild grasses so much that they cast their seed at the lightest touch. This was necessary for the perpetuation of the wild grass, but how was man to harvest ripened grain? The first task of man was, therefore, to break his favorite grasses of this bad habit. For millennia he cultivated only those individual grasses whose seed clung to the ear for an unusually long time, and he succeeded. The wild grasses he metamorphosed into cultivated wheat, cultivated rye, and all the other grains that became the great nourishers of mankind. These new varieties have fruit which clings so firmly to the pedicel that it can be removed only by trampling, shaking, or beating—that is, by what we call threshing. The threshing floor is the battlefield between the tenacity of the stalk and men's hunger for flour.

How prehistoric man accomplished such a miracle of selective breeding is a mystery. Such transformations, such operations upon the very source of life, were not again undertaken until the nineteenth century, by professional botanists working upon the basis of Gregor Mendel's laws of heredity. How did early man acquire such knowledge of the workings of nature? By what train of thought did he arrive at branding such knowledge as a secret science? One might perhaps remark that Gregor Mendel was also a priest. In early times the priests, who did not have other work, were excellent observers of all growing things. It is impossible to imagine that a priest invented the harrow, the plow, or any other tool that has changed the life of mankind. But it is extremely likely that it was the priest who interfered in the life habits of plants.

For fifteen thousand years the epic of grain has been one with the epic of man. We may say that man has transformed the wild grain into a domestic animal. It follows man everywhere because it needs the excrements of his economy—manures, phosphates, and nitrogen. And it would die at once without him. Grain is more dependent than is the dog upon the kindness of its master, for its seed adheres so steadfastly to the stalk that the wind can no longer sow it; it can reproduce itself only by artificial sowing.

The grain that gives life to man lives in its turn only through the grace of man. And yet the sower of grain for the past few thousand years has had the lot of the stepchild in human history.

A Knowledge of Herbs

from A History of Cultivated Vegetables

by Henry Phillips

NATURAL PHILOSOPHY has never been introduced with success into any country until its inhabitants had made considerable progress in other arts. The Assyrians, Chaldeans, and Egyptians had attained great proficiency in this science long before the existence of either the Greeks or Romans, who did not encourage it until they had learnt the art of war, and had in great measure become civilized by the very nations they had conquered.

In this kingdom, Lord Bacon was the first who cultivated natural philosophy; and it is from his torch that many excellent lights have since been kindled.

In the primitive times, when men were driven either by war, or a wandering disposition, to form colonies in distant countries, they lived upon such fruits as sprang out of the earth without art or cultivation. At Argos they fed chiefly on pears, at Athens on figs, in Arcadia on acorns; but, as their numbers increased, it became necessary for them to cultivate vegetables for the subsistence of themselves and their cattle; and we find that in those early days the labors of the agriculturists were so duly appreciated that the persons of the husbandmen and the shepherds were held sacred even by the enemies of their country.

Herodotus informs us that one of the greatest princes of the East, Xerxes, when he led his army into Greece, gave strict orders to his soldiers not to annoy the husbandmen. Among the Indians, it was held unlawful to take these men in war, or to devastate their plantations.

Cultivated vegetables afford the principal part of our subsistence: for without the aid of cultivation our numerous flocks and herds could not be supported; and it is from the same source that we derive every comfort and luxury that we enjoy. They furnish our wine, our oil, and our ale; as well as the greater portion of our garments and furniture; they are the natural medicine of all animals, as well as the principal one for man. A medical writer of eminence says, "Vegetable food is not only necessary to secure health, but long life. In infancy and youth we should be confined to it mostly; in manhood, and decay of life, use animal; and near the end, vegetable again."

"I am persuaded," says Dr. Veitch, "that it will be invariably found true, that those who are living on animal food, are more impetuous in temper than those who live on vegetable aliment." The same author says, "The influence of diet is of the most vital importance in the prevention and cure of insanity. Those living on animal food present great fullness of the vessels on the surface of the body, which is not confined to the visible and external frame, but will be felt in the brain and membranes of those who are afflicted with, or who have a tendency to this disease."

It is to vegetable productions that commerce owes its support. They form our ships, cordage, and sails; and it is for vegetable rarities, principally, that we cross the seas, and explore every clime from the equator to the poles.

The unlettered countryman examines vegetation with delight and instruction. The peasant, who is an attentive observer of Nature, substitutes the pimpernel and the chickweed for a weather-glass; finding, when these flowers fully expand, that no rain will fall for some hours. The husbandman finds also a barometer in the trefoil, which always contracts its leaves at the approach of a storm. The shepherd, when he sees the thistle-down agitated without an appearance of wind,

"And shakes the forest-leaf without a breath,"

drives his flock to shelter, and cries, Heaven protect yon vessel from the approaching tempest! Then

. . . "Chaff with eddy winds is whirl'd around,
And dancing leaves are lifted from the ground;
And floating feathers on the waters play."

—Virgil

Gardens have ever been esteemed as affording the purest of human pleasures, and the greatest refreshment to the spirits of man; and as these rural delights greatly promote sedateness and quietness of mind, while they afford the advantages of air and exercise, they must tend to the establishment of health and the prolongation of life. We notice with great satisfaction that the lives of the ancient as well as of the more modern herbalists have generally extended to an advanced age; and that some of them have even pursued their tranquil course without indisposition through life.

A knowledge of plants will prevent many of those ills, for the relief of which mineral aid is often sought in vain. We have found the perfume of flowers and shrubs in the garden not only refresh the sense, but inspire cheerfulness and good humor in those who walk, and create appetite in those who join in the labor, whether to turn the earth, or to prop the drooping flower. For where is the man who can forbear to join

... "the general smile
Of Nature? Can fierce passions vex his soul,
While every gale is peace, and every grove
Is melody?"

—THOMSON

"Where every breeze shall medicine every wound."

—SHENSTONE

The Chinese have no school for the study of physic; but they make use of simples and roots, and are generally well experienced in the knowledge of the several virtues of all the herbs growing in their country; and which every master of a family teaches his servant.

The predilection of the ancient Syrians for gardening gave rise to the proverb of the Greeks, "Many worts and potherbs in Syria."

The Greeks had physic-gardens in the time of Theophrastus; and Pliny often mentions the medicinal herb-gardens of the Romans.

We meet with no English work on plants prior to the sixteenth century. In 1552, all books on geography and astronomy in England were ordered to be destroyed, as being, it was supposed, infected with magic. It is very probable that works on the virtues of herbs underwent the same fate; as witchcraft was thought to be assisted by various plants.

... Our immortal bard, availing himself of the credulity of the age, makes the weird sisters, in their incantations, employ

"Root of hemlock, digg'd i' the dark;
Liver of blaspheming Jew:
Gall of goat, and slips of yew."

The English surgeons and apothecaries began to attend to the cultivation of medicinal herbs in the time of Henry the Eighth. Gerard, the father of English herbalists, had the principal garden of those days, attached to his house in Holborn, and which we think was in existence as late as 1659; for on the 7th of June in that year, Evelyn mentions in his Diary, that he "went to see the foundation laying for a street and buildings in Hatton Garden, designed for a little towne, lately an ample garden."

Gerard mentions several private herb-gardens in 1597, but does not notice any public establishment for the encouragement of his art. We therefore presume that Oxford has to boast of the earliest public physic-garden in this country, which appears to have been planted about the year 1640, when Parkinson first published his work on plants; . . .

We may infer how little the art of gardening was understood in this country at that period, when we find the garden at Oxford was put under the directions of a German, who continued to hold that situation in the time of Evelyn, as appears by his Diary: "24 Oct. 1664, I went to the Physic-garden at Oxford, where were two large locust-trees, as many platana,* and some rare plants, under the culture of old Bobart." Jacob Bobart was a German, and was appointed the first keeper of the Physic-garden at Oxford.

A botanic garden was planted at Padua in 1533, and one at Presburg in 1564. At the present time [1822] there are twenty-three botanic gardens in the Austrian monarchy. France has two noble establishments for the encouragement of this art; and Amsterdam may boast, not only of having enriched Europe, but the West Indies also, with plants from her public garden; while Sweden may justly pride herself on giving the world a Linnaeus.

. . . We find no authentic account of a public physic-garden in the vicinity of London, before the year 1673, although it appears in the minute-books of the Society of London, (June 21, 1674) that several members proposed to build a wall around Chelsea Garden, at their own expense, with the assistance of such subscriptions as they might be able to procure; provided the Court of Assistants would agree to pay two pounds every year for ever, to each of the six *Herborizings:* which proposal was accepted. The proprietors of the Laboratory Stock gave fifty pounds towards the building of this wall, on the condition that they were to be allowed a piece of ground in the garden for Herbs. . . .

Sir Hans Sloane was a great friend to the Chelsea Garden establishment, and by the deed of conveyance of the land from this great man, it will be seen how anxious he was for its prosperity; a clause is inserted which runs thus: "That the Master, Warden, and Society of Apothecaries shall render yearly to the President, Council, and Fellows of the Royal Society of London, fifty specimens of distinct

* Phillips presumes this was the Plantain tree, *Musa.*

plants, well dried and preserved, which grew in their garden the same year, with their names or reputed names; and those presented in each year to be specifically different from every former year, until the number of two thousand shall have been delivered." This part of the covenant has long since been much more than fulfilled.

In the same year that this conveyance was signed (1722), Mr. Philip Miller was appointed gardener to the establishment, which office he filled with great honor to himself and benefit to his country for the long space of forty-eight years. He had not been in that situation more than two years when he published his Gardener's Dictionary, in two volumes octavo, but which is not generally noticed by his biographers, although we deem it the germ and embryo from whence, in 1731, sprang his folio volume, which has since swelled into four large folios, and has been translated into the Dutch, German, and French languages.

Sir Joseph Banks, who was a liberal benefactor to this garden, commenced his botanical studies, it is said, under the tuition of the venerable compiler of the Gardener's Dictionary. Sir Joseph presented to the Chelsea Botanic Garden more than five hundred different kinds of seeds, which he had collected in his voyage round the globe. . . .

It is said that the finest and most interesting collection of hardy herbaceous plants that this country could ever boast of has been formed by the care and knowledge of Mr. William Anderson, the present gardener of the Apothecaries' Botanic Garden at Chelsea, who was recommended to that situation by the late Sir Joseph Banks in the year 1814. Aiton and Forsyth were transplanted from Chelsea Garden to Royal grounds. The former is succeeded by his son in the care of the King's gardens, particularly that of the exotic garden of Kew, which perhaps contains the finest collection of plants ever congregated in any one spot on the globe. . . .

The present Royal Family being greatly attached to the study of Botany, his late Majesty bestowed much attention of the garden at Kew, and had the satisfaction of seeing the example which he set, followed with such ardor by his subjects, that not less than 6756 rare exotic plants were introduced into these kingdoms during his reign, and exotic beauties are now seen blended with our natural verdure in every corner of the island. . . . History furnishes no instance where a country has so rapidly improved in the arts of agriculture and horticulture as Great Britain, under the protection of George the Third, of whom justice and gratitude compel us to say, "He made the land to flow with milk and honey." . . .

The example given by one of the best of Kings, and the attention shewn to agricultural pursuits by an enlightened Nation, will, we trust, never be forgotten, as no treasure can be so valuable as that which protects us from famine and pestilence.

Sterne says, "I am convinced there would be more attentive observers of Nature, if, for example, the spider spun threads of gold, if the lobster contained pearls, or if the flowers of the field made old people young."

Reason tells us that a well-tilled garden produces us more real luxuries than mines of gold or oceans of pearls could afford us; and experience teaches us that, although we are not made young by the virtue of plants, we may prevent premature old age by a knowledge of herbs.

A BOUQUET OF HERBS

WOE UNTO YOU, scribes and Pharisees, hypocrites! for ye pay tithe of mint and anise and cummin and have omitted the weightier matters of the law, judgment, mercy and faith: these ought ye to have done, and not to leave the other undone.

—MATTHEW, Chapter 23, verse 23

Savory and still more marjoram has a conspicuous fruitful seed, but in thyme it is not easy to find being somehow mixed up with the flower; for men sow the flower and plants come up from it. This plant is sought and obtained by those in Athens who wish to export such herbs . . . they say it can not be grown or become established where the breeze from the sea does not reach. This is why it does not grow in Arcadia while savory, marjoram and such plants are common in many parts.

—THEOPHRASTUS, Inquiry into Plants
(translation by Sir Arthur Hort)

Certain it is, Almighty God ordained Herbs and Fruits for the Food of Men speaks not a Word concerning Flesh for two thousand years . . . And what if it was held undecent and unbecoming the Excellency of Man's Nature, before Sin entered, and grew enormously wicked, that any Creature should be put to Death and Pain for him, who had such infinite store of the most delicious and nourishing Fruit to delight, and the Tree of Life to sustain him?

—JOHN EVELYN, A Discourse on Sallets, 1699

The Suspicious Mushroom and the Truffle

from A Book About the Table

by John Cordy Jeaffreson

IT IS UNIVERSALLY conceded that our mushrooms are good when gathered with care and treated skillfully. Nor can it be questioned that they were largely eaten by our ancestors of the Roman period, who adopted the cuisine of their conquerors. To die of bad mushrooms is not an heroic way of quitting life, but it was through a fish of poisonous fungi, administered treacherously by the niece and fourth wife, Agrippina, that the Emperor Claudius went to the unseen world. What troubled the Roman wits chiefly in this affair was their inability to discover, for their own safety and the good of all epicures, the particular species of fungus that killed this wearer of the purple. Similar "accidents" may have decided our mediaeval ancestors to relinquish a practice taken from the Romans, and, in their inability to distinguish clearly between good and noxious fungi, to neglect the mushroom altogether. Anyhow, our edible fungi were regarded with wholesome suspicion, if not with universal abhorrence, in the earlier part of our Tudor time, and the fashion of eating them did not revive till that period was drawing to a close. After glancing at the new vegetables of his day, Harrison says of their eaters, "Neither doo they now staie with such of these fruits as are wholesome in their kinds, but adventure further upon such as are verie dangerous and hurtful as the verangenes, mushrooms, etc." In the middle of the following century Edmund Gayton wrote against mushrooms,

> Pepper and oyl and salt, nay all cook's art,
> Can no way wholesomeness to them impart.

What Dr. Butler said of the cucumber,

> Of these ground-bucklers we the same aver,
> Dress them with care, then to the dung-hill throw 'um
> A hog won't touch 'um if he rightly knowe 'um!

The gluttonous propensities, always conspicuous in pigs, are combined with a considerable discernment of flavors that comes into operation as soon as the animals are in position to choose their own food and eat daintily. Unclean beasts, able to relish anything, they also exhibit strong gastronomic preferences; and they devour the more delicate and odorous of the fungoid growths with an avidity which goes some way to prove their kinship to epicures of our own species. With his delicate nerves of smell, the hog is no less quick and sure than the truffle-terrier in detecting the scent of the subterranean truffle; and in some districts he guides the truffle-hunter to the delicacy which Brillat-Savarin justly styled, "*le diamant de la cuisine.*"

This elegant tribute to the virtues of the truffle should not be mentioned without a passing allusion to the baneful properties of the esculent which has been known to destroy abruptly those whom it has fascinated for a few brief minutes. Even as a youth with weak lungs should refrain from the violent excitement of rowing, the epicure of weak stomach should avoid the perilous delight of the truffle-gourmand. Together with many votaries the truffle has had several victims. If Claudius died of mushrooms, it must be recorded of the Duc d'Escars, Louis the Eighteenth's superb Grand-Maître d'Hôtel, that he was killed by *truffes à la purée d'ortolans.* The duke and his royal master had labored, and enjoyed their labor's proper reward, for several hours in that strict privacy which often guarded their gastronomic inquiries and pleasures from vulgar observation. With their own hands they had prepared the fatal compound; and having eaten it with unqualified satisfaction, they had retired to rest with easy consciences. A few hours later, Louis le Désiré was roused from his tranquil slumber to be informed that his faithful maître-d'hôtel was already in the arms of death. The expiring duke had despatched a timely warning to his master, in order that the King might avoid disaster by prompt measures. Betraying an heroic conviction of his own safety, and a royal freedom from emotional weakness, the sovereign observed, "Dying! and of my *truffes à la purée?* Poor man! Then he sees I did him no injustice. I always said I had the better stomach of the two."

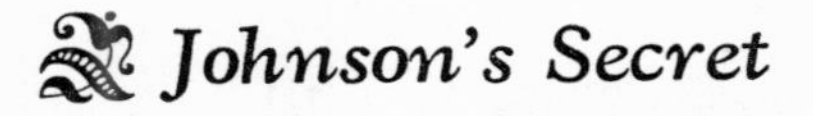

Johnson's Secret

from The Life of Samuel Johnson

by James Boswell

I WON A SMALL BET from Lady Diana Beauclerk, by asking him—Johnson—as to one of his particularities, which her Ladyship laid I durst not do. It seems he had been frequently observed at the Club to put into his pocket the Seville oranges, after he had squeezed the juice of them into the drink which he made for himself. Beauclerk and Garrick talked of it to me, and seemed to think that he had a strange unwillingness to be discovered. We could not divine what he did with them; and this was the bold question to be put. I saw on his table the spoils of the preceding night, some fresh peels nicely scraped and cut into pieces. "Oh,

Sir," said I, "I now partly see what you do with the squeezed oranges which you put into your pocket at the Club."

Johnson: "I have a great love for them."

Boswell: "And pray, Sir, what do you do with them? You scrape them it seems, very neatly, and what next?"

Johnson: "Let them dry, Sir."

Boswell: "And what next?"

Johnson: "Nay, Sir, you shall know their fate no further."

Boswell: "Then the world must be left in the dark. It must be said (assuming a mock solemnity) he scraped them, and let them dry, but what he did with them next he never could be prevailed upon to tell."

Johnson: "Nay, Sir, you should say it more emphatically:—He could not be prevailed upon even by his dearest friends to tell."

THREE COMMENTS ON DESSERT

FOR DESSERT we have Horace Walpole, a delectable literary dish himself, appearing in his noble title as Earl of Orford. The prolific and endlessly fascinating letter-writer of Strawberry Hill gives us an esoteric note on the history of desserts.

He is followed by the anonymous lover of good things and teller of marvelous tales who long preceded him, the creator of that treasure house, "The Thousand Nights and a Night." The episode given here from "The Tale of the Cobbler and the Vermicelli Cake" is not all the story, one of the most amusing of the 1001, but it does deal with a favorite Arabian dessert, and that is enough excuse for asking Scheherezade to join us.

Horace Walpole on Dessert

from Lord Orford's Works

THE LAST BRANCH of our fashion into which the close observation of nature has been introduced, is our dessert. Jellies, biscuits, sugar-plums, and creams, have long given way to harlequins, gondoliers, Turks, Chinese, and shepherdesses of Saxon china. But these, unconnected, and only seeming to wander among groves of curled paper and silk flowers, were soon discovered to be too insipid and unmeaning. By degrees meadows of cattle of the same brittle materials spread themselves over the table; cottages rose in sugar, and temples in barley-sugar; pigmies, Neptunes, in cars of cockle shells, triumphed over oceans of looking-glass or seas of silver tissue. Women of the first quality came home from Chevenix's laden with dolls and babies, not for their children, but for their housekeeper. At last even these puerile puppet-shows are sinking into disuse, and more manly ways of concluding our repasts are established. Gigantic figures succeed to pigmies; and it is known that a celebrated confectioner (Lord Albemarle's) complained that, after having prepared a middle dish of gods and goddesses eighteen feet high, his lord would not cause the ceiling of his parlor to be demolished to facilitate their entry. "*Imaginez-vous,*" said he, "*que Milord n'a pas voulu ôter le plafond!*"

But I will place this carefully fed pig
Within the crackling oven; and, I pray,
What nicer dish can e'er be given to man!

—AESCHYLUS

The Tale of the Cobbler and the Vermicelli Cake

from The Thousand Nights and a Night
(*Burton translation*)

THERE DWELT once upon a time in the God-guarded city of Cairo a cobbler who lived by patching old shoes. His name was Ma'aruf and he had a wife called Fatimah, whom the folk had nick-named "The Dung"; for that she was a whorish, worthless wretch, scanty of shame and mickle of mischief. She ruled her spouse and used to abuse and curse him a thousand times a day; and he feared her malice and dreaded her misdoings; for that he was a sensible man and careful of his repute, but poor-conditioned. When he earned much, he spent it on her, and when he gained little, she revenged herself on his body that night, leaving him no peace and making his night black as her book; for she was even as of one like her saith the poet:

> How manifold nights have I passed with my wife
> In the saddest plight with all misery rife
> Would Heaven when first I went in to her
> With a cup of cold poison I'd ta'en her life.

Amongst other afflictions which befell him from her one day she said to him, "O Ma'aruf, I wish thee to bring me this night a vermicelli-cake dressed with bees' honey." He replied, "So Allah Almighty aid me to its price, I will bring it thee. By Allah, I have no dirhams to-day, but our Lord will make things easy." She re-joined, "I wot naught of these words; whether He aid thee or aid thee not, look thou come not to me save with the vermicelli and bees' honey; and if thou come without it I will make thy night black as thy fortune whenas thou marriedst me and fellest into my hand." Quoth he, "Allah is bountiful!" and going out with grief scattering itself from his body, prayed the dawn-prayer and opened his shop, saying, "I beseech thee, O Lord, to vouchsafe me the price of the Kaunfah and ward off from me the mischief of yonder wicked woman this night!" After which he sat in the shop till noon, but no work came to him and his fear of his wife redoubled. Then he arose and, locking his shop, went out perplexed as to how he should do in the matter of the vermicelli-cake, seeing he had not even the wherewithal to buy bread. Presently he came up to the shop of the Kunafeh-seller and stood before it distraught, whilst his eyes brimmed with tears. The pastry-cook glanced at him and said, "O Master Ma'aruf, why dost thou weep? Tell me what hath befallen thee." So he acquainted him with his case, saying, "My wife is a shrew, a virago who would have me bring her a Kunafah; but I have sat in my shop till past mid-day and have not gained even the price of bread; wherefore I am in fear of her." The cook laughed and said, "No harm shall come to thee. How many pounds wilt thou have?" "Five pounds," answered Ma'aruf. So the man weighed him out five pounds of vermicelli-cake and said to him, "I have clarified butter, but no bees' honey. Here is drip-honey, however, which is better than bees' honey; and what harm will there be, if it be with drip-honey?" Ma'aruf was ashamed to object, because the pastry cook was to have patience with him for the price, and said, "Give it me with drip-honey." So he fried a vermicelli-cake for him with butter and drenched it with drip-honey, till it was fit to present to Kings. Then he asked him, "Dost thou want bread and cheese?"; and Ma'aruf answered, "Yes." So he gave him four half dirhams worth of bread and one of cheese, and the vermicelli was ten nusfs. Then said he, "Know, O Ma'aruf, that thou owest me fifteen nusfs; so go to thy wife and make merry and take this nusf for the Hamman; and thou shalt have credit for a day or two or three till Allah provide thee with thy daily bread. And straiten not thy wife, for I will have patience with thee till such time as thou shalt have dirhams to spare." So Ma'aruf took the vermicelli-cake and bread and cheese and went away, with a heart at ease, blessing the pastry-cook and saying, "Extolled by Thy perfection, O my Lord! How bountiful art Thou!" When he came home, his wife enquired of him, "Hast thou brought the vermicelli-cake?"; and, replying "Yes," he set it before her. She looked at it and seeing it was dressed with cane-honey, said to him, "Did I not bid thee bring it with bees' honey? Wilt thou contrary my wish and have it dressed with cane honey?" He excused himself to her, saying, "I bought it not save on credit"; but said she, "This talk is idle; I will not eat Kunafah save with bees' honey." And she was wroth with it and threw it in his face, saying, "Begone, thou pimp, and bring me other than this!" Then she dealt him a buffet on the cheek and knocked out one of his teeth. The blood ran down upon his breast and for stress of anger he smote her on the head a single blow and a slight, whereupon she clutched his beard and fell to shouting out and saying, "Help, O Moslems!" So the neighbors came in and freed his beard from her grip; then they reproved and reproached her, saying, "We are all content to eat Kunafah with cane-honey. Why, then, wilt thou oppress this poor man thus? Verily, this is disgraceful in thee!" And they went on to soothe her till they made peace between her and him. But, when the folk were gone, she sware that she would not eat of the vermicelli, and Ma'aruf, burning with hunger, said in himself, "She sweareth that she will not eat; so I will e'en eat." Then he ate, and when she saw him eating, she said, "Inshallah, may the eating of it be poison to destroy the fat one's body." Quoth he, "It shall not be at thy bidding," and went on eating, laughing, and saying, "Thou swarest that thou wouldst not eat of this; but Allah is bountiful, and tomorrow night, and the Lord decree, I will bring thee Kunafah dressed with bees' honey, and thou shalt eat it alone." And he applied himself to appeasing her, whilst she called down curses upon him; and she ceased not to rail at him and revile him with gross abuse till the morning, when she bared her forearm to beat him. Quoth he, "Give me time and I will bring thee other vermicelli-cake." Then he went out to the mosque and prayed. . . .

AFTER DINNER

After the dishes are cleared, coffee—or tea. For those who drink neither, perhaps a sip of punch.

The coffee drinkers will doubtless find something to interest them in the historical notes on coffee provided by John Ernest McCann, from an interesting collection of pieces about the brew, "Over the Black Coffee," compiled by Arthur Gray.

Tea drinkers may relish equally Agnes Repplier's remarks about Dr. Johnson's tea-drinking habits, from her charming book, "To Think of Tea."

As for punch, it comes here from an unlikely source, Sir Walter Scott, an episode from one of his lesser known novels, "St. Ronan's Well."

Drink, then, to your taste.

Coffee in History

from Over the Black Coffee
by John Ernest McCann

"There are two things Frenchmen will never swallow—Racine's poetry, and coffee," wrote Madame de Sévigné, in 1669, when Solomon Aga, the Sultan's ambassador to the court of Louis XIV, was treating the nobility of France to its first drink of coffee.

Mme. de Sévigné was not the only one to make wry faces over coffee, with its hot, black decoction of muddy grounds, thickened with syrup. She did not know what a stimulant to jaded brains it would be, nor what a restorative of sparkless wit. But she lived long enough to see her prophecy fail in both instances, for Racine's poetry was swallowed, and coffee was drunk by the gallon long before she died.

The liquids up to 1669 were: home-brewed beer, apple and pear cider, honey-and-water, water, milk, and the juice of the grape.

England was ahead of France in the drinking of coffee, for in 1657 (May 19th), the *Publick Advertiser* printed this quaint and curious ad:

> "In Bartholomew Lane, on the backside of the old Exchange, the drink called Coffee, which is a very sholesom and Physical drink, having many excellent virtues, closes the orifice of the Stomach, fortifies the heat within, helpeth Digestion, quickeneth the Spirits, maketh the heart lightsom, is good against Eye-sores, Coughs or Colds, Rhumes, Consumptions, Headache, Dropsie, Gout, Scurvy, King's Evel, and many others, is to be sold both in the morning, and at three of the clock in the afternoon."

But coffee's day did not last long, for tea came simmering into London shortly after its advent, and all London became tea drunkards.

In 1658, coffee was sold "at Sultaner's-head, a Cophee-house, in Sweeting's Rents, by the Royal Exchange, London."

Almost from its introduction to the present day, or for 233 years, coffee has been the favorite drink in Paris. That beats whisky in Ireland or Scotland, the great whisky-absorbing countries of the world, although beer holds the blue ribbon as the longest favorite drink on record—in England. Water, in England, is a side issue, and is valuable for dish-washing purposes only. It is drunk there on compulsion. But coffee is *the* drink of France. In 1669, France had no more nerves than England, nor for a century after, when she began to realize that she was a Nation of Nerves. One of the greatest things that ever happened would not have happened but for coffee. In other words, coffee changed the map of Europe, made Napoleon, and an Irish soldier the great Duke of Wellington. In a word, coffee made France a nation of nerves; nerves made the French Revolution; which made Napoleon; who made Mr. Arthur Wellesley a conqueror and duke.

The first coffee house in Paris opened in 1672, at the Fair of St. Germain. Was it Voltaire or Diderot who said, in the Café Procope, where they both took their coffee, tilted at creeds, and attacked Shakespeare and high heaven: "Our cradle was a café?" One of them said it, and truly said it, for the cradle of the French Republic of today surely was a café, and coffee made cafés.

Pascal, an Armenian, was the proprietor of the first cafe. He came to Paris all the way from Constantinople, little thinking of his great destiny in being the cause of the French Revolution and Napoleon, a reconstructed Europe, and the sale of Louisiana to the United States. But for that little insignificant Pascal, Albert Wettin might today be king of this country as he is of Great Britain; for without France's aid in the Revolution, where would our glorious Washington have been? and without Washington where would we be?

Pascal was accompanied from Constantinople by his own waiter-boys. Prior to his appearance upon the Parisian stage of life, other restaurants sold the before-mentioned liquids, with cakes, gingerbread, sausages, ham and sinkers, spices, preserves, Portuguese oranges, dates, figs, nuts, and fruits of many countries; but Pascal sold only coffee, and threw his competitors into a green and frightful rage. As business improved, Pascal sent his waiter-boys throughout the city with coffee-pots, heated by lamps, and little side-dishes of *nougat,* made of almonds and honey, and other Oriental sweets. He tempted the Parisian at his door and window, knowing, at that early day, that no Parisian could resist temptation. He made a fortune, and for seventeen years nobody ever dreamed that coffee could be made except by a little chap from Turkey. Lords and ladies, mere men and women, girls and boys, hooks and crooks, thugs and mugs, all drank the delicious new and strange concoction.

But in 1689, an Italian, who had been watching Pascal, saw a great white light and opened a café across the street from the Comédie Française. He had a royal license to sell spices, ices, barley-water, circus lemonade, and milk, when he added coffee to his menu, and it proved the beginning of his fortune. He called his place a café, and afterwards swore that his café was the first café. That was Procope, and his place was known as "The Café Procope." He called himself an Italian, but he was from Sicily. His was the greatest café the world has ever known, as it was the trundle-bed of Liberty.

Coffee was first found growing wild in Arabia, so the legend runs. Hadji Omar, a dervish, discovered it in 1285, six hundred and seventeen years ago. He was outlawed from Mocha for asking the ten-millionaire "boss" of Mocha: "Where *did* you get it?" He was dying of hunger in the wilderness, when his glazing eyes saw some small, round berries. He ate some, but they were bitter. He roasted some, and they were better. He steeped the roasted berries in a running brook's water, held in the hollow of his hand, and they were as good as solid food. He ran back to Mocha, found the "boss" dead and his filthy millions scattered, made some coffee, invited the wise men of Mocha to drink, and in their gratitude they made him a saint.

The little brown Arabian bean grows in the East and West Indies, and in Central and Southern America, too. It makes the one drink famous the wide world over. In the English provinces, it was once spelled without any letter that is in it today. That seems a reckless sort of statement, but here it is: KAWPHY. The Malays spelled it KAWAH; but from Kaffa, in Eastern Africa, it derived its present name, COFFEE, though originally spelled KAULI.

In 1554, it became the favorite drink at Constantinople, and robbed the mosques of their worshippers, to the disgust of the priests, who swore by Allah that the roasted berries were the coals of the evil one, and as such must be outlawed. To please the priests it was taxed, but it was drunk copiously in secret, then openly again. Refusing to supply a wife with coffee was a valid cause for divorce.

It was introduced in Venice, by a descendant of the *Merchant*, in 1615, and it was known in Marseilles in 1644, fifty-five years before it became popular in Paris.

In the last half of the seventeenth century, its popularity was at its height in London, and "Wills's Coffeehouse," at the corner of West Bow Street and Covent Garden, was also known as "The Wits," for in Wills's "Glorious John" Dryden, an earlier Doctor Johnson, but without Johnson's brutality in argument, let his pupils flatter him, as he laid down poetic and literary laws, as Samuel Johnson laid them down almost a century later in "The Cheshire Cheese." At Wills's and at "Button's," in Great Russell Street, across the way, Joseph Addison held forth in his happiest manner. Richard Steele was another literary light at Button's; so was Jonathan Swift. Little "Essay-on-Man" Pope was yet another, but he lasted only a year, leaving in disgust, because his irritable temper made him unpopular. Davenant, the first man to put scenery on the English stage, Carey, Ambrose Philips, and many lesser lights, drunk Button's coffee. Later on, every London had its coffee-house. At one time there were three "Tom's" coffee-houses in London; but the "Tom's" in Birchen Lane was the favorite, for that was patronized by the actor, David Garrick; the green-apple poet, Akenside; poor little Chatterton, on a few occasions; Edmund Burke, Boswell, Beauclerk, and infrequently, by the great Doctor Johnson. But, when another "Tom" opened up across the way from Billy Button's, Billy took to the small beer, for seven hundred of the nobility, literary, and political lights, at a guinea a throw, were the subscribers to it; which meant $35,000 a year for Tom. That Tom's coffee was the finest in England, and it was drunk and eaten, for Charles James Fox swore that it could be carved, in its thick richness.

In the reign of Queen Anne, London's coffee-houses really began to multiply. "Squire's" coffee-house was famous in Anne's time, for there "Sir Roger de Coverley" drank coffee with the "Spectator." That is, Messrs. Addison and Steele got together.

New Orleans used to be the first place in the whole world for pure coffee. The old French market there was wont to be alive, from early morning to almost high noon, with coffee-drinkers. Every family in New Orleans was a coffee-drinking family.

Boston, before, during, and after the Revolution, had many coffee-houses, as had Virginia and New York. Burns's coffee-house, northwest of Bowling Green, the present site of the Stevens House, was the first in New York. "The Liberty Boys" met there, and brewed dark plots for the overthrow of George the Third. The Merchants' coffee-house, also known as "The Merchants' Exchange," stood at the foot of Wall Street. "The Tontine Coffee-house" was at the northwest corner of Wall and Water Streets, and was opened in 1792.

Tea has always been women's favorite drink; coffee, men's. Dr. Johnson was one of the few famous men who preferred tea. Balzac, the great novelist, was almost a coffee drunkard. He thought nothing of drinking twenty and thirty cups in a day, or a night, almost to the day of his death, in 1849, at the age of fifty. When he was poor, and lived in an attic, he made it himself. When he could afford it, the best chef in Paris made it for him. Flaubert, Hugo, Baudelaire, Paul de Koch, Théophile Gautier, Alfred de Musset, Zola, Bernhardt, Coppée, Guy de Maupassant, and Francis Saltus, were all tremendous drinkers of the juice of the delicious Arabian berry; and George Sand smoked cigarettes and drank coffee to the last. Can more be said for coffee, when the works of that group are remembered? Yes:

Coffee makes a sad man, cheerful; a languorous man, active; a cold man, warm; a warm man, glowing; a debilitated man, strong. It intoxicates, without inviting the police; it excites a flow of spirits, and awakens mental powers thought to be dead. . . . Coffee clears the mind of vapors; the brain of cobwebs; the heart of pain; the soul of care. It invigorates the faculties, and makes an old man young. It is the terror of advancing age. Creditors fly from it; debtors cry for it. When coffee is bad, it is the wickedest thing in town; when good, the most glorious. When it has lost its aromatic flavor, and appeals no more to the eye, smell or taste, it is fierce; but when left in a sick room, with the lid off, it fills the room with a fragrance only jacqueminots can rival. The very smell of coffee in a sick room terrorizes death.

Ladies are creation's glory, but they are anti-climax, following a wine of a century old.

—George Meredith

On a Tea-Drinker

from To Think of Tea
by Agnes Repplier

DR. JOHNSON'S LIFE is punctuated by tea. Whether we look for him in London or at Streatham, in Boswell's company or in Mrs. Thrale's, we find him drinking it. He began his innocent potations an hour or so before getting up (commending them especially as being relished at that time), continued them for a goodly portion of the afternoon, and wound up his nights with as many cups as he could get anyone to make for him. When he was under his own roof (which was not often) he dispensed gallons of tea. It was commonly his only mode of entertainment, though he did surprise Boswell (whom, by the way, he first met over a cup of tea in the back parlor of Davie's bookshop) with a well-served dinner of soup, a boiled leg of mutton, spinach, a veal pie, and a rice pudding. After he gave up his house, and went to live in chambers in Inner Temple Lane, it was his habit to drink tea every night with Mrs. Williams at her lodgings in Bolt Court, before going home to bed....

No incident that Boswell thought worth relating has been oftener repeated than the story of his being taken for the first time to drink tea with Mrs. Williams, and of his being so elated by the honor, which he had long coveted, that he consumed cup after cup, "as if it had been the Heliconian spring"; albeit the blind lady's method of ascertaining how much she had poured by putting her finger in the cups seemed to him "a little awkward." Later he was informed that what Mrs. Williams really did was to put her finger on the outside rim of the cup, and feel the mounting heat; and later still, when the novelty of these visits had worn off, he made up his mind that she had a peevish temper, and ceased to enjoy her society....

While Johnson was willing to jest about the quantity of tea he drank, he did not relish the comments of his friends. He had his own conception of good manners, and such remarks appeared to him unmannerly. One night at Mr. Richard Cumberland's, Sir Joshua Reynolds reminded him that he had drunk eleven cups. Johnson, deeply affronted, replied: "Sir, I did not count your glasses of wine; why should you number my cups of tea?" Then, according to Cumberland, he grew suddenly good-humored, laughed and said: "Sir, I should have released the lady from any further trouble if it had not been for your words; but you have reminded me that I lack one of the dozen, and I must request Mrs. Cumberland to round up my number."

This his hostess hastened to do, and her gratified husband had the satisfaction of seeing Johnson restored to perfect complacency. Turning upon her "a kind and cheerful look," he took the twelfth cup with an air that was almost apologetic. "Madam," he said, "I must tell you for your comfort that you have escaped much better than a certain lady did a while ago, upon whose patience I intruded more than I have done upon yours. But the lady asked me for no other purpose but to make a zany of me, and set me gabbling to a parcel of people I knew nothing of. So I had my revenge of her; for I swallowed five-and-twenty cups of her tea, and did not treat her to as many words." "I can only say," comments Cumberland, "that my wife would have made tea for him as long as the New River supplied her with water."...

Careless, brusque and untidy, Johnson had nevertheless a strong sense of propriety, and it took a tea-table to illustrate it. During his brief sojourn in Paris in 1775, he paid a visit to Madame de Boccage, who, knowing his weakness, did her best to make him some real English tea. The leaves clogged the passage of a fine old teapot she was using, whereupon she blew gustily down the spout to remove the obstruction. "*Voilà,*" she cried, pleased with the ingenuity of the trick, "*j'ai regagné l'honneur de ma théière.*" But Johnson, who could stomach Mrs. Williams's finger out of pity and regard, balked at the French lady's *souffle,* and showed much manifest discomposure that Miss Strickland was fearful of annoying him further by using her fingers—in the absence of tongs—for the sugar. Seeing which, Madame du Boccage remarked with lively banter: "*O mon Dieu! quel grand quanquan les Anglais font de peu de chose!*" ...

It was after drinking his twelfth cup of tea that Johnson mused on the folly of travelers who desire to wander in far and dangerous lands; and it was tea that saved his life when he undertook his famous journey to the Hebrides. They were neither far nor dangerous, but teeming with discomfort. Why he ever consented to go to them, no man can understand; but that, having consented, he fared forth gallantly, all men must admit. He hated to be cold and wet; but, when he was both, he refrained from grumbling, and said hopefully: "Now for a dish of tea."

Mr. Winterblossom's Punch

from St. Ronan's Well

by Sir Walter Scott

THE CLAMOR WHICH attends the removal of dinner from a public room had subsided; the clatter of plates, and knives and forks—the bustling tread of awkward boobies of country servants, kicking each other's shins, and wrangling, as they endeavor to rush out of the door, three abreast—the clash of glasses and tumblers, borne to earth in the tumult—the shrieks of the landlady—the curses, not loud, but deep, of the landlord—had all passed away; and those of the company who had servants had been accommodated by their respective Ganymedes with such remnants of their respective bottles of wine, spirits, etc., as the said Ganymedes had not previously consumed, while the rest, broden in to such observance by Mr. Winterblossom, waited patiently until the worthy president's own special and multifarious commissions had been executed by a tidy young woman and a lumpish lad, the regular attendants belonging to the house, but whom he permitted to wait on no one, till as the hymn says,

"All his wants were well supplied."

"And, Dinah—my bottle of pale sherry, Dinah—place it on this side—there is a good girl;—and, Toby—get my jug with the hot water—and let it be boiling—and don't spill it on Lady Penelope, if you can help it, Toby."

"No—for her ladyship has been in hot water today already," said the Squire; a sarcasm to which Lady Penelope only replied with a look of contempt.

"And, Dinah, bring the sugar—the soft East India sugar, Dinah—and a lemon, Dinah, one of those which came fresh today—Go fetch it from the bar, Toby—and don't tumble down stairs, if you can help it. —And, Dinah—stay, Dinah—the nutmeg, Dinah, and the ginger, my good girl —And, Dinah—put the cushion up behind my back—and the footstool to my foot, for my toe is something the worse of my walk with your ladyship this morning to the top of Belvidere."

"Her ladyship may call it what she pleases in common parlance," said the writer; "but it must stand Munt-grunzie in the stamped paper, being so nominated in the ancient writs and evidents thereof."

"And, Dinah," continued the president, "lift up my handkerchief —and—a bit of biscuit, Dinah—and—and I do not think I want anything else—Look to the company, my good girl.—I have the honor to drink the company's very good health—Will your ladyship honor me by accepting a glass of negus?—I learned to make negus from old Dartineuf's son.—He always used East India sugar, and added a tamarind—it improves the flavor infinitely.—Dinah, see your father sends for some tamarinds—Dartineuf knew a good thing almost as well as his father—I met him at Bath in the year—let me see—Garrick was just taking his leave, and that was in," etc.

Beefe, mutton and porke, shred pies of the best,
Pig, veale, goose and capon and turkie well drest
Chese, apples and nuts, jolie carols to heare,
And then in the countrie, is counted good cheare.

—Tusser, *Five Hundred Points of Husbandry*

Praysynge God

When thy parentes downe to the table shall syt,
In place be ready for the purpose most fyt;
With sober countenance, lookynge them in the face,
Thy hands holdynge up, thus begin grace:
"Give thankes to God with one accorde
For that shall be set on this borde,
And be not careful what to eate,
To eche thynge lyvynge the Lord sends meats;
For foode he wyll not se you peryshe,
But wyll you fede, foster and cheryshe;
Take well in worth what he hath sent,
At thys time be therwith content
Praysynge God."
So treatablie speakyng, as possibly thou can,
That the hearers thereof may thee understan.
Grace beynge sayde, low cursie make thou,
Sayinge "much good may it do you."

—SEAGER'S *The Schoole of Vertue*

Chapter Twelve

EXOTICA

STRANGE AND CURIOUS affairs constantly appear in the old books on food, and in some of the new as well. We have collected here, as a fillip to the section "Customs and Manners," some of the stranger and more curious items that have come to light in the course of research.

"Eggs in Religion," for example, is an historical footnote drawn from a book by William Hutchinson, an obscure English county historian.

Athenaeus, on cabbage, is taken from "The Deipnosophists," or "Banquet of the Learned," a book which this immensely cultured and urbane Greek writer wrote sometime during the close of the second century. Egyptian born, he lived in Alexandria and later in Rome. Unfortunately, only fragments of the "Banquet" survive.

John Jeaffreson tells us more about the awful condiment of the Romans, garum, and Sir Eyre Coote, a British general who served in India and dabbled in gastronomy and history on the side, adds another footnote to this curious substance. After these, Abraham Hayward returns to speak of those odd birds, ruffs and reeves, and from the accomplished Jeaffreson again, notes on frogs and acorns.

The curious recipe for preserving cucumbers comes from an obscure volume, "Delightes for Ladies, to Adorne their Persons, Tables, Closets, and Distillatories," by High Plat, published in 1609 by Humfrey Lownes, of London. This is one of the earliest, if not the first, cookery and household recipe books printed in England.

Paul Pierce's directions for a nutting supper appeared in one of those turn-of-the-century (twentieth, that is) books designed to further home entertaining. The book, "Suppers," is dedicated "To that much abused, but very eminent class, the society women of America." It contains suggestions for entertaining with the chafing dish, then a most popular custom; Bohemian suppers for men, suppers for special occasions and a chapter on miscellaneous suppers. Among these latter, which includes a clam bake and a "butterfly supper," one of the most amusing is the nutting party described. It was, of course, written with an absolutely straight face.

We conclude with Mrs. C. F. Leyel's dissertation on soul medicines, from her book, "The Magic of Herbs," in which she anticipates Huxley and other moderns in describing the effects of narcotic herbs.

Eggs in Religion

from History of Northumberland
by William Hutchinson

EGGS WERE HELD by the Egyptians as a sacred emblem of the renovation of mankind after the Deluge. The Jews adopted it to suit the circumstances of their history, as a type of their departure from the land of Egypt, and it was used in the feast of the Passover as part of the furniture of the table, with the Paschal Lamb. The Christians have certainly used it on this day, as containing the elements of future life, for an emblem of the resurrection.

The Cabbage as an Ancient Remedy

from The Deipnosophists
by Athenaeus

NOW THAT THE Egyptians really are fond of wine this is a proof, that they are the only people among whom it is a custom at their feasts to eat boiled cabbages before all the rest of their food; and even to this very time they do so. And many people add cabbage seed to potions which they prepare as preventive against drunkenness. And wherever a vineyard has cabbages growing in it, there the wine is weaker. On which account the citizens of Sybaris also, as Timaeus says, used to eat cabbages before drinking. And so Alexis says—

> Last evening you were drinking deep,
> So now your head aches. Go to sleep;
> Take some boil'd cabbage when you wake;
> And there's an end of your headache.

And Eubulus says, somewhere or other—

> Wife, quick! some cabbage boil, of virtues healing,
> That I may rid me of this seedy feeling.

Garum

from A Book About the Table
by John Cordy Jeaffreson

IN MOMENTS OF uncertainty the Roman cook used the never-absent garum. Oil was silver, liquamen was gold. The rich and luxurious used the garum which was termed "optimum." There were inferior kinds of the sauce for the poor and thrifty.

This exquisite condiment was obtained from the intestines, gills, and blood of fishes, great and small, stirred together with salt, and exposed in an open vat to the sun, until the compound was putrid. Nothing is known as to the proportions of the several piscine ingredients; but whilst small fishes were thrown whole into the vessel, the large fishes—such as tunny, sturgeon, and mackerel—contributed nothing to the mess, save their gills, internal parts, and juices. When putrefaction had done its work, wine and spice-herbs were added to the liquescent garbage. Finally, the liquor of this loathsome compound was strained, and sent in amphorae from Greece to the Roman market. Something like this sauce might doubtless be obtained by an artful treatment of fetid catsup, and caviar, so far gone to the bad that the few and the many would agree in their estimate of its virtues. Anyhow, it was darksome, saltish, biting, and beastly.

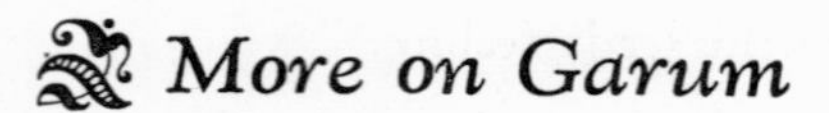

More on Garum

from Cuisine Bourgeoise of Ancient Rome
by Sir Eyre Coote

THIS BRINGS US to the real problem of Roman cookery, the flavor imported by that confection (garum) to the sauces with which it intercommunicated. Looking at this from the point of view of the kitchen, it is no other than a grave aesthetical question. If we can solve it in any way, we shall penetrate to the bottom of the Roman system. Without experiments, which will probably never be made, though Soyer vehemently desired them, we know so much as this, that the materials of the zest of fish, that salt was an adjunct, and that fermentation in the sun was the means of effecting a union more or less chemical between these well pronounced elements.

Beware of saladis, grene metis, and of frutes rawe,
for they make many a man have a feeble mawe,
therfore, of suche fresch lustes set not an hawe,
For such wantoun appetites ar not worth a strawe:

—JOHN RUSSELL, *Boke of Nurture*

Ruffs and Reeves

from The Art of Dining
by Abraham Hayward

THE GREATEST NOVELTY, perhaps, is the poachard or dun-bird, a species of wild fowl, supposed to come from the Caspian Sea, and caught only in a single decoy on the Misley Hall estate, Essex, in the month of January, in the coldest years. Their flesh is exquisitely tender and delicate, and may almost be said to melt in the mouth, like what is told of the celebrated canvas-back duck of America; but they have little of the common wild-duck flavor, and are best eaten in their own gravy, which is plentiful, without either cayenne or lemon juice. Their size is about that of a fine widgeon. The dotterel is also highly and deservedly valued by the epicure.

Ruffs and reeves are little known to the public at large, though honorable mention of them is made by Benwick. The season for them is August and September. They are found in fenny counties (those from Whittlesea Meer, in Lincolnshire, are best), and must be taken alive and fattened on boiled wheat or bread and milk mixed with hempseed for about a fortnight, taking good care never to put two males to feed together, or they will fight *à l'outrance*. These birds are worth nothing in their wild state; and the art of fattening them is traditionally said to have been discovered by the monks in Yorkshire, where they are still in high favor with the clerical profession, as a current anecdote will show. At a grand dinner at Bishopthorpe (in Archbishop Markam's time) a dish of ruffs and reeves chanced to be placed immediately in front of the young divine who had come up to be examined for priest's orders, and was considerately (or, as it turned out, inconsiderately) asked to dinner by his grace. Out of sheer modesty the clerical tyro confined himself exclusively to the dish before him, and persevered in his indiscriminating attentions to it till one of the resident dignitaries (all of whom were waiting only the proper moment to participate) observed him, and called the attention of the company by a loud exclamation of alarm. But the warning came too late: the ruffs and reeves had vanished to a bird, and with them, we are concerned to add, all the candidate's hopes of Yorkshire preferment are said to have vanished too.

A similar anecdote is current touching wheatears, which, in our opinion, are a greater delicacy. A Scotch officer was dining with the late Lord George Lennox, then commandant at Portsmouth, and was placed near a dish of wheatears, which was rapidly disappearing under his repeated attacks. Lady Louisa Lennox tried to divert his attention to another dish. "Na, na, my leddy," was the reply, "these wee birdies will do verra weel."

Frogs

from A Book About the Table
by John Cordy Jeaffreson

ON HIS RETURN from Italy, Thomas Coryate commended frogs as delicate fare to the notice of his fellow-countrymen; and the suggestion was ere long fruitful of the frog-pies which the epicures of Charles the First's London ate with infinite gusto. In his directions for cooking "frogs in the Italian fashion," Robert May orders that their thighs should be dressed with, and served in, pastry, together with the flesh of eels and fruit. "Season them both with pepper, nutmeg, and ginger," says the chef, "lay butter on your paste, and lay a rank of frog, and a rank of eel, some currants, gooseberries or grapes, raisins, pine-apple seeds, juyce of orange, sugar, and butter: this do three times, close up your dish, and being baked, ice it," i.e., with sugar. Frog-pies, thus compounded, was often seen at the best London tables, any time between James the First's later years and Charles the Second's death. Just as George the Third's commonalty scorned the French for living chiefly on frogs, the "populace" of England in the seventeenth century imagined that frogs were the principal food of the fantastic and vicious Italians.

Hunger and Acorns

from A Book About the Table

by John Cordy Jeaffreson

WHEN HISTORY FIRST condescended to notice our British forefathers, their cooking was of Poseidonian simplicity. Indeed, it is questionable whether their culinary practice covered all the operations noticed by the stoical observer. Diodorus Siculus, an authority on many matters at this date, albeit an arrant and ludicrously inaccurate book-maker, something less than two thousand years since, assures us that they lived chiefly on dried corn, which they grated in mortars, and worked into a heavy paste. The mightiest chieftain of them all had never a morsel of butter wherewith to lubricate this farinaceous mess. When corn failed these eaters of paste, hunger gave them appetite for acorns—the food of swine, and so bitter a substitute for meat, that the men of these luxurious days can scarcely believe it to have ever been a common article of diet. It is less generally known that the same nauseous fare was consumed in seasons of scarcity by our ancestors of much more recent time. But William Harrison, supremely first of Elizabethan chroniclers, assures us that, even in his day, the poorer folk of England sometimes ate a bread made partly or altogether of acorns.

There were hard times, when, in the dearth of mast, the aborigines of our productive land devoured herbs and roots, even more distasteful and indigestible than the fruit of the oak. But they had palliatives for the torments of famine. Harrison records that in the Northern districts they possessed a "certaine kind of confection," made, probably, of earth and the inspissated juices of narcotic herbs, a small pill of which alleviated wonderfully the pain of fasting. Another of their measures against hunger is more singular and incredible. In the extremity of their anguish, the famished wretches had recourse to a primitive kind of water-cure. Creeping out to the fens and morasses, they placed themselves in "moorish slits up unto their chins," and "sat for hours at a time in mud and water." They were of the opinion that the cold and wet "qualified the heats of their stomachs," and weakened their yearning for food. Strange to say, the efficacy of this process has not been fully tested in these days of scientific inquiry. But any reader of this work who is prone to be irritable when his wife keeps him waiting for dinner, may easily make trial of the frigid treatment. Instead of venting his displeasure at an absent wife in angry words, let him retire to his bathroom, turn on the cold water, and sit in it till she has returned from her afternoon's drive. He will, of course, select for the experiment a day in the sharpest season of winter.

To Preserve Cowcumbers All the Yeere

from Delightes for Ladies *by High Plat*

TAKE A GALLON of faire water, & a pottle of verjuice, and a pint of bay salt, and a handful of greene fennell or Dill: boile it a little, and when it is cold put it into a barrel, and then put your Cowcumbers into that pickle, and you shal keep them all the yeere.

A CONCEIPT OF THE AUTHORS, HOW BEEFE MAY BE CARRIED AT THE SEA, WITHOUT THAT STRONG AND VIOLENT IMPRESSION OF SALT WHICH IS USUALLY PURCHASED BY LONG AND EXTREME POWDRING.

Here, with the good leave and favour of those curteous gentlewomen, for whome I did principally, if not only, intend this little treatise; I will make bold to lanch a little from the shoare, and trie what may bee done in the vast and wide Ocean, and in long and dangerous voyages, for the better preservation of such usuall victuals, as for want of this skill doe oftentimes meerely perish, or else by the extreame pearching on the salte, doe lose even their nutritive strength and vertue: and if any future experience doe happen to controll my present conceipt, let this excuse a scholler, *quod in magnis est uolvisse satis*. But now to our purpose, let all the bloud bee first well gotten out of the beefe, by leaving the same some nine or tenne dayes in our usuall brine, then barrell up all the peeces in vessels full of holes, fastening them with ropes at the sterne of the ship; and so dragging them through the salte sea water (which by his infinite change and succession of water will suffer no putrefaction, as I suppose) you may happily find your beefe both sweet and savourie enough when you come to spend the same. And if this happen to fal out true upon some triall thereof had, then either at my next impression, or when I shall be urged thereunto upon any necessitie of service, I hope to discover the means also whereby everie Ship may carrie sufficient store of victuall for her selfe in more close and convenient cariages then those loose vessels are able to performe. But if I may be allowed to carrie either roasted or soffen flesh to the sea, then I dare adventure my poore credit therein to preserve for sixe whole monethes together, either Beefe, Mutton, Capons, Rabbets, &c. both in a cheape manner, and also as fresh as wee doe now usuallie eate them at our Tables. And this I hold to be a most singular & necessary secret for all our English Navie; which at all times uppon reasonable tearmes I will be readie to disclose for the good of my country.

A *Nutting Supper*

from Suppers

by Paul Pierce

A NUTTING PARTY is particularly appropriate to be given during the fall season.

The invitation may be written on paper, folded neatly and slipped inside an English walnut shell—which is then glued together and sent in a small box, labeled "A Nut to Crack."

Decorations should carry out, as far as possible, the effect of a woodland scene. The walls may be entirely covered with branches of autumn leaves, and mantels and over doorways banked with pine boughs and greenery of all sorts. Rustic tables and chairs, if available, are most appropriate, and lights shaded with red and yellow shades. As the guests arrive, each should be given a peanut shell, glued together or tied with ribbons. On a slip of paper inside is written the number of table and partner. To indicate progressions, ribbons may be glued to nuts of different kinds and one given for each game won. Or little baskets may be given into which a nut is dropped for each game won. Or if tally cards for finding partners are preferred, they may be painted to represent nuts of different kinds, not more than two being alike.

The nutting game itself is played similarly to that well known children's game, "jackstraws." On each table is placed a pair of bonbon tongs—the kind that come in candy boxes are best—and a tall tumbler heaped full of nuts—peanuts are best for the purpose —with one gilded nut. For the first game, lady No. 1 at all the tables begins play and after the first game the lady begins who lost in the game preceding. The gentleman opposing the lady who begins play, carefully turns out on the table the peanuts and the players proceed as in jackstraws, getting with the tongs as many peanuts as possible, one at a time, without shaking the others. The winners progress and change partners, after the bell rings at the head table. At the head table, as at the other tables, the winners progress and the losing lady remaining begins play for the next game. At the head table each player has two chances at the peanuts and then the bell is rung. The neutral-colored peanuts count one each and the gilded one ten.

Suitable prizes are: For the ladies, a silver English walnut thimble case; a linen centerpiece in chestnut design; a silver almond charm, "Philopena," which opens with kernel inside; a silver English walnut, exact size, which opens, containing powder puff, mirror, place for miniature, small scent bottle and pincushion, "All in a Nut Shell"; a real English walnut shell containing a fine lace-betrimmed handkerchief, enclosed in a series of boxes, one fitting within the other; a sterling silver almond set or almond scoop; a silver vinaigrette in exact reproduction of a peanut. For the gentlemen, a burnt wood nut bowl, with nut cracker and set of nut picks; a handsome edition of E. P. Roe's "Opening of a Chestnut Burr"; a silver peanut magic pencil, etc. . . .

The refreshments may perfectly carry out the nutting idea:

Peanut Sandwiches Walnut Sandwiches
Chicken and Nut Salad
Salted Nuts
Bisque of Almonds or Burnt Almond Ice Cream
Cocoanut, Hickory Nut, or Pecan Cake
Nut Bonbons, Festinos
Cheese Balls with English Walnuts
Coffee

Soul Medicines

from The Magic of Herbs

by Mrs. C. F. Leyel

LITTLE IS YET known about the immunity of individuals to particular poisons, but arsenic-eating is certainly practiced in Syria, where it is called "Hydrach" amongst the peasants. They take it as a tonic, as an aphrodisiac, and to help respiration in mountain-climbing, and in doses large enough to kill an ordinary man.

Narcotics, which are closely related to poisons (the same drugs being often used for both) have played two distinct parts in medicine from the time that plants with soporific properties were first discovered. Among the primitive races they have been more used as intoxicants than as anasthetics, but they have always served this two-fold purpose. The conscious or unconscious idea behind the use of them for intoxication has been the desire which is common to every man to get into touch with the supernatural.

These soul medicines are used by every savage tribe, except perhaps in Australia, where a strenuous form of dancing brings about the same results. To many tribes intoxicating liquor is unknown, but special herbs which they smoke or grind to powder and use as snuff have always been in use.

Hashish and mescal buttons are venerated by the Indians and Mexicans for the ecstatic visions they produce. In parts of America the natives smoke stramonium, and in California they make use of a poisonous toadstool. Opium, hemp, datura, mandrake and hemlock are all used for the purpose.

In ancient legend the exhilarating and drowsy property of plants is recognized in the ambrosia of the gods, the immortal amaranth, and the plant called athanasia.

Morpheus is the disoverer of the poppy, and Helen puts nepenthe into Ulysses' wine. The identity of this plant, with which the lovely Helen, after her return from Troy, provoked the guests of Menelaus to gaiety, has been the subject of ceaseless speculation. The knowledge, disclosed to her by the Egyptian Polydame, was well known to the Theban women, who were famous for their skill in compounding "nepenthes." Opium, hashish, henbane, mandragora and buglass have all been academically put forward as the nepenthe of the ancients, but the question has never been settled.

Hashish had been used in China to bring about insensibility as early as 220 B.C., and the Arabs and Indians made use of other plants and anaesthetics, though Dioscorides is the first European to describe drugs with soporific properties.

Mandragora was the popular pain-killer of the Middle Ages, and was universally used until the thirteenth century, when Hugh and Theodoric introduced "the soporific sponge," which was used until the seventeenth century.

This sponge, which was first referred to in the Jensen imprint of the Antidotarium of Nicolas of Salerno, published in Venice in 1471, has been immortalized by Elizabethan writers. It was steeped in a mixture of mandragora, hemlock, opium, hyoscyamus, mulberry juice, lettuce, and dried ivy, then moistened and inhaled. The patient was awakened by the application of fennel juice to his nostrils.

Wound drinks, to bring about a state of semi-consciousness, were sometimes given too. One is described by Jean Yperman in the early fourteenth century. The physicians of Myddrai used a sleeping potion, the recipe of which follows, with two others of the same date, and a decoction of henbane was sometimes employed as a footbath in cases of insomnia.

The following is a potion which will induce sleep whilst any diseased part is being opened.

"Drink the juice of orpine, eringo, poppy, mandrake, ground ivy, hemlock and lettuce, of each equal parts. Let clean earth be mixed with them, and a potion prepared, then without doubt the patient will sleep. When you are prepared to operate upon the patient, direct that he should avoid sleep as long as he can, and then let some of the potion be poured into his nostrils, and he will sleep without fail.

"When you wish to awake him, let a sponge be pounded in vinegar and put in his nostrils. If you wish that he should not awake for four days, get a pennyweight of the wax from a dog's ear and the same quantity of pitch; administer it to the patient, and he will sleep.

"When you would that he should awake, take an onion compounded with vinegar, and pour some into his mouth, and he will awake. Take care that you keep him quiet and warned of the operation, lest he should be disturbed."

A Sleeping Potion

"Take the juice of opium (poppy) and of eringo, or the seed of the latter, compound them into pills with milk. Let these be ministered to the patient. One will induce sleep in general, but if not let him take another again if required, taking care that two or three hours should intervene between each dose, in order to watch their effect before another is given."

To Produce Sleep

"Take corn poppy (for it is better than the foreign poppy) and eringo or the seed thereof; pound them well in a mortar and mix with wine. Wash the nostrils, eyes and ears of the patient frequently therewith, and he will sleep."

The lettuce and the cowslip have long been credited with minor somnolent powers, and were used to put an end to sleeplessness.

"If you need rest,
Lettuce and cowslip wine probatum est,"

is Pope's recognition of their drowsy properties, but if vinegar is mixed with lettuce its soporific virtue is destroyed.

The fumes from ignited puff balls are a well-recognized narcotic, and if these fungi are eaten when they are young and white, sliced and fried in butter, they are generally inducive of sleep.

Nutmeg tea was a remedy of our grandmothers for insomnia, and they generally carried a silver grater and nutmeg box on the chatelaines hanging from their waists. One nutmeg crushed was sufficient to make a pint of tea, and dose was a small cupful taken on going to bed.

Orange-flower water is a French substitute, and many women in France take a little of this scented essence in sugared water before retiring to rest. One tablespoonful of orange-flower, a pint of boiling water and an ounce of lump sugar are the right proportions. The water is poured over the sugar, and when dissolved and cold the orange-flower water is added.

Orange tea has the same merits, and is made by squeezing the juice of the fruit into a cup and pouring upon it boiling water, sweetened to taste. But even more efficacious and just as fragrant is tea prepared from the flowers of the lime tree. This is a French "nightcap" which we should do well to adopt in this country, for lime tea has a soothing effect on the nerves and is an exceedingly pleasant drink.

An infusion of primroses combines the same virtues, and if taken last thing at night has a decided narcotic tendency.

PART 3

INGREDIENTS OF GOOD DINING

Chapter Thirteen

A BED OF OYSTERS

A FINE DINNER, like the dishes which comprise it, is no better than its ingredients, a truism which the gourmet often recalls when the delectable entree is followed by an atrocious dessert, or the taste of a splendid soup is ruined past recall by an insufferable salad.

These refinements do not trouble those of us who are sub-epicureans. We are grateful for whatever we find that is superior, and pleasantly surprised when the entire production of a meal is beyond reproach. No doubt it is better that way. To live on the gourmet's high plane, always on the brink of gastronomic disaster, would be wearing.

However, it does no harm to contemplate the ingredients of good dining, which is the object of this section. We have no intention of contemplating all of them, because that would take a rather large book by itself, but rather to make a choice selection of ingredients which are capable of making a meal memorable for sub-epicureans, or else may be essential items for epicures.

We begin with oysters. Not everyone does. The compilers of this book are equally divided on the subject, devotedly for and revoltedly against, oysters. The popularity of the oyster in literature, however, attests to the esteem earned by this curious bivalve since the first man who summoned enough courage to eat one. They are the "loveliest of all foods," as Hector Bolitho attests, although somehow a symbol of the poor, according to Sam Weller, an authority on both subjects.

From a little known book by one of the best American humorists, Artemus Ward, we learn the Yankee method of opening oysters. A Swiftian eighteenth century fillip leads us to some odd anecdotes, no doubt apocryphal, about oysters, taken from a delightful nineteenth century book of essays about food written by a London bon vivant, Frank Schloesser.

Loveliest of All Foods

from The Glorious Oyster

by Hector Bolitho

PEOPLE WHO KNOW the oyster only as one of a company of twelve on a plate, cannot imagine what oyster covered rocks are like, nor can they possibly conjure up an idea of the pleasure of breaking them off, prising them open and eating them alive, half an hour after the tide has receded from the bed.

We found a little bay where the sand was clean and silver. The beach was so hot that we could not bear to put our hands upon it. The water was blue and smooth, with gulls sweeping down to it and piercing it with their beaks. The vast dome of the sky was filled with silver light. At the end of the beach the rocks rose calmly to the hills. We walked this way, where there were pools with colored seaweed and darting fishes and anemones in them. Wise old crabs scuttled slowly over the rocks.

We came upon a place where the oysters grew, packed together, as closely as grapes. My English companion put the basket on the ground. He was a smiling, good-looking fellow, with a shirt and collar cut so well that they filled me with envy. He opened the basket and took out two bottles, two glasses, two plates and two forks. I produced nothing but a chisel. I broke the oysters off, one by one, choosing the big ones of tidy shape. The outsides of their shells were still wet from the sea. We prised them open and placed them, eighteen upon each plate. My friend producd lemon and red pepper and I began to eat.

"Wait," he said. He brought the two bottles from a place behind the rock, where they had been cooling in a pool. One was champagne, and the other was stout. And thus was I introduced to the pleasure of eating oysters with *black velvet*. The drink was two thirds of stout and one of champagne.

When I rush back over the years of my life, that summer day stands out as vividly as any. The calm, warm sea, the sand, the log against which we leaned, the plate of succulent fat oysters on my knee, and the first glass of this magic drink, which made the oysters more wonderful than any I had eaten before. And then my friend talked about food, of avocado pears dressed with vinegar and oil he had eaten in Africa, of stuffed lobsters—I remember the pleasure with which he described the color of the red shell against the blue plate, as he had eaten them in Paris. He talked, too, of Russian soups, and fish stuffed with mushrooms, and duck dressed with yellow tiger lilies, snails, perfectly cooked, brought out from their houses with the aid of a slender two-pronged silver fork.

"But the oyster is the loveliest of all foods, raw or cooked," he said. "You know that the Romans did not really want to capture the Britons at all," he added. (We had gathered another thirty oysters by then, and our glasses were refilled.)

"No!" I answered, in wonder.

"Did you know that one of the most eminent of the Roman writers said, 'The poor Britons—there is some good in them after all—they produce an oyster.' "

Sam Weller on Oysters

from Pickwick Papers

by Charles Dickens

AND AWAY WENT the coach up Whitechapel, to the admiration of the whole population of that pretty densely-populated quarter.

"Not a wery nice neighborhood this, sir," said Sam, with the touch of the hat which always preceded his entering into conversation with his master.

"It is not indeed, Sam," replied Mr. Pickwick, surveying the crowded and filthy street through which they were passing.

"It's a wery remarkable circumstance, sir," said Sam, "that poverty and oysters always seems to go together."

"I don't understand you, Sam," said Mr. Pickwick.

"What I mean, sir," said Sam, "is, that the poorer a place is, the greater call there seems to be for oysters. Look here, sir; here's a oyster stall to every half-dozen houses—the streets lined vith 'em. Blessed if I don't think that ven a man's wery poor, he rushes out of his lodgings, and eats oysters in reg'lar desperation."

"To be sure he does," said Mr. Weller senior, "and it's just the same with pickled salmon!"

"Those are two very remarkable facts, which never occurred to me before," said Mr. Pickwick. "The very first place we stop at, I'll make a note of them."

Opening Oysters, Yankee Style

from The Encyclopedia of Food

by Artemus Ward

There is a story of two "smart" Yankees, one named Hosea and the other Hezekiah, who met in an oyster shop in Boston. Said Hosea, "As to opening oysters, why nothing's easier if you know how."

"And how's *how?*" asked Hezekiah.

"Scotch snuff," replied Hosea, very gravely. "Scotch snuff. Bring a little of it ever so near their noses, and they'll sneeze their lids off."

"I know a man who knows a better plan," observed Hezekiah. "He spreads the bivalves in a circle, seats himself in the center, reads a chapter of Artemus Ward to them, and goes on until they get interested. One by one they gape with astonishment at A. Ward's whoppers, and as they gape my friend whips 'em out, peppers away, and swallows 'em."

Byron on Oysters

from Don Juan, Canto LXXXI

by Lord Byron

"AN OYSTER may be cross'd in love," and why?
Because he mopeth idly in his shell,
And heaves a lonely subterraqueous sigh,
Much as a monk may do within his cell:
And apropos of monks, their piety
With sloth has found difficult to dwell;
Those vegetables of the Catholic creed
Are apt exceedingly to run to seed.

Swift on Oysters

from Dialogue II

by Jonathan Swift

Lady Smart: Ladies and gentlemen, will you eat any oysters before dinner?

Colonel: With all my heart. (*Takes an oyster.*) He was a bold man that first eat an oyster.

Lady Smart: They say, oysters are a cruel meat, because we eat them alive; then they are an uncharitable meat, for we leave nothing to the poor; and they are an ungodly meat, because we never say grace.

Neverout: Faith, that's as well said as if I had said it myself.

Some Anecdotes About Oysters

from The Greedy Book
by Frank Schloesser

A STORY WHICH I venture to think apocryphal is quoted by W. R. Hare in a curious little book, "On the Search for a Dinner," published in London in 1857. Speaking of dining in Paris, he refers to the celebrated restaurant the *Rocher du Cancale*, and relates how an English "Milord" drove up to the establishment and ordered (and ate) a hearty meal of twenty-nine dozen oysters; after which Milord died suddenly—and no wonder! They carried him down with great difficulty to the carriage. The groom, on seeing his master's body arrive, exclaimed with great coolness, "It is the third time that Milord gives himself the pleasure of dying of indigestion." "He will not die a fourth time," answered the *patron*, with sorrow. Milord was buried at Père-la-Chaise. His facetious friends deposit every year by the remains of the defunct an enormous quantity of oyster-shells. The tomb is about five-and-twenty yards from that of Héloise and Abelard. On a slab of black marble the following epitaph is inscribed: "Here lies——, dead for the third time in a duel with the oysters of the Rocher du Cancale."

I confess that I have not had the curiosity to verify the tombstone.

Brillat-Savarin has an oyster anecdote to the effect that he was at Versailles in the year 1798 as Commissary of the Directory, and had frequently to meet the Registrar of the Tribunal, M. Laperte. The latter was so fond of oysters that he used to grumble about never having had enough to satisfy him. Being determined to procure him that satisfaction, Brillat-Savarin asked Laperte to dinner, and the latter accepted. "I kept up with him," says the host, "to the third dozen, letting him then go on by himself. He went on steadily to the thirty-second dozen—that is to say, for more than an hour, as they were opened but slowly—and as in the meantime I had nothing else to do—a state quite unbearable at table—I stopped him just as he was beginning to show more appetite than ever. 'My dear friend,' I said, 'it must be some other day that you have enough to satisfy you; let us now have some dinner.' We took dinner, and he showed all the vigor and hunger of a man who had been fasting."

These oyster-gorges are, however, mere epitomes of vulgar gluttony. There is no more gastronomic satisfaction to be got out of thirty-three dozen than out of the conventional two dozen. In fact, doctors rarely prescribe more than one dozen at a time. . . .

There is a story told of an astute Roman epicure named Fulvius Hirpinus who constructed on his estate, close to the seashore, a fishpond where he stored or "parked" oysters, which he fattened with paste and cooked wine, worked to the consistency of honey. He was certainly astute because besides regaling himself and his friends on these artificially fattened oysters, he drove a roaring trade in selling them wholesale and retail to the nobility and gentry of Rome. . . .

When Thackeray went to Boston in 1852 he had some trouble with the very large American oyster. "He first selected the smallest one of the half-dozen (rejecting a larger one because, as he said, it resembled the High Priest's servant's ear that Peter cut off), and then bowed his head as though he were saying Grace. Opening his mouth very wide, he struggled for a moment, after which all was over. I shall never forget the comic look of despair he cast upon the other five over-occupied shells. I asked him how he felt. 'Profoundly grateful,' he said, 'as if I had swallowed a small baby.' "

. . . Between 1775 and 1818 there lived and flourished (more or less) in Malta, Naples, Paris, and elsewhere, a notable composer, Nicolo Isouard, more generally known as Nicolo. He wrote many operas, all of which are now forgotten. Having lived in Naples he was a great macaroni eater, and prepared the dish himself in a somewhat original manner. He stuffed each tube of macaroni with a mixture of marrow, *pâté de foi gras,* chopped truffles, and cut-up oysters. He then heated up the preparation, and ate it with his left hand covering up his eyes, for he asserted that he could not afford to allow the beautiful thoughts engendered by such exquisite food to be disturbed by an extraneous mundane sight. No wonder he died young.

Chapter Fourteen

FISH AND FLESH

After the appetizer comes the fish, perhaps as a second course in the classic style, or as an entree—unless, of course, the entree is flesh of fowl or animal.

But then, what is an entree? Thomas J. Murrey tells us what they are, properly, in an excerpt from a book he wrote on the subject in 1886 and which is still authoritative.

Although it covers considerably more than fish or flesh, we have quoted nearly whole the essay on choosing the best in market, from the first American cookbook, simply because the advice is, in general, as good now as it was in the eighteenth century. Considerably older are the quoted legends about the origin of sirloin, which may well be taken with a little Béarnaise sauce.

The Reverend Sydney Smith's poem in praise of fish is one of those passionate little lyrics which may not be immortal in the grand sense but has long been cherished by lovers of good food, who can only sigh with Smith over salmon and turbot. No less passionate is the ode by the French poet, Raoul Ponchon, in praise of gigot, which may well be the nearest to simple ecstasy the food bard will ever come.

We turn then to an apostrophe in prose, this one to foie gras, the ingredient which ennobles goose and enhances the truffle. It is written by that elegant English stylist, Lord Lytton, excerpted from his almost forgotten novel, "Pelham."

Much more might be said of fish and flesh, but we have already spoken well of them, and will speak of them again. We give the last word here to Kenneth Roberts, a man who often enjoyed having it. In his unexcelled novel of the Revolution, "Arundel," he suggests a breakfast which may have been appropriate to the times, but leaves nothing more to be said on the subject today.

Some people have a foolish way of not minding, or pretending not to mind, what they eat. For my part, I mind my belly very studiously, and very carefully; for I look upon it, that he who does not mind his belly will hardly mind anything else.

—Dr. Johnson

Remarks on Entrées

from The Book of Entrées

by Thomas J. Murrey

Entrées are the middle dishes of the feast, and not the principal course, as many suppose; they are a series of dainty side dishes, in the preparation of which the cook demonstrates the extent of her capabilities. Should they be prepared in a careless, indifferent manner, they cloy the palate and prevent that much-abused organ from appreciating the more important dishes of the feast. They should not only be nicely prepared, but much care and ingenuity should be shown in the arraying of them on the platter. To prepare palate-pleasing entrées one must study to please the eye quite as much as the palate.

How to Choose the Best in Market

from American Cookery

by Amelia Simmons

Salmon. The noblest and richest fish taken in fresh water—the largest are the best. They are unlike almost every other fish, are ameliorated by being 3 or 4 days out of water, if kept from heat and the moon, which has much more injurious effect than the sun.

In all great fish-markets, great fish-mongers strictly examine the gills—if the bright redness is exchanged for a low brown, they are stale; but when live fish are bro't flouncing into market, you have only to select the kind most agreeable to your palate and the season. . . .

. . . A shad 36 or 48 hours out of water, may not cook so hard and solid, and be esteemed so elegant, yet give a higher relished flavor to the taste. . . .

Of all fresh water fish, there are none that require, or so well afford haste in cookery, as the *Salmon Trout,* they are best when caught under a fall or cataract—from what philosophical circumstances is yet unsettled yet true it is, that at the foot of a fall the waters are much colder than at the head; Trout choose those waters; if taken from them and hurried into dress, they are genuinely good; and take rank in point of superiority of flavor, of most other fish. . . .

Poultry. Having before stated that the female in almost every instance, is preferable to the male, and peculiarly so in the *Peacock,* which, tho' beautifully plumaged, is tough, hard, stringy, and untasted, and even indelicious—while the *Pea Hen* is exactly otherside, and the queen of all birds . . .

All birds are known, whether fresh killed or stale, by a tight vent in the former, and a loose open vent if old or stale; their smell domosted their goodness; speciled rough legs denote age, while smooth legs and combs prove them young.

Butter—Tight, waxy, yellow Butter is better than white or crumbly, which soon becomes rancid and frowy. Go into the centre of balls or rolls to prove and judge it; if in firkin, the middle is to be preferred, as the sides are frequently distasted by the wood of the firkin—altho' oak and used for years. New pine tubs are ruinous to the butter. To have sweet butter in dog days, and thro' the vegetable season, send stone pots to honest, neat, and trusty dairy people, and procure it pack'd down in May, and let them be brought in in the night, or cool rainy morning, covered with a clean cloth wet in cold water, and partake of no heat from the horse, and set the pots in the coldest part of your cellar, or in the ice house. Some say that May butter thus preserved, will go into the winter use, better than fall made butter.

Eggs—Clear, thin shell'd, longest oval and sharp ends are best;

to ascertain whether new or stale—hold to the light, if the white is clear, the yolk regularly in the centre, they are good—but if otherwise they are stale. The best possible method of ascertaining, is to put them into water, if they lye on their bilge, they are *good* and *fresh*—if they bob up an end they are stale, and if they rise they are addled, proved and of no use.

Potatoes, take rank for universal use, profit and easy acquirement. The smooth skin, known by the name of How's Potatoe, is the most mealy and richest flavor'd; the yellow rusticoat next best; the red, and red rusticoat are tolerable; and the yellow Spanish have their value . . .

A roast Potatoe is brought on with roast Beef, a Steake, a Chop, or Fricassee; good boiled with a boiled dish; make an excellent stuffing for a turkey, water or wild fowl; make a good pie, and a good starch for many uses. . . .

Garlicks, tho' used by the French, are better adapted to the uses of medicine than cookery.

Horse Radish, once in the garden, can scarcely ever be totally eradicated; plowing or digging them up with that view, seems at times rather to increase and spread them.

Thyme, is good in soups and stuffings.

Sweet Marjoram, is used in Turkeys.

Summer Savory, ditto, and in Sausages and salted Beef, and legs of Pork.

Sage, is used in Cheese and Pork, but not generally approved.

Parsley, good in *soups,* and to *garnish roast Beef,* excellent with bread and butter in the spring.

Sweet Thyme, is most useful and best approved in cookery.

Apples, are still more various, yet rigidly retain their own species, and are highly useful in families, and ought to be more universally cultivated, excepting in the compactest cities. There is not a single family but might set a tree in some otherwise useless spot, which might serve the two fold use of shade and fruit; on which 12 or 14 kinds of fruit trees might easily be grafted, and essentially preserve the orchard from the intrusions of boys, etc. which is too common in America. If the boy who thus planted a tree, and guarded and protected it in a useless corner, and carefully engrafted different fruits, was to be indulged free access into orchards, whilst the neglectful boy was prohibited—how many millions of fruit trees would spring into growth—and what a saving to the union. The net saving would in time extinguish the public debt, and enrich our cookery.

Origins of Beef Sirloin

A sirloyne of beef was set before him, (so knighted saith tradition, by this King Henry), on which the king laid lustily.

—FULLER'S *Church History*

Our Second Charles of fame facete
On loin of beef did dine;
He held his sword, pleas'd, o'er the meat,
Arise thou fam'd Sir Loin.

—THE NEW SIR JOHN BARLEYCORN

Poem in Praise of Fish

MUCH DO I love, at civic treat,
The monsters of the deep to eat;
To see the rosy salmon lying,
By smelts encircled, born for frying;
And from the china boat to pour,
On flaky cod, the flavor'd shower.
Thee, above all, I much regard,
Flatter than Longman's flattest bard,
Much honor'd turbot!—sore I grieve
Thee and thy dainty friends to leave.
—REV. SYDNEY SMITH

The Gigot *by Raoul Ponchon*

THE GIGOT'S HERE (on table neatly spread)
Fragrant with garlic, couched on seemly bed
Of many a bedded bean.

There's magic in the air, and hearts are light
As we recover waning appetite,
Now sharp and keen.

So far, so good. We'd tried, with moderate zest,
Hors d'oeuvre-ish snacks. But now each anxious guest
Wonders "Which roast?"

Joy! It's a gigot; borne by serving-maid
Sturdy of build, yet ceremonially staid.
Ah, precious load! Our host,

Father of all the flock, with critic's gaze,
Inspects it. Is it worthy of his praise?
Well browned, well done?

Pink of perfection, as we all agree,
When his proud blade cleaves irresistibly,
And streamless run,

Rose-red, from a pierced gold pourpoint, to disclose
The flesh, as sweet and wholesome as a rose.
The dreariest guest

But lately wordless, blossoms at the sight,
And scatters telling phrases left and right
Becomes, indeed, a pest.

Often a sad, spoiled soup will, from the start,
Ruin a meal, and nullify the art
Of many a wit.

Then comes the "leg." Tongues wag. In highest glee,
"Knuckle!" claims one. "Pope's eye!" cries one, "for me,"

"Some underdone," for him. For her "Cooked through."
No problem here. A third, between the two
Can't quite decide.

(A leg of mutton, when correctly done,
Ensures that every whim, of everyone,
Is gratified.)

Sometimes the talk . . . art, science, politics,
Gets out of hand, emphatic, or prolix,
Reaches some peril-point.

The gigot comes, and turgid speeches die.
"Quite right!" says one. And then, "Shall you and I
Discuss this joint?"

Unrivaled creatures! In the springing green
You lived on flowers. On flowers alone, I mean,
And never a weed.

Tender you are as any youthful bride,
O generous gigots! Dewey-fresh beside,
Lovely indeed.

When in the daisied vales you danced quadrilles,
Cropped the salt pastures, gamboled on the hills,
Butchers unheeded,

Sweet babes you seemed, gracious in infancy,
But more affecting still, at least to me,
On bean-layer bedded.

We munch you, then, in frankest, purest greed,
Slice after slice, and far beyond our need,
Sated, replete.

Still, as the Sorbonne doctor said: "Good mutton
Never yet harmed the most outrageous glutton."
Hungry or not—let's eat!

Foie Gras

from Pelham

by Lord Lytton

WE ALL THREE once more entered the fiacre, and drove to the celebrated restaurateur's of the Rue Mont Orgeuil. O, blissful recollections of that dinner! . . . Lonely and sorrowful as I now sit, digesting with many a throe the iron thews of a British beefsteak . . . I see the grateful apparitions of *Escallopes de Saumon* and *Laitances de Carpes* rise in a gentle vapor before my eyes . . . And thou most beautiful of all, thou evening star of *entremets*—thou that delightest in truffles, and gloriest in a dark cloud of sauces—exquisite *foie gras!*—Have I forgotten thee? Do I not, on the contrary, see thee (smell thee, taste thee), and almost die with rapture of thy possession? What though the goose, of which thou art a part, has, indeed, been roasted alive by a slow fire, in order to increase thy divine proportions—yet has not our almanach truly declared that the goose rejoiced amid all her tortures . . . because of the glory that awaited her? Did she not, in prophetic vision, behold her enlarged and ennobled *foie* dilate into *patés* and steam into *sautés*—the companion of truffles—the glory of dishes—the delight—the treasure—the transport of gourmands! O, exalted among birds—the apotheosized goose, did not thy heart exult even when thy liver parched and swelled within thee, from that most agonizing death; and didst thou not, like the Indians at the stake, triumph in the very torments which alone could render thee illustrious?

Pork for Breakfast

from Arundel
by Kenneth Roberts

"DAMN HER!" Cap Huff said. "She swears to God she don't know how to cook, and I'm beginning to believe her. It's a disgrace to the town of Arundel and the whole damned province of Maine, if you ask me! Can't cook! Gosh! I never expected to live to see the day that a Maine woman couldn't cook!"

Mary never looked at him, nor at me, but she spoke in a husky voice. "Maine woman? I? You take me for a filthy Bostonnais?"

Cap's jaw dropped. He put a hand on each knee, squatting, open-mouthed, to stare at her the more strickenly. "Filthy who?"

"Mind your own business!" I told him. "There's plenty of women in Maine that can't cook, either, not any more than a chipmunk can, though they call it cooking. Why don't you cook your own breakfast?"

"Well, mebbe I better," Cap said, straightening up. "Us filthy Bostonnais have got to have our food."

"What can we have?" I asked.

"Why," said Cap, in some surprise, "There ain't anything left in the world but pork, is there? Pork and wine wouldn't be bad for breakfast, Stevie: a little pork and a lot of wine."

Chapter Fifteen

VEGETABLES IN VARIOUS FORMS

FOR SOME REASON vegetables have not been celebrated as much as other ingredients of good dining, although their virtues are surely as great as the other items on the menu. How often, for example, does one see the onion, so much a part of so many dishes, treated in prose or poetry with the respect it deserves? More often its unfortunate effect on the lachrymal ducts makes it the subject of literary comment than the subtle touch it gives to a variety of potables.

This discrepancy is set somewhat to rights by Elizabeth Pennell's little hymn to the onion, which is followed by her observations on salads and her praise of the also neglected radish, which she suggests for breakfast—perhaps an accompaniment for Kenneth Roberts' pork and wine. The first of these excerpts is from "A Guide for the Greedy," and the latter two from "The Feasts of Autolycus," both popular books about food which this graceful English writer published near the end of the nineteenth century.

The Incomparable Onion

from A Guide for the Greedy
by Elizabeth Robins Pennell

TOO OFTEN THE POET sees but the tears that live in an onion; not the smiles. And yet the smiles are there, broad and genial, or subtle and tender. "Rose among roots," its very name revives memories of pleasant feasting; its fragrance is rich forecast of delights to come. Without it, there would be no gastronomic art. Banish it from the kitchen, and all pleasure of eating flies with it. Its presence lends color and enchantment to the most modest dish; its absence reduces the rarest dainty to hopeless insipidity, and the diner to despair . . .

The fragrance of this "wine-scented" esculent not only whets the appetite; it abounds in associations glad and picturesque. All Italy is in the fine, penetrating smell; and all Provence; and all Spain. An onion or garlic-scented atmosphere hovers alike over the narrow *calli* of Venice, the cool courts of Cordova, and the thronged amphitheatre of Arles. It is the only atmosphere breathed by the Latin peoples of the South, so that ever must it suggest blue skies and endless sunshine, cypress groves and olive orchards. For the traveler it is interwoven with memories of the golden canvases of Titian, the song of Dante, the music of Mascagni. The violet may not work a sweeter spell, nor the carnation yield a more intoxicating perfume.

And some men there have been in the past to rank the onion as a root sacred to Aphrodite: food for lovers. To the poetry of it none but the dull and brutal can long remain indifferent . . .

One word more. As the *ite missa est* of the discourse let this truth—a blessing in itself—be spoken. As with meat, so with vegetables, few are not the better for the friendly companionship of the onion, or one of its many offshoots. Peas, beans, tomatoes, eggplant are not indifferent to its blandishments. If honor be paid to the first pig that uprooted a truffle, what of the first man who boiled an onion? And what of the still mightier genius who first used it as seasoning for his daily fare? Every gourmet should rise up and call him blessed.

On Salads

from The Feasts of Autolycus
by Elizabeth Robins Pennell

As much depends upon the mixing as upon the proportions. The foolish pour in first their oil, then their vinegar, and leave the rest to chance, with results one shudders to remember. The two must be mixed together even as they are poured over the salad, and here the task but begins. For next, they must be mixed with the salad. To "fatigue" it the French call this special part of the process, and indeed, to create a work of art, you must mix and mix and mix until you are fatigued yourself, and your tomatoes or potatoes reduced to one-half their original bulk. Then will the dressing have soaked through and through them, then will every mouthful be a special plea for gluttony, an eloquent argument for the one vice that need not pall with years.

Radishes for Breakfast

from The Feasts of Autolycus

by Elizabeth Robins Pennell

WHEN SOFT RAINS FALL, and winds blow milder, and bushes in park or garden are sprouting and spring is at hand, grace your table with this same sweet promise of spring. Let rosy radish give the touch of color to satisfy the eye, as chairs are drawn in close about the spotless cloth: the tiny, round radish, pulled in the early hours of the morning, still in its first virginal purity, tender, sweet, yet peppery, with all the piquancy of the young girl not quite a child, not yet a woman. In great bunches, it enlivens every stall at Covent Garden, and every greengrocer's window; on the breakfast-table it is the gayest poem that uncertain March can sing. Do not spoil it by adding other *hors d'oeuvres;* nothing must be allowed to destroy its fragrance and its savor. Bread and butter, however, will serve as sympathetic background, and enhance rather than lessen its charm.

Vague poetic memories and aspirations stirred within you by the dainty radish, you will be in fitting humor for *oeufs aux saucissons,* a dish, surely, invented by the Angels in Paradise. There is little earthly in its composition of flavor; irreverent it seems to describe it in poor halting words. But if language prove weak, intention is good, and should others learn to honor this priceless delicacy, then will much have been accomplished. Without more ado, therefore, go to Benoist's and buy the little truffled French sausages which that temple of delight provides. Fry them, and fry half the number of fresh eggs. Next, one egg and two sausages place in one of those irresistible little French baking-dishes, dim green or golden brown in color, and, smothering them in rich wine sauce, bake, and serve—one little dish for each guest. Above all, study well your sauce; if it fail, disaster is inevitable; if it succeed, place laurel leaves in your hair, for you will have conquered. "A woman who has mastered sauces sits on the apex of civilization."

An Addenda of Cheese and Eggs

FIRST, a poem in praise of cheese by that noted gastronome, Saint-Amant, surnamed "Le Gros," an illustrious member of the *Société Bachique,* in seventeenth-century France. As a poet he did not confine himself to gastronomy, but his poems on food comprise the best known of what has survived, which is understandable when we contemplate his moving ode to cheese.

Then a dissertation on eggs by Anne Walbank Buckland, an English lady who flourished near the close of the last century as a member of the Anthropological Institute and a writer on food. This excerpt is from her book, "Our Viands," subtitled "Whence they come and how they are cooked, with a bundle of old recipes from cookery books of the last century."

On Cheese

by Saint-Amant

AND MAY I, every time I think
Of Cheese, be moved to take a drink!
Kneel, sinners all, and on your knees,
Sharers of my discrepancies,
Loudly and boldly yell with me:
"Heaven bless the boil that gives us Brie!
May its green pastures, fertile plains,
Never be vexed with lashing rains!
May Flora, with her jewels, her smiles,
Her half-a-million amorous wiles,
On lawns and meadows never old,
(In spite of winter's cruel cold,
His visage glacial and unkind)
Detain for ever, intertwined
In arms of alabaster white,
Sweet Spring, her loving satellite."

Get far behind me, Pont l'Eveque
Cheese of Auvergne . . . Milan . . . betake
Those charms elsewhere, for only Brie
Deserves my matchless minstrelsy.
Golden its glory! Golden, too,
Pure yellow is my cheese's hue,
Yet not from spleen! The moment after
You press its skin, it splits with laughter,
And richest cream, no stay, no stint,
Oozes beneath your fingerprint.

Hold hard, you guzzlers! Wait for me!
A cheese that's fit for royalty
Consumed at such unseemly speed—
The devil take you. And your greed!
Each single bite is worth a crown,
And muscatel to wash it down.
Your very teeth for shame should chatter
For making Brie a trivial matter!
. . . So, may I, every time I think
Of cheese, be moved to take a drink!

Lackey, more wine!

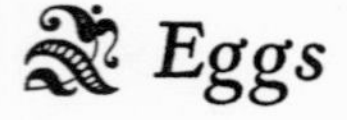

Eggs

from Our Viands

by Anne Walbank Buckland

Of all articles of diet, eggs are perhaps the most generally accepted; they are relished alike by sage and savage, and form a nutritious meal for prince or peasant. Nor is the taste for this universal food confined to mankind, for the hens themselves, the providers of the feast, often develop cannibalistic tendencies, and will peck and devour the very egg they have just deposited with so much care and cackling; whilst snakes will lie in wait for the delicate morsel, and will either swallow it whole, or tap it with their teeth and suck out the contents; and rats are credited with making wheelbarrows of themselves, allowing themselves to be pulled along by the ears by their comrades, in order to secure the prize held safely in their paws. Dogs also often develop a taste for eggs, which they will steal from the nest without compunction, the only cure for the propensity being to hold a hot egg in the mouth of the delinquent. Monkeys, and particularly baboons, will also diligently seek for and greedily devour all the eggs they can lay their hands on, and are consequently much dreaded by small birds. But, probably, rapacious birds are the greatest devourers of the eggs of other species. It seems a well authenticated fact that the grey crow in Africa, will carry stones up to a considerable height and drop them into an ostrich nest, in order to crack the hard shell which would otherwise be prohibitive of the coveted feast; whilst travelers assert that wild ostriches always place several eggs round the nest to serve as food for the young when first hatched.

Happily for mankind, the eggs of noxious reptiles and insects are relished as well as hen's eggs, and thus the excessive increase of deadly reptiles is prevented. The ichneumon greedily devours the eggs of snakes and crocodiles, and white ants' eggs are considered delicacies, even by men. In our own country the magpie and the jay are notorious thieves of the eggs of smaller birds; whilst turkeys, pheasants, and guinea-fowls, will swallow millions of ant eggs in a day, if they can get them.

The problem which puzzled the learned, centuries ago, as to which was first created, the egg or the hen, has never yet been unraveled. Theologians would probably say, the hen, certainly; but Darwin would be in favor of the egg, as being of the nature of that protoplasm from which all life originates. The ancients were certainly of Darwin's opinion, and looked upon the earth itself as developed from an egg by the power of various divinities, hence the egg became a sacred symbol in many countries, was hung up in Egyptian temples, and represented in paintings and sculptures as encircled in the folds of the good Agathodaemon, the serpent worshipped in so many lands, and which was doubtless connected with that other famous egg of antiquity, the serpent's egg of the Druids.

If we visit the British Museum we shall see eggs and egg-stands of various shapes and sizes, which have been found in tombs in Egypt, Greece, and Etruria; among the Etruscan relics are several ostrich eggs beautifully painted. These sepulchral eggs were, doubtless, symbolic of a future life, but were also probably designed as food for the dead, for it was well-nigh a universal practice to provide food for the departed spirit, a practice still in use among savages.

The eggs which are given at Easter time are supposed to symbolize the Resurrection, but it is certain that the custom originated in pre-Christian times. . . . It is both curious and interesting to note that in almost all countries this custom of giving and receiving brightly colored eggs at a spring festival, has prevailed from time immemorial; hence, probably, we see in the painted ostrich eggs from Etruscan tombs, which are at least two thousand years old, the spring gift of friends to the beloved dead. . . .

It may be well here to give a few of the uses of eggs in medicine, for they are valuable in many ways as household remedies.

"The white is the most efficacious of remedies for burns, and the oil extractable from the yolk is regarded by the Russians as an almost miraculous salve for cuts, bruises, and scratches. A raw egg, if swallowed in time, will effectually detach a fish-bone in the throat, and the white of two eggs will render the deadly corrosive sublimate as harmless as a dose of calomel. They strengthen the consumptive, invigorate the feeble, and render the most susceptible all but proof against jaundice in its more malignant phase." The old saw had it—

> "An egg, an apple, and a nut,
> You may eat after any slut."

That, however, is not quite true as regards eggs, for the shell being porous readily absorbs anything malodorous which is placed near it, so that it is not uncommon to meet with eggs tasting of onions. . .

The ostrich egg is the largest egg at present known, but that of the giant dinornis of New Zealand exceeded it in size as much as the turkey's egg exceeds that of the hen. One of these gigantic eggs was exhibited, with the skeleton of the extinct bird, at the Colonial and Indian Exhibition, and a cast of one may be seen at the Natural History Museum, with an ostrich egg near it by way of comparison; but the dinornis egg is unique and unattainable, as well as uneatable, and we must be content with that of the ostrich as the largest now used for eating, one of which makes a tolerable meal for five or six people, being considered equal to twenty-four hens' eggs. It is, however, rather strong in flavor, but makes excellent sponge-cakes, pancakes, or omelets, and a find of ostrich eggs in the desert is matter of great rejoicing to the wandering bushman or the hungry traveler.

Besides the dinornis, there is another extinct bird, the great auk, which has left behind it two or three eggs, which are so much coveted as to fetch an extraordinary price; one of these famous eggs was sold a year or two ago for £225. . . .

We are not likely to find eggs of dinornis or great auk; but it is reported that eggs larger than that of the ostrich have occasionally been found in the deserts of Africa, and any traveler coming across such may find it a profitable investment, although not as an article of food, for as the bird which laid these eggs is unknown, and perhaps extinct, the eggs would probably be partially petrified, although it is possible that they may be found to be those of the gigantic ostrich recently discovered in the interior, a specimen of which has lately been forwarded as a present to the Queen.

Of eggs good for food we may mention, in addition to those of the hen, duck, turkey, goose, guinea-fowl, and plover, those of the penguin, which are much relished by sailors, and dwellers on the sea-coasts where these birds abound, as also the eggs of other sea-birds, although they are apt to have a somewhat rank and fishy flavor. The eggs of the turtle are eagerly sought by the epicure, and it is related that one gentleman, having found what he supposed to be a nest of them, took some home and cooked them, leaving the rest in the sand, but returning in a day or two for the remainder, found instead a number of lively young crocodiles, which would go far to prove that there is very little to choose between turtles' eggs and those of the crocodile, and probably those of snakes and lizards would be equally palatable if prejudice did not interfere with their consumption.

Chapter Sixteen

HERBS, TEA, WINE AND LIQUEURS

We know that herbs do not go with tea, wine and liqueurs, but the question is, where else to put them? They might be accompaniment to any of the other ingredients of good dining, but they stand by themselves. The literature of herbs is a library in itself. The excerpts chosen here are small flavorings, one a brief essay on tisanes by the contemporary English food writer, Mrs. C. F. Leyel, the other a comment on saffron by our old friend, John Jeaffreson, who seems to keep on cropping up. Wash it all down, then, with an Oriental expert's words on the philosophy of tea and the irrepressible Captain Marryat's comment on mint julep.

Tisanes

from Herbal Delights

by Mrs. C. F. Leyel

TISANES COME TO us from France. Other countries have adopted them, and other countries have introduced them into their official pharmacopaeias, but in France tisanes are a national habit. A tisane of herbs is the Frenchman's way of relieving a condition that is not serious enough to see a doctor about. A bad sleeper takes a tisane of tilleul before going to bed; poor digestion is improved by a cup of camomile tea; a chill is cured with peppermint and elderflower tea, or a tisane of anise and menthe. The Frenchman is too much of a gourmet to choose any herbs that are not pleasant to the taste; and, as the carminative herbs are usually the aromatic ones, his needs do not, as a rule, go beyond these. Melilot, Hyssop, Lovage, Golden Rod and Costmary are some of them, and all the other herbs found in this chapter make fragrant tisanes if they are not infused long enough to become bitter. They cover a wide range of minor illnesses which can be dealt with successfully in this simple and pleasant way.

The Camellia, from which the tea we usually drink is gathered, is also included, for it is a herb like any other, and is sometimes mixed with Bergamot, Speedwell, Wood Betony or other herbs. Bergamot is better known by its old name of Oswego tea, and Speedwell was at one time so universally used as an adulterant of ordinary tea, or as a substitute for it, that it was called "*Thé de l'Europe*." Ground-Ivy was called Gill tea. Willow Herb went by the name of Kaporie tea in Russia, and Ceanothus was the well-known Jersey tea of America.

Dittany tea is another old-fashioned tisane, a pleasant and effective remedy for indigestion. The plant grows in the island of Candy in Dalmatia and is a species of Marjoram.

Last, and pleasantest of all, are Rosemary, Lavender and Queen Meadow—so sweetly scented and so English that for centuries they have figured in royal household accounts as a necessary expenditure for strewing floors, making potpurri and for scenting linen. Amongst those who work in the Lavender and Rosemary fields a tea made from either of these flowers is a quick cure for a nervous headache. Rosemary has become the symbol for remembrance because it is actually used in herbal medicine to cure forgetfulness.

The Fable of Saffron

from A Book About the Table

by John Cordy Jeaffreson

Brilliant colorists, the medieval chefs seized the lessons of the missal-painters, and delighted the eye with chromatic effects, that were equally daring and felicitous. . . . Some of their "made dishes" were red, others crimson; some were of vermilion brightness, and some of delicate carmine tint. For these uses they were indebted chiefly to red sanders, alkanet, mulberry-juice, and the coloring particles of blood. Throwing in these vivid hues with masterly boldness, they were also prodigal of yellow, from the faintest maber to the deepest orange. It was their favorite color, and was conspicuous in breads and cakes, pottages and hashes, brewets and twists of pastry. Two-thirds of their dishes were thus enriched to the eye, with the various tints of a dye which they obtained from the bright petals of a delicate flower, whose story, beginning in fable and ending in homeliest prose, is so strange and whimsical as to merit especial notice in the annals of Good Cheer.

When Crocus, the beloved friend of Smilax, fell beneath Mercury's murderous quoit, the blood which dripped from the wounded boy moistened the turf, which, after his death, brought forth a bell-shaped blue flower with reddish-yellow stigmata—the Crocus Sativus of botanists. Poetry declared that the lad was changed to a saffron plant. Prose admitted that the flower abounded on the ground where he was said to have received his death-blow. Scepticism remarked that probably the plant had grown there long before the incident, whatever it was, that occasioned the fable. One of the utterers of this skeptical sentiment was an Elizabethan scholar, William Harrison, author of the Introduction to Holinshed's Chronicles, who remarked quaintly, "A certain yong gentleman called Crocus went to playe at coits in the field with Mercurie, and being heedlesse of himselfe, Mercurie's coit happened by mishap to hit him on the head, whereby he received a wound that ere long killed him altogither, to the great discomfort of his friends. Finallie, in the place where he bled, saffron was found to grow, whereupon the people seeing the colour of the chive as it stood, (although I doubt not it grew there long before), adjudged it to come of the blood of Crocus, and therefore they gave it his name."

The Cup of Humanity

from The Book of Tea

by Okakura Kakuzo

TEA BEGAN as a medicine and grew into a beverage. In China, in the eighth century, it entered the realm of poetry as one of the polite amusements. The fifteenth century saw Japan ennoble it into a religion of aestheticism—Teaism. Teaism is a cult founded on the adoration of the beautiful among the sordid facts of everyday existence. It inculcates purity and harmony, the mystery of mutual charity, the romanticism of the social order. It is essentially a worship of the Imperfect, as it is a tender attempt to accomplish something possible in this impossible thing we know as life.

The Philosophy of Tea is not mere aestheticism in the ordinary acceptance of the term, for it expresses conjointly with ethics and religion our whole point of view about man and nature. It is hygiene, for it enforces cleanliness; it is economics, for it shows comfort in simplicity rather than in the complex and costly; it is moral geometry, inasmuch as it defines our sense of proportion to the universe. It represents the true spirit of Eastern democracy by making all its votaries aristocrats in taste.

The long isolation of Japan from the rest of the world, so conducive to introspection, has been highly favorable to the development of Teaism. Our home and habits, costume and cuisine, porcelain, lacquer, painting—our very literature—all have been subject to its influence. No student of Japanese culture could ever ignore its presence. It has permeated the elegance of noble boudoirs, and entered the abode of the humble. . . .

The outsider may indeed wonder at this seeming much ado about nothing. What a tempest in a tea-cup! he will say. But when we consider how small after all the cup of human enjoyment is, how soon overflowed with tears, how easily drained to the dregs in our quenchless thirst for infinity, we shall not blame ourselves for making so much of the tea-cup. . .

Strangely enough humanity has so far met in the tea-cup. It is the only Asiatic ceremonial which commands universal esteem. The white man has scoffed at our religion and our morals, but has accepted the brown beverage without hesitation. The afternoon tea is now an important function in Western society. In the delicate clatter of trays and saucers, in the soft rustle of feminine hospitality, in the common catechism about cream and sugar, we know that the Worship of Tea is established beyond question. The philosophic resignation of the guest to the fate awaiting him in the dubious decoction proclaims that in this single instance the Oriental spirit reigns supreme. . . .

There is a subtle charm in the taste of tea which makes it irresistible and capable of idealization. Western humorists were not slow to mingle the fragrance of their thoughts with its aroma. It has not the arrogance of wine, the self-consciousness of coffee, nor the simpering innocence of cocoa. . .

Charles Lamb, a professed devotee, sounded the true note of

Teaism when he wrote that the greatest pleasure he knew was to do a good action by stealth, and to have found it out by accident. For Teaism is the art of concealing beauty that you may discover it, of suggesting what you dare not reveal. It is the noble secret of laughing at yourself, calmly yet thoroughly, and is thus humor itself—the smile of philosophy. All genuine humorists may in this sense be called tea-philosophers. . . . Perhaps nowadays it is our demure contemplation of the Imperfect that the West and the East can meet in mutual consolation.

The Taoists relate that at the great beginning of the No-Beginning, Spirit and Matter met in mortal combat. At last the Yellow Emperor, the Sun of Heaven, triumphed over Shuhyung, the demon of darkness and earth. The Titan, in his death angony, struck his head against the solar vault and shivered the blue dome of jade into fragments. The stars lost their nests, the moon wandered aimlessly among the wild chasms of the night. In despair the Yellow Emperor sought far and wide for the repairer of the Heavens. He had not to search in vain. Out of the Eastern sea rose a queen, the divine Niuka, horn-crowned and dragon-tailed, resplendent in her armor of fire. She welded the five-colored rainbow in her magic cauldron and rebuilt the Chinese sky. But it is also told that Niuka forgot to fill two tiny crevices in the blue firmament. Thus began the dualism of love—two souls rolling through space and never at rest until they join together to complete the universe. Everyone has to build anew his sky of hope and peace.

The heaven of modern humanity is indeed shattered in the Cyclopean struggle for wealth and power. The world is groping in the shadow of egotism and vulgarity. Knowledge is bought through a bad conscience, benevolence practiced for the sake of utility. The East and West, like two dragons tossed in a sea of ferment, in vain strive to regain the jewel of life. We need a Niuka again to repair the grand devastation; we await the great Avatar. Meanwhile, let us have a sip of tea. The afternoon glow is brightening the bamboos, the fountains are bubbling with delight, the soughing of the pines is heard in our kettle. Let us dream of evanescence, and linger in the beautiful foolishness of things.

Mint-Julep—A Delightful Potation

from A Diary in America

by Captain Marryat

But the Americans do not confine themselves to foreign wines or liqueurs; they have every variety at home, in the shape of compounds, such as mint-julep and its varieties; slings in all their varieties; cock-tails,—but I really cannot remember, or if I could, it would occupy too much time to mention the whole battle array against one's brains. I must, however, descant a little upon the mint-julep, as it is, with the thermometer at 100°, one of the most delightful and insinuating potations that ever was invented, and may be drank with equal satisfaction when the thermometer is as low as 70°. There are many varieties, such as those composed of Claret, Madeira, etc.; but the ingredients of the real mint-julep are as follows. I learnt how to make them, and succeeded pretty well. Put into a tumbler about a dozen sprigs of the tender shoots of mint, upon them put a spoonful of white sugar, and equal proportions of peach and common brandy, so as to fill it up one-third, or perhaps a little less. Then take rasped or pounded ice, and fill up the tumbler. Epicures rub the lips of the tumbler with a piece of fresh pineapple, and the tumbler itself is very often encrusted outside with stalactites of ice. As the ice melts, you drink. I once overheard two ladies talking in the next room to me, and one of them said, "Well, if I have a weakness for any one thing, it is for a mint-julep"—a very amiable weakness, and proving her good sense and good taste. They are, in fact, like the American ladies, irresistible.

The Virginians claim the merit of having invented this superb compound, but I must dispute it for my own country, although it has been forgotten of late. In the times of Charles I and II it must have been known, for Milton expressly refers to it in his Comus:—

"Behold this cordial *julep* here
Which flames and dances in its crystal bounds
With spirits of *balm* and *fragrant syrups* mixed.
Not that Nepenthes, which the wife of Thone
In Egypt gave to Jove-born Helena
Is of such power to stir up joy like this,
To life so friendly, or so *cool to thirst*."

If that don't mean mint-julep, I don't know the English language.

PART 4

SOME GASTRONOMIC ECCENTRICITIES

Chapter Seventeen

THERE IS, apparently, no limit to what a man will put in his stomach if he has a fancy for it, and what is one man's delicacy is another's emetic. Most of us have our list, large or small, of things we cannot possibly eat unless under the threat of imminent starvation. It shocks us sometimes to see a friend regard us with undisguised horror as we munch away at something which to him is anathema. (Anathema with a white wine sauce, incidentally, is a rare delight.)

Our collection here, however, goes beyond mere everyday likes and dislikes, into the realm of sheer exotica, beginning with an excerpt from that remarkable book, "The Pantropheon, or History of Food, and Its Preparation, from the Earliest Ages of the World," by the equally remarkable Alexis Soyer, the eminent Victorian cook. The book sold a quarter of a million copies. The author was far better known than any of his books through the pages of *Punch,* as a character in a novel by Thackeray, and as a man as much involved in English politics as he was in English kitchens. This Frenchman who lived most of his life in England was a man of parts. "The Pantropheon" is only one of his many excellent cookery books. He also wrote poems, a ballet, and letters to the *Times*. Soyer was a born inventor; he could not help inventing. Sometimes it was a new marvel in food or drink, sometimes a utensil to cook in, or whole kitchens for special uses, as the one he devised for the British Navy, or a specific stove, which the British Army used for decades. Yet he was not above inventing small things, like a gadget for keeping money in dress boot heels. As a chef, Soyer cooked for small intimate gatherings of royalty, and for twenty thousand of London's poor on Christmas Day. He could, as he demonstrated in the Crimea, even perform the miracle of making army salt pork a palatable dish.

This is only a small sampling of Alexis Soyer's many-faceted personality, which is entirely too comprehensive to dwell on any longer here. The essay on "Dogs, Peacocks and Elephant Trunks," which we have excerpted, at least conveys a suggestion of his incredible gastronomic erudition, and it will surely gag dog lovers.

Cat lovers will be fully as nauseated by Sam Weller's description of an opportunistic veal pie man, if they have forgotten it, but between Soyer and Dickens, they will have had a breathing space to contemplate Mrs. Buckland's excursion into the eccentric cuisine and Hector Bolitho's reminiscent fragment about cannibalism.

There follows a small oddity by an English writer of the late nineteenth century who signed himself Fin-Bec. "The Book of Menus," which was published in London in 1876, has an almanac of gastronomic events, articles on dinners and wines, royal menus, Shakespeare dinners, ceremonial entertainments, city menus, menus for the year, and notes from the author's scrapbook. The menu for the horse, mule and donkey banquet at the Grand Hotel in Paris, April 1875, is a veritable *tour de force* of the subject.

Only a few years earlier, Paris had been under siege and horse meat appeared eventually on the menus of the best restaurants, as Madame Ritz describes so vividly in the biography of her famous chef husband, César Ritz.

The section concludes with poor Gulliver's attempts to get a square meal from the rather odd people he visited on his voyages.

We forbear to wish *bon appétit* to readers of the section.

Dogs, Peacocks and Elephant Trunks

from Soyer's Pantropheon

WE MUST BEG pardon of the reader for informing him that the dog presented a very relishing dish to many nations advanced in culinary science. To them, one of these animals, young, plump, and delicately prepared, appeared excellent food. The Greeks (we grieve to say) ate dogs, and even dared to think them good: the grave Hippocrates himself—the most wise, the least gluttonous, and therefore the most impartial of their physicians—was convinced that this quadruped furnished a wholesome, and at the same time, a light, food. As to the Romans, they also liked it, and no doubt prepared it in the same manner as the hare, which they thought it resembled in taste.

Atheneus, describing a feast of the most exquisite elegance, names double tripe among a host of dishes. He also says, speaking of a state dinner, that first of all there appeared large basins containing the intestines of animals, disposed with art around their heads.

At Rome the peacock had a prodigious success. When alive the Romans praised its beauty; when dead it appeared on the tables of its most enthusiastic admirers. Ultimately more savory or more rare dishes took the place of peacock's flesh, which then began to be thought hard, unwholesome, and of difficult digestion. However, it re-appeared in the Middle Ages at the nuptial festivities of the rich, where one of these birds was served as if alive, with the beak and claws gilded. To do that well, it was necessary to skin the bird very carefully, and then cook it with aromatics, such as cinnamon, cloves, etc. It was then covered with its skin and feathers, and served without any appearance of having been stripped. This luxury was to gratify the sight. Nobody touched it. The peacock was thus preserved for several years without being damaged—a property believed to be peculiar to its flesh, but which was owing no doubt to the aromatics just mentioned. . . .

Certain wandering tribes of Asia and Africa were thought formerly to be very fond of grilled elephant.

In our days also some semi-savage nations partake of the same taste. Le Vaillant, a celebrated traveler, and a most distinguished gastronomist, tells us that the first time he partook of an elephant's trunk, which was served him by the Hottentots, he resolved that it should not be the last; for nothing appeared to him of a more exquisite flavor. But he reserves his greatest praises for the foot of the colossal quadruped. We will let him speak for himself:—"They cut off the four feet of the animal, and made in the earth a hole about three feet square. This was filled with live charcoal, and, covering the hole with very dry wood, a large fire was kept up during part of the night. When they thought that the hole was hot enough it was emptied: a Hottentot then placed within it the four feet of the animal, covered them with hot ashes, and then with charcoal and small wood; and this fire was left burning until the morning . . . My servants presented me at breakfast with an elephant's foot. It had considerably swelled in the cooking; I could hardly recognize the shape, but it appeared so good, exhaled so inviting an odor, that I hastened to taste it. I could not conceive how so heavy, so material, an animal as the elephant, could furnish a dish so fine and delicate, and I devoured without bread, my elephant's foot, while my Hottentots, seated around me, regaled themselves with other parts which they found equally delicious."

The Romans never evinced fondness for the flesh of the elephant. This animal, with its gigantic proportions and rare intelligence, was found to be so amusing to the nation of kings, when dancing on the tightrope, or in the terrible combats of the circus, that they hardly thought of roasting it, or making it into fricassees. We cannot, however, affirm that the gastronomic eccentricity of some Roman epicure did not dream of a monstrous feast in which he may have offered to his guests an elephant *à la Troyenne* on a silver dish made purposely for the occasion!

Heliogabalus, who understood good living, contented himself with the brains of ostriches. Six hundred of these animals furnished enough for one meal. The devastation was great, but the Emperor had made a good supper.

The red mullet, which is still much esteemed, was considered one of the most delicate of dishes, and the Romans in fashionable circles employed it in a refinement of pleasure of a singular kind. It is well known that this fish, when the scales are removed, still remains of a fine pink color. The fops of Rome having remarked that at the death this color passed through a succession of the most beautiful shades, the poor mullet was served alive, inclosed in a glass vessel; and the guests, attentive, and greedy of emotions, enjoyed this cruel spectacle which presented to them a gradation of colors which insensibly disappeared.

Crassus, who displayed so little tenderness towards his servants, had an extraordinary weakness concerning his fine sea-eels. He passed his life beside the superb fishpond where he lovingly fattened them from his own hand. Ornamented with necklaces of the finest pearls, and earrings of precious stones, all, at a signal, swam towards him; several fearlessly took the food he offered them; and some allowed their master to caress them without seeking to bite or avoid him. It was a much more exciting spectacle to witness a swarm of sea-eels tearing to pieces an awkward or rebellious slave; besides, it greatly improved the fish. The atrocious Vedius Pollio, who understood these matters, never failed to have sea-eels served him after their odious repast, that he might have the pleasure of eating some part of the body of his victim.

Unappreciated Trifles

from Our Viands

by A. W. Buckland

'Necessity knows no law,' says the proverb, and starvation will cause people to eat anything, but nothing short of that would induce the average English man or woman to partake of some of the dishes which foreigners relish. There are, however, some who are ready to experiment upon anything and everything presented to them in the shape of food. The late Dr. Buckland made soup of the bones of extinct animals, and his son, Mr. Frank Buckland, tasted every animal he could get at from the Zoo, and induced some of the members of the Zoological Society to join him in his 'feast of reason,' although it is doubtful whether the 'flow of soul' was quite up to that which would have followed a feast of turtle, oysters, etc., followed by mutton, beef, and game. And yet there seems no reason why turtle should occupy the proud position it enjoys, while we reject the land tortoise, its near relation, and why oysters should be prized and snails rejected.

In eating and drinking there is a great deal of fashion and prejudice. We know that during the siege of Paris the Parisians were reduced to the necessity of eating all the animals in the Jardin des Plantes, as well as 'rats and mice and such small deer,' and since then they have retained a fondness for horseflesh, to which we have never yet attained, although, as we know, it has been eaten from time immemorial by the Tartars; whilst hunters in Africa, as well as natives, highly appreciate the meat of the zebra or quagga, and that of the donkey is said to be superior to both; but, if placed upon the London market, in all probability all three of these kindred meats would be allowed to rot unpurchased. In like manner the porcupine is esteemed a delicacy in South Africa, but its next-of-kin here, the hedgehog, is only eaten by gipsies. The eel, and even the great conger, is eaten with relish; but the snake, which is said to be good and wholesome, is regarded with horror and loathing by men rendered squeamish by civilisation.

The lordly elephant is made to contribute his quota of food to his pursuers, the foot being the tit-bit; but the lion and tiger, being carnivorous, are not appreciated by civilized man any more than the shark, the eagle, the vulture, and many other birds of the air, beasts of the earth, and fishes of the great sea, which are greedily devoured by savages. Even the hyena is eaten by the Bushmen, although it is so hated by them that every one passing the carcase gives it a blow with a whip or stick.

The whale and the seal are highly appreciated by the Greenlanders and Eskimos, although hunger alone would cause them to be relished by ourselves. Yet a whale or a good fat seal would have saved the lives of many an Arctic voyager, and the eagerness with which Greely and his starving followers hunted foxes and the great Polar bears, shows how hunger will whet the appetite. . . .

When, however, we turn to countries where food is plentiful, we are surprised at the singularities of taste in the choice of viands. Take, for instance, China, with its fatted dogs, its bird-nest soup, and trepang, all of which seem to us disgusting, yet doubtless had we been bred in China we should have esteemed them delicacies, as the Chinese do. There is no reason why dogs should not be good eating when well and carefully fed; but we from time immemorial have made of them such pets and companions that to eat them would seem like cannibalism. As to the birds' nests, they are of a peculiar kind, made of a gelatinous substance, and might probably be esteemed a delicacy by ourselves, were they not too scarce for export. Rats and mice are also relished by the Celestials, and in the account of the astonishing escape from death of some entombed miners in America, we read that they managed to preserve life by catching and eating the rats which came to prey upon them. This was, of course, a case of dire necessity; but an African traveler tells of a little Bushman, who picked up the mice which had been caught, and after putting them in the hot ashes for a few moments, devoured them greedily half-raw, entrails and all.

There is no one in England so poor as to eat these rodents willingly, but we remember hearing a French gentleman relate how, during the siege of Paris, he and his companions were attracted by a savory smell in a restaurant, and determined *coûte qui coûte* to satisfy their hunger with the appetizing delicacy. Upon paying a good round sum they secured the dish, and learnt with surprise that they had partaken of a ragout of rats. This was, of course, an exceptional dish; but the French habitually indulge in some viands which we despise, as, for instance, frogs. Of these, the hind legs only are taken, skinned, and claws twisted together. In this form they resemble delicate little lamb cutlets, and are, as we can testify, extremely palatable. Then, all along the sea coasts of France and Italy may be seen the octopus occupying a place in the fishermen's baskets, and often boiled in cauldrons of oil in the streets, and taken out to be offered for sale to the passerby, always with the recommendation, 'It is good, very good'; and, indeed, it smells good, and is said to enter largely into the savory soups at the hotels.

Again, in the south of France and Italy you see people eating with relish the sea urchin, brought to table, like oysters, in the shell, and scooped out with a spoon. Having purchased some of these to bring home as curiosities, I could not induce the natives to believe I did not want to eat them, so they invariably cut and trimmed them for table, thus spoiling them as specimens. . . .

We have left to the last a favorite French and Italian dish, namely snails—in French escargots—which several writers have lately been advocating both as food and medicine. It would seem from these articles that snails and slugs are still sought and eaten in some parts of Wiltshire, being in season only when dormant during the winter, when they are taken, soaked in salt and water, and grilled on the bars of the grate. Probably they are quite as good as the periwinkle, so greedily devoured by those who would look upon the snail with disgust, and who would reject a dish of spring cabbage because a careless cook had allowed a slug to remain ensconced in the leaf upon which it had been feeding when consigned to the pot. . . .

Much has been written of late in recommendation of insect food, including caterpillars, cockchafers, ants, and even spiders and wire-worms. (Kirby and Spence tell us that spiders are eaten by Bushmen and the inhabitants of New Caledonia; and Reaumur relates that a young lady cracked and ate every spider she came across. Anna Maria Schurman ate them like nuts. Lalande, the astronomer, was equally fond of them; and a German, immortalized by Rosel, used to spread them on his bread like butter.) Locusts are certainly much relished in those countries which are subject to their depredations, and we have seen boys in Germany greedily devour the cockchafer alive, first depriving it of its legs and wings, and declaring it was just like a nut. Fried white ants are also highly esteemed in some countries, and the grubs of bees are relished even by Englishmen, but we think some considerable time must elapse before we adopt of free will the articles of diet of which we have been writing. . . .

Nevertheless, our forefathers were certainly less squeamish than we are; they ate the queerest conglomerations, and seasoned their dishes with ambergris and other strange sauces, nor has the taste for odd combinations quite died out from among us, as witness the Scotch haggis and the Cornish pasties, for which a writer in the *Western Antiquary*, quoted the Cornish saying that 'the devil will not venture into Cornwall for fear of being put in a pie.'

The Spanish *olla podrida* seems nearly related to these Cornish pasties. . . .

All these things are, however, as nothing to some of the dainties enjoyed by the old Romans, who not only feasted upon snails, and the maggots found in old timber, but thought

'A lamb's fat paunch was a delicious treat,'

and revelled upon water rats and stewed sow's teats, which Martial says were prepared by a certain cook with so much art as to appear still full of milk, and upon sucking puppies, which Pliny declared were worthy of being served at a supper for the gods.

Then there were dormouse sausages, of which a quaint writer remarks: 'Petronius delivers us an odd receipt for dressing 'em and serving 'em up with Poppies and Honey, which must be a very Soporiferous Dainty, and as good as Owl Pye to such as want a Nap after Dinner.' ('The Art of Cookery,' by the author of 'A Journey to London.')

After such an account of the dainties indulged in by the highly civilized masters of the world, we need not feel any disgust at the taste of the Chinese and Red Indians for dog's flesh, or of the poor Australian savages, who regale themselves upon the larvae of beetles found in decaying timber, that from the acacia tree being, says Lumholtz, of excellent flavor, in size the thickness of a finger, and glittering white, the taste resembling nuts. . . .

It would seem that nothing in the way of food comes amiss to savages; but they do not, as a rule, eat their meat raw. The iguana and its eggs are considered delicacies by the Australians, and so are snakes, which they will hunt fearlessly. Some tribes eat even the poisonous kinds, but others content themselves with the non-poisonous, of which the python, being often twenty feet long, makes a splendid meal. . . .

In Soyer's 'History of Food' we are given the menu of a Roman supper which is worth transcribing: 'First course—Sea hedgehogs, raw oysters, all sorts of shell fish and asparagus. Second course—A fatted pullet, a fresh dish of oysters and other shell fish, different kinds of dates, univalve shell fish, as whelks, conchs, etc., more oysters of different kinds, sea nettles, beccaficos, chines of roebuck and wild boar, fowls covered with a perfumed paste, a second dish of shell fish and purples (a very costly crustacean). Third course—A wild boar's head, fish, a second set of *hors d'oeuvres,* chicks, potted river-fish, leverets, roast fowls, and cakes from the marshes of Ancona.'

Here we see several curious combinations, many of the favorite dishes of modern times mixed with others which would now be relished only by Chinese, such as sea hedgehogs (which, however, are still eaten in Italy), sea nettles, whelks, conchs, and fowls covered with perfumed paste, reminding one of the ambergris and rose water so much used in the last century. After all, we are constrained to see that the tastes of civilized man do not vary much from those of the savage, and that the unappreciated trifles of today were highly esteemed by those who, in former ages, were regarded as the most fastidious of epicures.

Cannibalism

from The Glorious Oyster
by Hector Bolitho

WHEN I WAS almost sixteen, I went to live on an island, in a little hotel where the food was stodgy and dull. It was a romantic island, and about a mile inland there was a place where the Maoris used to eat each other, before our ancestors arrived to cure them of their primitive habits. Even these poor cannibals had more imagination in preparing their food than the people in the hotel. There is a pleasant record of the cooking of a cannibal feast, which I shall include in this chapter to prove my point. The writer was Barnet Burns, master of a schooner which traded between New South Wales and New Zealand. He tired of the sea, went on shore and married a chief's daughter. He was present at the cooking of a Maori woman when—

"She was ordered to prepare some potatoes for cooking with herself, and to gather green leaves for the oven. The savage made a large earth stove, laid the leaves on the hot stones, tied both her legs together. When this was done, she took a friendly leave of two or three persons that she knew, and then threw herself down on the leaves. . . . They laid potatoes over her, and covered her with earth until she was cooked fit for eating."

In the cannibal banqueting hall upon my island people still found pieces of human bone, which were kept as souvenirs of the great feasts which took place, before the advent of the white man. Froude stayed on this island when he was gathering material for "Oceana." He, too, saw this cannibal banqueting hall like the horrid shade of some Druid's grove . . . Here, at the beginning of this century, the Maori pirates of the island had held their festivals. To this place they had brought their prisoners; here they had slain them and hung their carcasses on these branches to be cut and sliced for spit or cauldron . . . I could fancy that I saw the smoking fires, the hideous preparations, the dusky groups of savage warriors. I could hear the shrieks of the victims echoing through the hollows of the forest. We ourselves picked up relics of the old scenes, stone knives and chisels and axeheads. . ."

Sam Weller's Weal Pie

from Pickwick Papers

by Charles Dickens

"WEAL PIE," said Mr. Weller, soliloquizing, as he arranged the eatables on the grass. "Wery good is weal pie, when you know the lady as made it, and is quite sure it ain't kittens; and arter all, though, where's the odds, when they're so like weal that the wery piemen themselves don't know the difference?"

"Don't they, Sam?" said Mr. Pickwick.

"Not they, sir," replied Mr. Weller, touching his hat. "I lodged in the same house with a pieman once, sir, and a wery nice man he was—reg'lar clever chap, too—make pies out o' anything, he could. 'What a number o' cats you keep, Mr. Brooks,' says I, when I'd got intimate with him. 'Ah,' says he, 'I do—a good many,' says he. 'You must be wery fond o' cats,' says I. 'Other people is,' says he, winkin' at me; 'they an't in season till the winter though,' says he. 'Not in season!' says I. 'No,' says he, 'fruits is in, cats is out.' 'Why, what do you mean?' says I. 'Mean?' says he. 'That I'll never be a party to the combination o' the butchers, to keep up the prices o' meat,' says he. 'Mr. Weller,' says he, a squeezing my hand wery hard, and vispering in my ear—'don't mention this here ain—but it's the seasonin' as does it. They're all made o' them noble animals,' says he, a pointin' to a wery nice little tabby kitten, 'and I seasons 'em for beef-steak, weal, or kidney, 'cordin' to the demand. And more than that,' says he, 'can make a weal a beef-steak, or a beef-steak a kidney, or any one on 'em a mutton, at a minute's notice, just as the market changes, and appetites wary!' "

"He must have been a very ingenious young man, that, Sam," said Mr. Pickwick, with a slight shudder.

"Just was, sir," replied Mr. Weller, continuing his occupation of emptying the basket, "and the pies was beautiful."

A little before our times, a goose was wont to be brought to the table of the King of Arragon, that was roasted alive, as I have heard by old men of credit.

—Baptista Porta's *Natural Magick*

At last I discovered, with some joy, a pig at the lower end of the table, and begged a gentleman that was near to cut me a piece of it. Upon which the gentleman of the house said with real civility, "I am sure you will like the pig, for it was whipt to death."

—Addison's No. 148, *The Tatler*

Horse, Mule and Donkey Banquet

from The Book of Menus

by Fin-Bec

April 3, 1875

GRAND HOTEL, PARIS

MENU

Potage

Le Consommé aux Trois Animaux Diffamés.

Hors d'Oeuvre

Les Saucissons de Cheval aux Piments des Anglais.

Relevés

Le Turbot à la sauce algérienne.
Le Filet de Cheval Borâk rôti à l'Orientale.
L'Aloyau de Coursier à la Phébus.

Entrées

Les Langues de Cheval, de Mulet, et d'Ane à la Cosaque.
Le Fricandeau d'Oreilles d'Ane braisé.
Le Filet de Mulet à la Gelée Obstinée.

Rôt

Poulardes truffées.
Salade à l'Huile Chevaline.

Entremets

Les Cèpes sautés à l'Entente Cordiale.
Les Asperges en branches à la sauce présidente.
Les Sylphides à la Reine des Fleurs.
Les Croûtes Triomphales.

Glaces

Longchamps.—Pons Asinorum.—Chantilly.
Les Sorbets aux Grands Mulets du Mont Blanc.

Dessert Assorti

Vins.

Haute-Sauterne.—Pomard.—Saint-Émillion.—Médoc vieux en carafe.—Champagne frappé.—Madère.

Voisin's During the Siege of Paris (1870-71)

from César Ritz

by Marie Louise Ritz

FOR A TIME—probably for much longer than any other Paris restaurant—Voisin's stood out against the newest culinary innovations. But in December beef was unprocurable, horse meat was growing scarce, and well-dressed bourgeois citizens were glad to join the queues of people outside groceries where a few tinned foods might still be found. The business of preserving foods was given quite an impetus by the Franco-German war, when more than one French town suffered a prolonged siege and the mortality from malnutrition exceeded the mortality from wounds in battle. Escoffier told me that his experience in Metz, where he was *chef de cuisine* at General Headquarters, gave him the first idea of the possibility and of the dire necessity the world had for tinned foods. And he was the first great chef to study seriously the preservation of meats, vegetables, and sauces and to manufacture them in quantities. Only the other day an Englishman who had lived many years in India told me, "Thanks to Escoffier's tinned and bottled foods, I was able for many years to enjoy good French cooking in the wilds." Tinned foods now became a rare and much appreciated luxury.

Rats were being sold openly in the market for from one franc to one franc fifty, depending upon their size. Ragout of rabbit and saddle of lamb still figured on restaurant menus, but stray cats and dogs had become mysteriously rare! Roast donkey was a gourmet's luxury. The small lake in the Luxembourg Gardens had been dragged for tiny fish. The banks of the Seine were crowded with earnest fishermen, in respectable bourgeois black, in army red, in workmen's blouses. And one by one the animals in the Jardin des Plantes were killed. . . .

Both Escoffier and Ritz used to torment me with descriptions of the food they had eaten at this time. In Metz the cavalry horses had eventually all been slaughtered and before the end of the siege there even the teams for heavy artillery had been sacrificed. "Horse meat," thus Escoffier would hold forth, his eyes twinkling, "is delicious, when you are in the right condition to appreciate it!" "A little sweet, perhaps," César would add. "I found, too, that it is hard to digest. But cat-meat! Now, there is a gourmet's dish! The best ragout of rabbit I ever ate was made of alley-cat." "And as to rat-meat, it approaches in delicacy the taste of roast pig!" "But you should taste a stew of elephant trunk! A little oily—but with marvelous flavor—" Etc., etc., until they saw I could stand no more!

Bellenger [the proprietor] stood out as long as possible, then he had to capitulate. One day he had a consultation with the chef, and the following menu was the result—the first of a long series of such menus:

Purée de lentilles
Sardines à l'huile
Vol-au-vent
Selle d'Epagneul
Haricots blancs et rouges
Oranges

The chef complained most bitterly of the lack of butter, coco-butter being but a poor substitute in cooking for the real thing. The clients did not worry about such details, but they did, for the most part, object to the saddle of spaniel. But according to César, the worst feature of the menu was the quite rightly anonymous *vol-au-vent*.

Before the siege was over, the chef had an opportunity to prepare more exotic dishes. Castor and Pollux, the two elephants of the Zoo, were killed and their carcasses fetched good prices. The trunks were considered tidbits, and the price for them was accordingly high. Bellenger put in a supply of elephant; and Voisin's soon became famous for its "elephant trunk, *sauce chasseur,*" and elephant blood-pudding was pronounced by people of cultivated taste to be most excellent.

But happier days came to Voisin's, and eventually to César Ritz's Parisian emporium of gastronomy, which was capable of producing the kind of perfect dining described herewith. It was only a small dinner, but the meal Ritz produced was memorable.

There were ten guests, all men, all world-known financiers, German, French, and Belgian. The host consulted with Rey, with Olivier, with Gimon. "Money doesn't count," he said to Rey. "I only want you to see that the food and wine are perfect, regardless of cost. Here's a little to go on with." And the great financier produced ten crisp one-thousand-franc notes! The ten thousand francs were, as it turned out, not enough to cover the costs, and before the day arrived Rey asked for and received a couple of thousand more.

Here is the menu that was finally decided upon:

Consommé de Faisan en Tasse
Mousseline de Sole Empire
Cassolette de Queues d'Ecrevisses
Escalope de Foi gras au Beurre noisette
Velouté de Petits Pois frais
Carré de Veau braisé à la crême
Pommes de Terre Anna
Pointes d'Asperges
Sorbets au Montrachet
Bécasses au Fumet
Salade de Laitue
Truffes en Papillotes
Mandarines de Nice givrées
Friandises
Les plus beaux Fruits de France

Now, that is a good menu, it is even an excellent menu, and Rey, Olivier, and Gimon are to be complimented upon its composition. Fresh peas and asparagus in December, and truffles and woodcock at any time, are apt to be expensive. But why should this dinner, no matter how exquisitely prepared, cost more than one thousand francs per person? Ah, but I have not yet mentioned the wines. The host, a famous connoisseur, knew the type of wine which he wished to be served with each course—as did Rey. And he insisted that Rey should furnish from the Ritz cellars or elsewhere just the right wines, vintage wines all of them, and of the best years.

Here is the list of wines which were served, in their correct order:

Sherry Carta Oro Viejo
Meursault Goutte d'Or 1915
Magnum de Château Léonville Barton 1878
Jeroboam de Château Lafitte 1870
Pommery 1911
Grand Chambertin 1906
Romanée 1881
Giesler 1906
Château Yquem 1869
Cognac Hennessy (Réservée Privée)

To procure these wines was not in every case easy. The Jeroboam of Château Lafitte 1870 and the Château Yquem 1869 had to be brought specially from Bordeaux by messenger! The messenger sat up all night with his precious package, never let it leave his hand for a moment, was careful to see that it received the minimum of shock in movement. Both messenger and wine were heavily insured, and their arrival was awaited with much tenseness on the part of all concerned. As to the Romanée 1881, that was "found" by Rey in the private cellars of a princely friend. The Château Yquem, served with the dessert, tasted, Rey assures me, "like flowers."

The liqueur, Cognac Hennessy, from our private stock, and of which there is still a small supply in our cellars, was entirely worthy of the wines that had preceded it. Guyot, our present chief cellarer, who is young, but who knows his métier if anyone does (this would amaze Julian Street, who maintained in one of his books that "a *sommelier* must be grey-haired"), assures me that it is "priceless." Three-star Hennessy, bearing no date whatever, not cobwebbed in the least—our cellarmen scorn factitious spiderwebs—yet is wondrous old and wondrous good, and could follow, with no loss of dignity, a list of wines which is almost incomparable.

If the assembling of these wines had caused trouble, their serving did likewise. Aside from the business of bringing them all to the exact, the absolutely exact temperatures required, there was the business of the glasses. Not the finding of the correct shapes and sizes or the perfect thinness and fragility, for our glasses were designed with care and beautifully made by Baccarat; but with such wines with which to fill them, Rey took especial pains that they should be polished to an unheard-of degree. And he personally supervised their washing, adding lemon to the water in which they were rinsed.

At last the tables were set, the waiters held themselves ready, and Rey took one last look to see that all was well. He had emphasized the importance of keeping the glasses in their polished state, and a waiter, in an agony of zeal, had—oh, tragedy!—covered them lightly with clean table-napkins. Rey lifted a glass towards his nose. Horrors! There was a smell—a faint smell, but still, enough!—of fresh laundry! Back to the kitchens went those glasses, to be washed, rinsed, and polished anew. This at the last minute.

Well, the dinner was a success. The guests sat down to it at half past eight, and coffee was not served until eleven o'clock! When Rey saw that the guests intended to sit long over their coffee, liqueurs and cigars—and I wonder what momentous conversation? —he skillfully had arm-chairs substituted for the chairs. The guests continued to sit in comfort. And the party did not break up until two o'clock in the morning.

But as a test of the perfection of that menu, the superb quality of the food and wine, Rey always adds when he recites the epic story of this dinner: "And none of the guests felt in the least indisposed on the following morning." The host, in fact, telephoned next day to each of his guests, and put to them the same questions: Had they slept well? Were they feeling well? And the report in each case was favorable.

Are such efforts worth while to achieve so transient a work of art as a dinner? The host and the guests in this case, all connoisseurs, all gourmets, apparently thought so. Rey, Olivier, and Gimon still think so. Our chief cellarer, Guyot, who presides over his domains with the zeal of a priest guarding sacred altars, thinks so, and thinks so passionately.

Gulliver Dines

from A Voyage to Lilliput

by Jonathan Swift

Being almost famished with hunger, having not eaten a morsel for some hours before I left the ship, I found the demands of nature so strong upon me, that I could not forbear shewing my impatience (perhaps against the strict rules of decency) by putting my finger frequently to my mouth, to signify that I wanted food. The Hurgo (for so they call a great lord, as I afterwards learnt) understood me very well. He descended from the stage, and commanded that several ladders should be applied to my sides, on which above an hundred of the inhabitants mounted, and walked towards my mouth, laden with baskets full of meat, which had been provided and sent thither by the king's orders, upon the first intelligence he received of me. I observed there was the flesh of several animals, but could not distinguish them by the taste.There were shoulders, legs, and loins, shaped like those of mutton, and very well dressed, but smaller than the wings of a lark. I eat them by two or three at a mouthful, and took three loaves at a time, about the bigness of musket bullets. They supplied me as they could, shewing a thousand marks of wonder and astonishment at my bulk and appetite. I then made another sign that I wanted drink. They found by my eating, that a small quantity would not suffice me, and being a most ingenious people, they flung up with great dexterity one of their largest hogsheads, then rolled it towards my hand, and beat out the top; I drank it off at a draught, which I might well do, for it did not hold half a pint, and tasted like a small wine of Burgundy, but much more delicious. They brought me a second hogshead, which I drank in the same manner, and made signs for more; but they had none to give me. When I had performed these wonders, they shouted for joy, and danced upon my breast, repeating several times as they did at first, *Hekinah degul. . . .*

I had three hundred cooks to dress my victuals, in little convenient huts built about my house, where they and their families lived, and prepared me two dishes apiece. I took up twenty waiters in my hand, placed them on the table, an hundred more attended below on the ground, some with dishes of meat, and some with barrels of wine and other liquors, slung on their shoulders, all of which the waiters above drew up as I wanted, in a very ingenious manner, by certain cords, as we draw the bucket up a well in Europe. A dish of their meat was good mouthful, and a barrel of their liquor a reasonable draught. Their mutton yields to ours, but their beef is excellent. I have had a surloin so large, that I have been forced to make three bites of it; but this is rare. My servants were astonished to see me eat it bones and all, as in our country we do the leg of a lark. Their geese and turkeys I usually eat at a mouthful; and, I must confess, they far exceed ours. Of their smaller fowl, I could take up twenty or thirty at the end of my knife.

(*from* A Voyage to Brobdingnag)

It was about twelve at noon, and a servant brought in dinner. It was only one substantial dish of meat (fit for the plain condition of an husbandman), in a dish of about four and twenty feet diameter. The company were the farmer and his wife, three children, and an old grandmother. When they were set down, the farmer placed me at some distance from him on the table, which was thirty feet high from the floor. I was in a terrible fright, and kept as far as I could from the edge, for fear of falling. The wife minced a bit of meat, then crumbled some bread on a trencher, and placed it before me. I made her a low bow, took out my knife and fork, and fell to eat, which gave them exceeding delight. The mistress sent her maids for a small dram cup, which held about two gallons, and filled it with drink; I took up the vessel with much difficulty in both hands, and, in a most respectful manner, drank to her ladyship's health, expressing the words as loud as I could in English, which made the company laugh so heartily that I was almost deafened with the noise. This liquor tasted like a small cyder, and was not unpleasant. Then the master made me a sign to come to his trencher-side; but as I walked on the table, being in great surprise all the time, as the indulgent reader will easily conceive and excuse, I happened to stumble against a crust, and fell flat on my face, but received no hurt. I got up immediately, and observing the good people to be in much concern, I took my hat (which I held under my arm out of good manners) and, waving it over my head, made three huzzas, to show I had got no mischief by my fall. . . .

The queen became so fond of my company that she could not dine without me. I had a table placed upon the same at which Her Majesty ate, just at her left elbow, and a chair to sit on. Glumdalclitch stood on a stool on the floor, near my table, to assist and take care of me. I had an entire set of silver dishes and plates, and other necessaries which, in proportion to those of the queen's, were not much bigger than what I have seen of the same kind in a London toy-shop for the furniture of a baby-house. These my little nurse kept in her pocket in a silver box, and gave me at meals as I wanted them, always cleaning them herself. No person dined with the queen but the two princesses royal, the elder sixteen years old, and the younger at that time thirteen and a month. Her Majesty used to put a bit of meat upon one of my dishes out of which I carved for myself; and her diversion was to see me eat in miniature. For the queen (who had, indeed, but a weak stomach) took up at one mouthful as much as a dozen English farmers could eat at a meal, which, to me, was for some time a very nauseous sight. She would crunch the wing of a lark, bones and all, between her teeth, although it were nine times as large as that of a full-grown turkey; and put a bit of bread into her mouth as big as two twelve-penny loaves. She drank out of a golden cup, above a hogshead at a draught. Her knives were twice as long as a scythe, set straight upon the handle. The spoons, forks, and other instruments were all in the same proportion. I remember, when Glumdalclitch carried me out of curiosity to see some of the tables at court, where ten or a dozen of these enormous knives and forks were lifted up together, I thought I had never, till then, beheld so terrible a sight.

(*from* A Voyage to the Land of the Houyhnhnms)

The sorrel nag offered me a root, which he held (after their manner, as we shall describe in its proper place) between his hoof and pastern; I took it in my hand, and, having smelt it, returned it to him again as civilly as I could. He brought out of the Yahoo's kennel a piece of ass's flesh, but it smelt so offensively that I turned from it with loathing; he then threw it to the Yahoo, by whom it was greedily devoured. He afterwards shewed me a wisp of hay, a fetlock full of oats; but I shook my head, to signify that neither of these were food for me. And, indeed, I now apprehended that I must absolutely starve, if I did not get to some of my own species: for as to those filthy Yahoos, although there were few greater lovers of mankind, at that time, than myself, yet, I confess I never saw any sensitive being so destestable on all accounts, and the more I came near them, the more hateful they grew, while I stayed in that country. This the master horse observed by my behavior, and therefore sent the Yahoo back to his kennel. He then put his fore-hoof to his mouth, at which I was much surprised, although he did it with ease, and with a motion that appeared perfectly natural; and made other signs to know what I would eat; but I could not return him such an answer as he was able to apprehend; and, if he had understood me, I did not see how it was possible to contrive any way for finding myself nourishment. While we were thus engaged, I observed a cow passing by, whereupon I pointed to her, and expressed a desire to let me go and milk her. This had its effect; for he led me back into the house, and ordered a mare servant to open a room, where a good store of milk lay in earthen and wooden vessels, after a very orderly and cleanly manner. She gave me a large bowl full, of which I drank very heartily and found myself well refreshed.

About noon, I saw coming towards the house a kind of vehicle, drawn, like a sledge, by four Yahoos. There was in it an old steed, who seemed to be of quality; he alighted with his hind feet forward, having, by accident, got a hurt in his fore-foot. He came to dine with our horse, who received him with great civility. They dined in the best room and had oats boiled in milk for the second course, which the old horse eat warm, but the rest cold. Their mangers were placed circular in the middle of the room, and divided into several partitions, round which they sat on their haunches upon bosses of straw. In the middle was a large rack, with angles answering to every partition of the manger; so that each horse and mare ate their own hay, and their own mash of oats and milk, with much decency and regularity. The behavior of the young colt and foal appeared very modest; and that of the master and mistress extremely cheerful and complaisant to their guest. The grey ordered me to stand by him; and much discourse passed between him and his friend concerning me, as I found by the stranger's often looking on me, and the frequent repetition of the word Yahoo. . . .

When dinner was done, the master horse took me aside, and by signs and words, made me understand the concern that he was in, that I had nothing to eat. Oats, in their tongue, are called hluunh. This word I pronounced two or three times; for although I had refused them at first, yet, upon second thoughts, I considered that I could contrive to make of them a kind of bread, which might be sufficient, with milk, to keep me alive, till I could make my escape to some other country, and to creatures of my own species. The horse immediately ordered a white mare servant, of his family, to bring me a good quantity of oats on a sort of wooden tray. These I heated before the fire, as well as I could, and rubbed them till the husks came off, which I made a shift to winnow from the grain; I ground and beat them between two stones, then took water, and made them into a paste or cake, which I toasted at the fire, and ate warm with milk. It was at first a very insipid diet, though common enough in many parts of Europe, but grew tolerable by time; and, having been often reduced to hard fare in my life, this was not the first experiment I had made, how easily nature is satisfied. And I cannot but observe, that I never had one hour's sickness while I stayed in this island. It is true, I sometimes made a shift to catch a rabbit, or bird, by springs made of Yahoo's hairs; and I often gathered wholesome herbs, which I boiled, or eat as salads with my bread; and now and then for a rarity I made a little butter and drank the whey. I was first at a great loss for salt; but custom soon reconciled the want of it; and I am confident that the frequent use of salt among us is an effect of luxury, and was first introduced only as a provocative to drink; except where it is necessary for preserving of flesh in long voyages, or in places remote from great markets. For we observe no animal to be fond of it but man: and as to myself, when I left this country, it was a great while before I could endure the taste of it in anything that I ate.

PART 5

LIFE WITH THE CHEFS

Chapter Eighteen

SIX MASTER CHEFS

THOSE PRINCES of the kitchen, the great chefs, are well known to us and yet they are not. Most moderately knowledgeable people know of Escoffier, of Brillat-Savarin, and perhaps two or three other masters, but in scant detail. Of Carême, who may be the greatest of them all, they know little if anything. It is hardly surprising. Except to a few gourmets, the personalities of the chefs are of far less interest than the food they produce, although the flavor of one may be as distinctive as the other.

We hope to make a beginning of correcting this neglect, or at the least to throw a few random shafts into some relatively dark corners, in the eight sketches offered here. It is instructive, for example, to begin with the superb Carême and view him from three angles: the authoritative eyes of Alexandre Dumas, the somewhat eccentric gaze of Fin-Bec, and the solid nineteenth century spectacles of Dr. John Doran.

Those who followed in Carême's soup spoons may not have been as distinguished, but they are worth saving from oblivion, as George H. Ellwanger, an early twentieth century food historian, shows us in his brief history, "From Carême to Dumas."

Then our (by now) old friend Abraham Hayward discourses on the famed Brillat-Savarin, which is at least a change from hearing Brillat-Savarin discourse on himself, and adds some notes on two little known masters, Ude and Francatelli.

We suppose there will be some objectors to the inclusion of Mme. de Sévigné's account of Vatel's suicide, on the ground that it is thrice familiar to students of literature as well as to gourmets. Admitting, without the least shame, that it may be the best known anecdote in the literature of food, we have included it anyway, on the ground that if anyone has missed the story, he should not die without reading it.

Concluding, there is a short and authoritative history of Escoffier by Craig Claiborne, who is food editor of the New York *Times*.

Life of Carême

from Grand Dictionnaire de Cuisine

by Alexandre Dumas
(translated by Louis Colman)

CARÊME, MARIE-ANTOINE. This is a name that certainly did not seem predestined to acquire the gastronomic fame it now has. Since the death of Carême on January 12, 1833, many princes have lost their principalities and many kings have fallen from their thrones. Carême, by his genius of cookery, has stood up, and no rival has obscured his glory. Like Theseus and Romulus, like all founders of empires, Carême was a sort of lost child. He was born in Paris in 1784, in a woodyard where his father was employed. There were fifteen children, and the father did not know how to feed them all.

One day, when Marie-Antoine was eleven years old, his father took him to the town gate for dinner. Then, leaving him in the middle of the street, he said to him: "Go, little one. There are good trades in this world. Let the rest of us languish in the misery in which we are doomed to die. This is a time when fortunes are made by those who have the wit, and that you have. Tonight or tomorrow, find a good house that may open its doors to you. Go with what God has given you and what I may add to that." And the good man gave him his blessing.

From that time on, Marie-Antoine never again saw his father and mother, who died young, nor his brothers and sisters, who were scattered over the world.

Night fell. The boy saw a lighted window and knocked on it. It was a cookshop whose proprietor's name has not been preserved in history. He took in the boy and put him to work next day.

At sixteen, he quit this dingy tavern and went to work as assistant to a restaurateur. His progress was rapid, and he already knew what he wanted to be. He went to work for Bailly, a famous pastry-cook on the Rue Vivienne, who excelled in cream tarts and catered to the Prince de Talleyrand. From that moment he saw his future clearly. He had discovered his vocation.

"At seventeen," he says in his *Memoirs*, "I was chief pastrycook at Bailly's. He was a good master and took an interest in me. He gave me time off to study designs from prints. He put me in charge of preparing several set pieces for the table of the First Consul. I used my designs and my nights in his service, and he repaid me with kindness. In his establishment I began to innovate. The illustrious pastrycook Avice was then flourishing. His work aroused my enthusiasm, and knowledge of his methods gave me courage. I sought to follow without imitating him. I learned to execute every trick of my trade, and made unique, extraordinary pieces by myself. But to get there, young people, how many sleepless nights! I could not work on my designs and calculations until after nine or ten o'clock, and I worked three quarters of the night.

"I left M. Bailly with tears in my eyes and went to work for the successor of M. Gendron. I made it a condition that if I had opportunity to make an 'extra' I could have someone replace me. A few months later, I left the great pastryshops behind altogether, and devoted myself to preparing great dinners. It was enough to do. I rose higher and higher and earned a lot of money. Others became jealous of me, a poor child of labor, and I have often been the butt of attacks from little pastrycooks who will have far to climb to where I am now."

During the prodigality of the Directoire, Carême refined cooking into the delicate luxury and exquisite sensuality of the Empire. The Talleyrand household was served with wisdom and grandeur, Carême says. It gave an example to others and kept them in mind of basic principles.

The culinary director in his household was Bouche, or Boucheseche, who came from the Condé household, famous for its fine fare. So Talleyrand's cuisine was simply a continuation of the cuisine of the Condé household. Carême dedicated his *Patissier royal* to Bouche. It was there he made the acquaintance of Laguipiere, the Emperor's cook, who died in the retreat from Moscow. Until that time, Carême had followed his art. After Laguipiere, he learned to improvise. But practice did not satisfy him any longer. He wanted to go more profoundly into theory, to copy designs, to read and analyze scientific works and follow through with studies parallel to his profession. He wrote and illustrated a *History of the Roman Table,* but, unfortunately, both manuscript and drawings have been lost. Carême was a poet. He placed his art on the same level as all the others. And he was right to do so.

"From behind my stoves," he says, "I contemplated the cuisines of India, China, Egypt, Greece, Turkey, Italy, Germany, and Switzerland. I felt the unworthy methods of routine crumble under my blows."

Carême had grown up under the Empire, and you can imagine his distress when he saw it crash. He had to be forced to execute the gigantic royal banquet in the Plaine des Vertus in 1814. The following year, the Prince Regent called him to Brighton as his chef. He stayed with the English Regent two years. Every morning he prepared his menu with His Highness, who was a blasé gourmand. During these discussions he went through a course in gastronomic hygiene that, if printed, would be one of the classic books on Cookery.

Bored with the gray skies of England, Carême returned to Paris but went back when the Prince Regent became King. From London he went to St. Petersburg as one of the Emperor Alexander's chefs, then to Vienna to direct a few great dinners for the Austrian emperor. He returned to London with Lord Stuart, the English ambassador, but soon quit to return to Paris to write and publish. He was constantly torn from his study of theory by calls from monarchs and congresses. His work shortened his life. "The charcoal is killing us," he said, "but what does it matter? The fewer the years, the greater the glory." He died before reaching the age of fifty, on January 12, 1833.

Women can spin very well, but they cannot make a good book on Cookery.
—Dr. Johnson

The Epicure

from The Book of Menus

by Fin-Bec

CARÊME, IN HIS DAY, was deemed a necessary presence at the congresses of Aix-la-chapelle, Laybach, and Verona. Who shall say that he exercised no influence at these diplomatic gatherings? After a dinner conceived and cooked by a Carême the mind is disposed to calm judicial action; for, be it observed, the epicure abhors excess, and rises from his dinner as calm as a judge from the bench. Cooking for a congress, to whose hands the fate of nations is committed, is a solemn duty. A bad dish may twist a protocol; a tough bird may make an unyielding plenipotentiary. It was in this way that Carême, among others, understood his art, and practiced it. When he was in the service of the Prince Regent, his master observed to him one morning:—

"Carême, the dinner yesterday was succulent. I find everything you offer me delicious; but you will make me die of indigestion."

Carême replied, "Prince, my duty is to tempt, to flatter your appetite, and not to regulate it."

Such an eater as the finest gentleman in Europe was not worthy of Carême. He preferred the delicacy and moderation at table of such masters as Talleyrand and Rothschild. He was in Rothschild's house for five years, and he observed of it: "There only people know how to live! And Madame the Baroness Rothschild, who does the honors of this magnificent hospitality, deserves to be reckoned among the women who make you love to contemplate wealth, because of the charm and happiness she makes it yield to others, of the dignity of her habits, and the delicate luxury of her table."

The Epicure is the antithesis of the glutton . . . He is simply the moderate, cultivated man who knows what to eat, and how to eat it. He is an economist also, and a hater of waste. He is to be found not only in great houses or West End clubs but in very humble quarters indeed, living with refinement on some little pension, which in gross hands, would provide little better than a journeyman's fare.

I remember a gentleman of the fine old formal school, who had spoken to Napoleon, and known Louis Philippe well. He had been in Lafitte's house, and subsequently a banker on his own account in Brussels. The Revolution of 1830 ruined him, and he fled to London. He was a philosopher, and a gay one. He had the manners of an old French marquis, and they gave a grace to his threadbare coat and rusty velvet waistcoat. He lived in a narrow street by Covent Garden, and in an attic. Yet, when he received you, he did the honours of his *mansarde* with the ceremony that had become second nature to him. He was too proud a man to apologize for the more than homeliness of his surroundings. They were accidents of fortune which in no way affected the intercourse of gentlemen. They were just something to philosophize upon pleasantly, and to put in their place, which was far away from, and below the serious consideration of, a cultivated man.

But my friend looked his best—when he was cooking! He was a tall, sparse man—very like De Lamartine in the face; and he wore a black skull cap, and embroidered dressing-gown (which a marquis of historic name had given him many a long year ago), and a deep Regency stock. I have talked of Castlereagh and Talleyrand, and the bad conduct of the Duke of York (who was the ruin of my friend's father), while this stately personage has whipped eggs for his omelette; and I have known him to pause with an egg-shell in either hand, while he related a conversation that occurred between him and the Citizen King. Draining a shell, he would say:—

"As empty, sir, as the pockets of His Royal Highness the Duke of York."

And in a minute there would be the music of the omelette in the pan. Presently the omelette, golden brown, and cooked *à point*, would be upon the table. The old gentleman was great on salads, and had one, as he would relate, for a few pence, all the year round. It would be such a salad as no spendthrift was eating in Pall Mall that evening. The arrangements for coffee-making were of a learned kind. The old gentleman was for the biggin; and he would throw off very eloquent periods on the loss of aroma, the too much roasting, the misuse of chicory. He had invented a mustard, of which he was very proud: and he would carry a jar of it off with him when he dined *en ville*, and present it with many courtly phrases to his host. He dealt in as refined a manner in that Covent Garden back street as he had lived in his prosperous days when a *chef* worked for him. Yet his income was barely one hundred pounds a year.

Let it not be imagined for a moment that my venerable friend gave an undue time to the pleasures of the palate. He was a studious man. He used to frequent the great reading-room of Gliddon's divan, where he played his game of chess, and devoted his afternoons to solid reading, and to the writing of his experiences. I had arranged to help him in the preparation of his papers for publication, but death gently overtook him before the work was begun, and I could never discover where he had laid his treasures. Just enough remained to bury my friend. He had arranged it so, and he begged that his funeral should not exceed the money set aside for it by one shilling.

"His late Royal Highness," he used to say, but not bitterly, "lies in Genoa velvet, but plain cloth will do for the son of his creditor."

That noble old man was one for whom a Carême would have worked for nothing.

Sketch of Carême

from Table Traits

by Dr. John Doran

HE WAS ILLUSTRIOUS by descent; for one of his ancestors had served in the household of a Pope, who himself made more sauces than saints, Leo X. But Carême was one of so poor and so numerous a family that when he came into the world he was no more welcome than Oliver Goldsmith was: the respective parents of the little-cared-for babes did not know what future great men lay in naked helplessness before them. One wrote immortal poetry, and starved: the other made delicious pastry, and rode in a chariot! We know how much Oliver received for his "Vicar"; while Anthony Carême used to receive twice as much for merely writing out a recipe to make a "*paté*". . . .

Carême studied under various great masters, but he perfected his studies under Boucher, *chef des services* of the Prince Talleyrand. The glory of Carême was co-eval with that of Napoleon: those two individuals were great men at the same period; but the glory of one will, perhaps, be a little more enduring than that of the other. I will not say *whose* glory will thus last the longer; for as was remarked courteously by the Oxford candidate for honors, who was more courteous than "crammed," and who was asked which were the minor Prophets, "I am not willing to draw invidious distinctions!"

In the days of the Empire—the era of the greatness, of the achievements, and of the reflections of Carême,—the possession of him was as eagerly contested by the rich as that of a nymph by the satyrs. He was alternately the glory of Talleyrand, the boast of Lavalette, and the pride of the Saxon Ambassador. . . .

But Carême was capricious. It was not that he was unfaithful, but he was *volage;* and he passed from kitchen to kitchen, as the bee wings from flower to flower. The Emperor Alexander dined with Talleyrand, and forthwith he seduced Carême: the seduction money was only £100 sterling per month, and the culinary expenses. Carême did not yield without much coyness. He urged his love for study, his desire to refine the race of which he made himself the model, his love for his country; and he even accompanied, for a brief moment, "Lord Stewart" to Vienna; but it was more in the way of policy than pastry: for Count Orloff was sent after him on a mission, and Carême, after flying, with the full intention of being followed, to London and Paris, yielded to the golden solicitation, and did the Emperor Alexander the honor of becoming the head of the Imperial kitchen in whatever palace His Majesty presided. But the delicate susceptibility of Carême was wounded by discovering that his book of expenses was subjected to supervision. He flung up his appointment in disgust, and hastened across Europe to England. The jealous winds wished to detain him for France, and they blew him back on the coast between Calais and Boulogne, exactly as they did another gentleman, who may not be so widely known as Carême, but who has been heard of in England under the name of William Wordsworth. Carême accepted the omen, repaired to Paris, entered the service of the Princess Bagration, and served the table of that capricious lady, *en maître d'hôtel*. . . .

The Princess, however, ate herself into a permanent indigestion, and Carême transferred his services to the English Ambassador at the Court of Vienna. . . .

Carême, two years before George IV was King, had been for a short period a member of the Regent's household. He left Vienna to be present at the Coronation; but he arrived too late; and he does not scruple to say, very ungenerously, that the banquet was spoiled for want of his presence, nor to insinuate that the colleagues with whom he would have been associated were unworthy of such association—an insinuation at once base and baseless. After being the object of a species of semi-worship, and yielding to every new offer, yet affecting to despise them all, Carême ultimately tabernacled with Baron Rothschild in Paris; and the superhuman excellency of his dinners, is it not written in the "Book without a name" of Lady Morgan? And was not his residence there the object of envy, and cause of much melancholy, and opportunity for much eulogy, on the part of George IV? Well, Anthony Carême would have us believe as much with respect to himself and the King; but we do not believe a word of it; for the royal table was never better cared for by the royal officers, whose duty lay in such care, than at this very period. George IV is said to have tempted him by offering triple salaries; but all in vain; for London was too *triste* an abiding place for a man whose soul, out of kitchen hours, was given to study. And so Carême remained with his Jewish patron until infirmity overtook his noble nature, and he retired to dictate his immortal works (like Milton, very!) to his accomplished daughter. *Les beaux restes* of Carême were eagerly sought after; but he would not heed what was no longer a temptation; for he was realizing twenty thousand francs a year from the bookseller, besides the interest of the money he had saved. Think of it, shade of Milton!

Eight hundred pounds sterling *yearly*, for writing on kitchen-stuff! Who would compose epics after that? But Carême's books were epics after their sort, and they are highly creditable to the scribe who wrote them from his notes. Finally, even Anthony Carême died, like cooks of less degree; but he had been the imperial despot of European kitchens, had been "beringed" by monarchs, and been smiled on by Princesses; he had received Lords in his kitchens, and had encountered ladies who gave him a great deal for a very little knowledge in return; and finally, as Fulke Greville had inscribed on his tomb that he had been a friend of Sir Philip Sidney, so the crowning joy of Carême's life might have been chiseled on his monument, indicating that he had been the friend of one whom he would have accounted a greater man than the knightly hero in question—namely, *il Maestro Rossini!* Carême's cup was thereat full; and he died, perfectly convinced that paradise itself would be glad at his coming.

From Carême to Dumas

from The Pleasures of the Table

by George H. Ellwanger

AMONG THE GREAT professional cooks who were not alone notable practitioners, but who have written understandingly on the art, the names of Beauvilliers, Carême, Ude, Francatelli, Soyer, Urbain-Dubois, and Gouffé are preeminent. We have already considered the important role enacted by Beauvilliers as chef, restaurateur, and author. The unctuous name of Carême, however, is more often uttered with reverence, and even yet evokes visions of all that is most delectable in sauces and *entremets de douceur*.

Indeed, were one to wish that he might turn on Aladdin's ring and summon some genius of the range who would be most gladly welcomed, surely on Carême the choice would fall. As for the dinner one might wish to command, what better than the feast at the Chateau de Boulogne, so eloquently described by Lady Morgan, when he presided at the Baron Rothschild's villa—that dinner of an estival eventide when the landscape lay sweltering in the heat, without, but where all was deliciously cool within the vast pavilion which stood apart from the mansion in the midst of orange trees "where distillations of the most delicate viands, extracted in silver dews, chemical precision,

" 'On tepid clouds of rising steam,'

formed the base of all; where every meat presented its own natural aroma, and every vegetable its own shade of verdure; where the mayonnaise was fried in ice (like Ninon's description of Sévigné's heart); and the tempered chill of the *plombière* anticipated the stronger shock, and broke it, of the exquisite *avalanche*, which, with the hue and odor of fresh gathered nectarines, satisfied every sense and dissipated every coarser flavor."

The age of Carême was the era of quintessences—of the *cuisine classique*, when chemistry contributed new resources and fish, meats, and fowls were distilled, in order to add heightened flavors to the sauces and viands that their etherealized essences were to accentuate. One thinks of Lucullus and Apicius, and of the "exceeding odoriferous and aromatical vapour" of the ovens of the artist mentioned by Montaigne.

That success in any walk of life is the result not only of natural aptitude but of persevering application, Carême's history affords abundant proof, if such were required. Left to shift for himself when but seven years old, at fifteen he had already served his apprenticeship as a cook to advance with rapid strides in his chosen profession. Constant sobriety, which called for much self-sacrifice on his part, and an iron constitution enabled him to carry out the most arduous labors. "My ambition was serious," he states in his memoirs, "and at an early age I became desirous of elevating my profession to an art."

The better to perfect himself in its various branches, he studied for ten years under the most distinguished masters, including Robert and Laguipière. For years, also, he was a daily student at the Imperial Library and Cabinet of Engravings, perfecting himself in drawing and in the literature of his profession. He likewise made an exhaustive study of old Roman cookery, only to arrive at the conclusion that it was intrinsically bad and abominably heavy—an opinion confirmed by the Marquis de Cussy, who declared that he would rather dine at a Parisian restaurant for twenty francs than with Lucullus in the saloon of Apollo. It was Carême's habit to take notes nightly of his progress and the modifications he had made in his work during the day, thereby fixing those ideas and combinations that otherwise would have escaped his memory.

Amid the luxurious kitchens of the Empire he reigned supreme—the king of pastry-cooks and marvelous in his sauces, galantines, and inventions. Crowned heads soon became his suitors, and princes implored his services. It was Talleyrand, one of the wittiest and most epicurean princes of the Empire, who inspired him perhaps with his greatest enthusiasm, and of whom he says, "M. de Talleyrand understands the genius of a cook, he respects it, he is the most competent judge of delicate progress, and *his expenditures are wise and great at the same time.*" Of Laguipière, the chief cook of Murat, to whose talents he ascribes the elegance and eclat of the culinary art of the nineteenth century, he is unstinted in his praises. Of Beauvilliers and Carême, one fancies that the proverbial jealousy of cooks was not wanting in their case.

Carême has modified the adage *on se fait cuisinier, mais on est né rotisseur,* claiming that to become a perfect cook one must first be a distinguished pastry-maker, and citing as instances his favorite teacher Laguipière, with Robert, Lasne, Riquette, and numerous other celebrities. He speaks of the "lightness," the "grace," and the "color" of pastry; of the "order, perspicuity, and intelligence" required in its preparation. "It is easier," he says, "to cook pastry than to make it.". . .

Many anecdotes of the famous gastronomers and great personages of his time have been recounted by Carême. To Cambacérès he refers at length, disputing his claim to a distinguished place among epicures. The cuisine of the arch-chancellor, he states decisively, never merited its great reputation. This was through no fault of his chef, M. Grand 'Manche, an excellent practitioner, but was due solely to the excessive parsimony of his employer, who at each service was in the habit of noting the entrees that were untouched or scarcely touched, and of forming his *carte* for the morrow from their remains.

"Cambacérès was never a gourmand in the scientific acceptance of the word; he was naturally a great and even voracious eater. Can one believe that he preferred, above all dishes, the *paté chaud* with forcemeat balls?—a heavy, unsavory, and vulgar dish. As a *hors-d'oeuvre* he had frequently a crust of paté reheated on the grill, and had brought to table the *combien* of a ham that had done duty for the week. And his skillful cook who never had the grand fundamental sauces! neither his under-cooks or aids nor his bottle of Bordeaux! What parsimony! what a pity! what an establishment!

"Neither M. Cambacérès nor M. Brillat-Savarin knew how to eat. Both were fond of strong and vulgar things, and simply filled their stomachs. This is literally true. M. de Savarin was a large eater, and talked little and without facility, it seemed to me; he had a heavy air and resembled a parson. At the end of a repast his digestion absorbed him, and I have seen him go to sleep."

Charles Monelet has termed Savarin a mere seltzer drinker, while Dumas says he was neither a gastronomer nor a gourmet, but simply a vigorous eater. "His large size, his heavy carriage, his common appearance, with his costume ten or twelve years behind the times, caused him to be termed the drum-major of the Court of Cassation. All at once, and a dozen years after his death, we have inherited one of the most charming books of gastronomy that it is possible to imagine—the 'Physiologie du Gout.' "...

Louis Eustache Ude, once chef of Louis XVI, and founder of the modern French school in England, exerted considerable influence upon the better cookery of his day. His "French Cook" appeared in 1822, and a few years afterwards he became chef of Crockford's Club, the year during which his former employer, The Duke of York, died. The story is told that, on hearing of the duke's illness, Ude exclaimed, "*Ah, mon pauvre Duc,* how greatly you will miss me where you are going!" Of the finesse that appertains to cookery, of the difficulty to become perfect in the art, Ude wrote as follows:

"What science demands more study? Every man is not born with the qualifications necessary to constitute a good cook. Music, dancing, fencing, painting, and mechanics in general possess professors under twenty years of age, whereas in the first line of cooking preeminence never occurs under thirty. We see daily at concerts and academies young men and women who display the greatest abilities, but in our line nothing but *the most consummate* experience can elevate a man to the rank of chief professor. Cookery is an art appreciated by only a very few individuals, and which requires, in addition to most diligent and studious application, no small share of intellect and the strictest sobriety and punctuality; there are cooks and cooks—the difficulty lies in finding the perfect one."

Ude was succeeded in England by Charles Elme-Francatelli, a distinguished pupil of Carême, who presided as chef at Chesterfield House and various clubs until he became *officier de bouche* to the queen. His "Modern Cook" is still a superior treatise, and although little adapted to the average household, it will well repay careful study on the part of the expert amateur. "The palate is as capable and nearly as worthy of education as the eye and the ear," says Francatelli—a statement which his volume abundantly bears out.

A scholar of Carême, Francatelli was quick to note that *si l'habit fait l'homme, il fait aussi l'entrée*—that the sense of sight has its delight as well as the taste, and one sees, accordingly, an ornate observance of decoration in his grand army of side-dishes. These are excellent throughout, but generally very elaborate, while his sauces and recipes for pastry are especially good. The same may be said of his quenelles and timbales. A competent hand will find his work a valuable guide from which to obtain ideas; it is not a practical book for the majority. . . .

After Francatelli, Alexis Soyer did his part towards the improvement of the higher classes of England. As an author he was ambitious, if not distinguished, his published works numbering four, viz.: "The Gastronomic Regenerator," "The Modern Housewife, or Ménagère," "The Pantropheon or History of Food," and "A Shilling Cookery for the People." From the fact that the last-named volume reached its two hundred and forty-eighth thousand, it may be concluded it was not a distinguished work, and was written to attract the multitude who do not appreciate. The warm reception given to his "Ménagère," according to a reviewer in "Fraser's Magazine," indicated, "with a statistical accuracy very superior to the census, the lamentably small number of educated palates and self-comprehending stomachs which this country possesses." Like Carême, Soyer had studied the cuisine of the ancients attentively, and in this respect his "History of Food" becomes a valuable addition to the student's library. But his execution is said to have been far below his conception, and his soups much inferior to his soup-kitchens. He refrains from giving a certain recipe for crawfish *à la Sampayo,* which appeared in one of his bills of fare, on account of an agreement between himself and M. Sampayo, adding that the reason of the enormous expense of the dish was that "two large bottles of Perigord truffles, which do not cost less than four guineas, are stewed with them in champagne." But inasmuch as the virtues of the truffle are sadly dissipated in its preserved state, and chefs generally use an ordinary Chablis or other wine in place of champagne, one need not be seriously concerned with the loss of the crawfish. . . .

From the somewhat stilted style of Soyer it becomes doubly pleasing to turn to the laughing pages of Dumas, at once suggestive and inspiring, pointed in paragraph and scintillant with anecdote.

The author of "Monte Cristo" and "The Three Musketeers" has also left an illustrious name as a cook, a host, and an epicure. And if, of all celebrated artists, it might be Carême whom one would wish to prepare the dinner, who more delightful than Dumas as a *vis-à-vis* at the repast? But his expansive smile and his *bonhomie* are reflected in his writings, and his "intuition of all" is no less apparent when dealing with cookery than when detailing the intrigues of cardinals and courtiers. A chartreuse becomes as important as the missing necklace of a queen, and the theory of frying no less momentous than the fate of the prisoner of the Chateau d'If. As Octave Lacroix has phrased it, "Assuredly it is a great attainment to be a romancist, but it is by no means a mediocre glory to be a cook . . . Romancist or cook, Alexandre Dumas is a chef, and the two vocations appear in him to go hand in hand, or rather to be joined in one."

The two introductory epistles, an anecdotal review of the art, are among the most felicitous in the language. Nor should we forget the many references to the table in the "Impressions de Voyage" and numerous other volumes. The Marquis de Cussy, Jules Janin, Charles Monselet, and others have treated the same subject at more or less length, but none of them so comprehensively. "I wish to conclude," Dumas often said, "my literary work of five hundred volumes by a work on cookery." This was his great ambition, and to it he devoted his most zealous efforts. "I see with pleasure," he remarks in one of his volumes, "that my culinary reputation is increasing, and soon promises to efface my literary reputation. . . . I therefore make the announcement that as soon as I am freed from the claims of certain editors I will show you a book of practical cookery by which the most ignorant in matters gastronomical will be able to prepare, as easily as my honorable friend Vuillemot, an *espagnole* or a *mirepoix*."

With Dumas to promise was to fulfill and in due time his book—the last volume from his pen—appeared, a tall folio of over a thousand pages, with the spirited etching of the author by Rajon. While this is more especially devoted to the French kitchen, it contains a large number of recipes from foreign countries where the author had traveled. It thus becomes a compendium of many different schools, offering a wide range for selection. Written, moreover, by an amateur, it is also an easier guide than many of the professional manuals of the *haute cuisine*. In the "Dictionary" everything is passed under review—from snails *à la provençale* to the feet of elephants, from filets of kangaroo to lamb's tail *glacées à la chicorée*, the list of fishes including an account of the origin of the term "Poisson d'Avril" (April fool). . . .

There are recipes from Beauvilliers, Carême, the Marquis de Cussy, and the cook of King Stanislas; from the manuals of the times of Louis XIV and XV; from the cafés Anglais, Verdier, Brebant, Magny, Grignon, Véfour, and Véry; from Elzéar-Blaze, La Reynière, the Provincial Brothers, and Vuillemot, proprietor of the Tête Noire at St. Cloud. One's mouth waters as he reads the vast alphabet of dishes. There are, for example, thirty-one modes presented for preparing the carp, and fifty-six for dressing the egg, apart from the omelet, with sixteen recipes for artichokes and a dozen for asparagus. There is the Java formula for cooking halcyons' nests, and that of the cook of Richelieu for *godiveau,* a dissertation on the hocco, and a prescription for bustards *à la daube.* No wonder that Dumas has defined the dinner as a daily and capital action that can be worthily accomplished only by *gens d'esprit*. . . .

Rossini, a contemporary and friend of Balzac and Dumas, was not alone a famous musician—composer of "Tell" and the "Stabat Mater"—but was also a distinguished *fourchette* and a cook of ability. One of his most celebrated compositions—that of a certain manner of preparing macaroni which is said to have vied in seductiveness with the sweetest strains of the "Barbier de Seville"—is unfortunately lost to the world through a prejudice of Dumas.

One day the great romancist, who never ate macaroni in any form, asked the noted composer for his recipe, being anxious to add it to his culinary repertoire. "Come and eat some with me tomorrow at dinner, and you shall have it," was the answer. But the host, perceiving that his guest would not touch a dish on which he had bestowed so much pains, refused to give him the formula, whereupon Dumas circulated the report that it was his cook, not Rossini, who was master of the secret, and forthwith presented at length a recipe given him by the famous Mme. Ristori as "the true, the only, the unique manner of preparing macaroni *à la néapolitaine*.". . .

Among the most distinguished of modern professional cooks was Jules Gouffé, former *officer de bouche* of the Jockey Club of Paris, whose "Livre de Cuisine" and "Livre de Patisserie" are unexcelled as guides to the greatest triumphs of the art of which they treat. The "Livre de Cuisine," which first appeared in 1865, is not a manual that can be utilized in the ordinary establishment, however; but a volume on a grand scale, written by a great chef for chefs. Francatelli, though very elaborate, is much more simple. At any rate, it is possible to simplify his recipes, or to derive many new ideas from them, even where his formulas may not be executed in the average household. But to follow Gouffé calls for the very highest professional skill and the most lavish expenditure,—the hand of a master, a larder of cockscombs, crawfish, truffles, plover and pheasants' eggs, not to mention a cellar of Château Margaux, champagne, and Chabile Moutonne. . . .

With Jules Gouffé, Urbain-Dubois, a chef of the highest order, and author of six important works on cookery, will be known to posterity as one of the greatest masters of the range of the second half of the nineteenth century.

In marked contrast to those of Gouffé and Dubois are the numerous culinary works of Ildefonse-Leon Brisse, more familiarly known as Baron Brisse, and who was sometimes termed the Baron Falstaff. Two of his manuals, molded on somewhat similar lines, are excellent mentors for the modest household—"The 366 Menus" (1868) and "La Petite Cuisine" (1870), of which many editions have appeared. In these a large number of foods, uncommon, and simple dishes are presented, and both works may be comprehended by all who have a fair practical knowledge of cookery at command. According to Théodore de Banville, Baron Brisse was "at once an accomplished cook, a fine and delicate gourmet, and a gourmand always tormented with an insatiable hunger." It may therefore be assumed that all his recipes have been personally tested, and that those he particularly recommends are well worthy of trial, bearing out the sentiment he expresses in the preface of "La Petite Cuisine." "This book is a good action for which I will be duly credited in this world or the other." Besides his numerous volumes on cookery, he founded and contributed to several culinary journals. He laughed and ate. He was of enormous stature, and always one was obliged to secure two places in the diligence between Paris and his home at Fontenay-aux-Roses, where he resided previous to his death in 1876. With Jules Gouffé he instituted a series of dinners where the guests were expected to dine in white frocks and round white caps, like the fat old cooks that Roland has painted—dinners presided over by the baron, whose *bonhomie* was proverbial, one executed under the directions of Gouffé himself. But apart from his excellent cookery-books, Baron Brisse should be held in abiding reverence by all entertainers that are worthy of the name, if only for his splendid axiom—"The host whose guest has been obliged to ask him for anything is a dishonored man!"

Brillat-Savarin

from The Art of Dining
by Abraham Hayward

THE *Almanach de Gourmands* was the first serious and sustained attempt to invest gastronomy with the air of an intellectual and refined pursuit. But incomparably the completest essay on what may be termed the aesthetics of the dinner table is the famous *Physiologie du Goût,* a short biographical sketch of the author may not be unacceptable as an introduction to a few extracts from the work.

Anthelme Brillat-Savarin, judge of the Court of Cassation, member of the Legion of Honor, and of most of the scientific and literary societies of France, was born in 1755 at Belley. He was bred up to his father's profession of the law, and was practicing with some distinction as an advocate when (in 1789) he was elected a member of the Constituent Assembly, where he joined the moderate party, and did his best to avert the ruin that ensued. At the termination of his legislative duties, he was appointed President of the Civil Tribunal of the department of *L'Ain,* and on the establishment of the Court of Cassation he was made a judge of it. During the reign of terror he found himself amongst the proscribed, and fled for refuge to Switzerland, where he contrived to while away the time in scientific, literary, and gastronomical pursuits. He was afterwards compelled to emigrate to America, where also his attention seems rarely to have been diverted from the study in which he was destined to immortalize himself. It is related of him, that once, on his return from a shooting expedition, in the course of which he had the good fortune to kill a wild turkey, he fell into conversation with Jefferson, who began relating some interesting anecdotes about Washington and the war, when, observing the distracted air of M. Brillat-Savarin, he stopped, and was about to go away: "My dear sir," said our gastronomer, recovering himself by a strong effort, "I beg a thousand pardons, but I was thinking how I should dress my wild turkey." He earned his subsistence by teaching French and music, an art in which he excelled. He returned to France in 1796, and, after filling several employments of trust under the Directory, was re-appointed to his old office of judge of the Court of Cassation, in which he continued until his death in 1826. The *Physiologie du Goût* was published some time in the year 1825, and ran rapidly through five or six editions, besides reprints in Belgium. Its great charm consists in the singular mixture of wit, humor, learning, and knowledge of the world—*bon mots,* anecdotes, ingenious theories, and instructive dissertations—which it presents; and if, as is currently related, Walton's Angler has made thousands turn fishermen, we should not be at all surprised to hear that the "Physiology of Taste" had converted a fair portion of the reading public into gastronomers. . . .

It may not be deemed beside the purpose to state that M. Brillat-Savarin was of a sober, moderate, easily satisfied disposition; so much so, indeed, that many have been misled into the supposition that his enthusiasm was unreal, and his book a piece of badinage written to amuse his leisure hours. . . . An anecdote (related to Colonel Damer by Talleyrand) may help to rescue the fair fame of Brillat-Savarin from the reproach of indifference, and illustrate the hereditary quality of taste. He was on his way to Lyons, and was determined to dine at Sens. On his arrival he sent, according to his invariable custom, for the cook, and asked what he could have for dinner? The report was dispiriting. "Little enough," was the reply. "But let us see," retorted M. Savarin, "let us go to the kitchen and talk the matter over." In the kitchen he found four turkeys roasting. "Why!" exclaimed he, "you told me you had nothing in the house. Let me have one of these turkeys." "Impossible!" said the cook, "they are all bespoken by a gentleman upstairs." "He must have a large party to dine with him then?" "No, he dines by himself." "I should like much to be acquainted with the man who orders four turkeys for his own eating." The cook was sure that the gentleman would be glad of his acquaintance; and M. Brillat-Savarin immediately paid his respects to the stranger, who turned out to be his own son. "What, you rogue, four turkeys all for yourself?" "Yes, sir; you know that, whenever I dine with you, you eat up the whole of *les-sots-les-laissent*"—titbit which we call the *oyster* of the turkey or fowl—"I was resolved to enjoy myself for once in my life, and here I am, ready to begin, although I did not expect the honor of your company."

Ude and Francatelli

from The Art of Dining
by Abraham Hayward

AT THE HEAD of the celebrities we must not forget to place Louis Eustache Ude. For upwards of twenty years he had the honor of educating the palate of the late Earl of Sefton, who, in his day, was considered a great *gourmet* as well as a great gourmand —and, be it understood, these qualifications are seldom united. The difference between a *gourmet* and a *gourmand* we take to be this: a *gourmet* is he who selects, for his nice and learned delectation, the most choice delicacies, prepared in the most scientific manner; whereas, the *gourmand* bears a closer analogy to that class of great eaters ill-naturedly (we dare say) denominated, or classed with, aldermen. Ude was also once *maître d'hôtel* to the late Duke of York, from whom he contrived to elicit many a hearty laugh through his clever mimicry. Under his auspices, also, it was that "the great playhouse" in St. James, yclept Crockford's, was ushered into its destructive career.

Louis Eustache Ude was verily the Gil Blas of the kitchen. He had, in his latter days, a notion of writing his memoirs; and if they had not proved deeply interesting, those who knew him well can with truth assert that many would have relished the curious scandal and pleasant gossip with which his astonishing memory was so well stored. Ude's mamma was an attractive and lively milliner, who married an underling in Louis XVI's kitchen. She thought Master Eustache too pretty a boy to be sacrificed to the "*Dieu ventru.*" The consequence was, that after an attempt made by his sire to train him in his own "glorious path," the youngster absconded, and apprenticed himself, first to a "*bijoutier en faux,*" then to an engraver, next to a printer, and lastly to a haberdasher! after which he became traveler for a mercantile house at Lyons. Something occurred at this point which occasioned him to change his vocation once more. He returned to Paris, and there tried his genius as an actor at a small theatre in the Rue Chantreine. He soon, however (aided by a discriminating public), discovered that his share of the world's cake was not on that stage, and, by some means, he set up an office and a "*cabriolet,*" and forthwith started into life as an "*agent de change.*" This scheme did not last long; he got "cleaned out" on 'Change, and shortly after was installed as an inspector of gambling-houses. He soon tired of this appointment, and, on relinquishing it, determined to return to his original calling, and became once again a cook.

After practicing in the culinary profession some few years in the early dawn of the fortunes of the house of Bonaparte, Ude raised himself to the post of *maître d'hôtel* to Madame Letitia Bonaparte. Here our artist remained for about two years, when, owing to some difference of opinion between Madame Letitia and himself in matters arithmetical, he somewhat suddenly left that lady's service to honor our land with his presence; and ever after, when fitting opportunity presented itself, he was wont to express his indignation against the "*usurpateur*" and all his family. Good cooks were scarce in England in those days, and, shortly after his arrival, the late Earl of Sefton secured his services at a salary of 300 guineas per annum; and not only proved himself a liberal and kind-hearted patron during his lifetime, but, with that benevolence for which he was remarkable, handsomely provided for the old age of his favorite cook by leaving him 100 pounds for life.

On Ude's retirement from the active duties of his high vocation at Crockford's, his mantle fell on Charles Elmé Francatelli—an author of merit, and a man of cultivation and accomplishments, as well as an eminently distinguished artist. His treatises on Gastronomy, published by Bentley, were alone sufficient to place him in the front rank of the scientific professors of the art. He was many years chef at Chesterfield House, when its dinners were the admiration of the gastronomic world of London. We subsequently trace him by his reputation to Rossie Priory (Lord Kinnaird's), Sir W. M. Stahley, Mr. Rowland Errington, Mr. Lyne Stevens, and the late Count Matuzavicz were the members. He succeeded Ude as *maître d'hôtel* at Crockford's, and was afterwards, through the discriminating patronage of the late Earl of Errol, promoted to the honorable and enviable post of *maître d'hôtel* and chief cook to the Queen. It is generally understood that his skill, zeal, and judicious economy obtained the full approval of her Majesty and her Royal Consort; what can such exalted personages know of the intrigues of the basement story of a palace? or how can they be fairly made responsible for the heart-breaking humiliation and injustice that may be perpetrated by their authority? At the end of two years Francatelli was displaced, or reluctantly resigned, the victim (he doubtless believes) of some pantry, scullery, still-room, or steward's-room cabal, and the Coventry Club was fortunate enough to possess him for a period. At present, if we are not misinformed, he is in the full enjoyment of the *otium cum dignitate*, and of a handsome competence to boot—a circumstance at which we should rejoice more cordially, did it not militate very seriously against the gratification of our palates.

THE TURNSPIT

His arguments in silly circles run,
Still round and round, and end where they begun,
So the poor turnspit, as the wheel runs round,
The more he gains, the more he loses ground.

—Pitt's *Art of Preaching*

The Suicide of Vatel

from Letters
by Mme. de Sévigné

(Mme. de Sévigné to Mme. de Grignan.)
Paris, Sunday, April 26th, 1671

I HAVE JUST LEARNED from Moreuil of what passed at Chantilly with regard to poor Vatel. I wrote to you last Friday, that he had stabbed himself; these are the particulars of the affair. The King arrived there on Thursday night; the walk, and the collation, which was served in a place set apart for the purpose, and strewed with jonquils, were just as they should be. Supper was served, but there was no roast meat at one or two of the tables, on account of Vatel's having been obliged to provide several dinners more than were expected. This affected his spirits, and he was heard to say several times, "I have lost my fame! I cannot bear this disgrace! My head is quite bewildered," said he to Gourville. "I have not had a wink of sleep these twelve nights, I wish you would assist me in giving orders." Gourville did all he could to comfort and assist him; but the failure of the roast meat (which, however, did not happen at the King's table, but at some of the other twenty-five) was always uppermost with him. Gourville mentioned it to the Prince, who went directly to Vatel's apartment, and said to him "Everything is extremely well conducted, Vatel; nothing could be more admirable than His Majesty's supper." "Your Highness's goodness," replied he "overwhelms me; I am sensible that there was a deficiency of roast meat at two tables." "Not at all," said the Prince. "Do not perplex yourself, and all will go well." Midnight came: the fireworks did not succeed, they were covered with a thick cloud; they cost sixteen thousand francs. At four o'clock in the morning, Vatel went round, and found everybody asleep; he met one of the under-purveyors, who had just come in with only two loads of fish. "What!" said he, "is that all?" "Yes, Sir," said the man, not knowing that Vatel had dispatched other people to all the seaports round. Vatel waited for some time, the other purveyors did not arrive; his head grew distracted; he thought there was no more fish to be had; he flew to Gourville: "Sir," said he, "I cannot outlive this disgrace." Gourville laughed at him; Vatel, however, went to his apartment, and setting the hilt of his sword against the door, after two ineffectual attempts, succeeded in the third, in forcing the sword through his heart. At that instant the carriers arrived with the fish; Vatel was inquired after to distribute it; they ran to his apartment, knocked at the door, but received no answer; upon which they broke it open, and found him weltering in his blood. A messenger was immediately dispatched to acquaint the Prince with what had happened, who was like a man in despair. The Duke wept, for his journey to Burgundy depended upon Vatel. The Prince related the whole affair to His Majesty, with an expression of great concern: it was considered as the consequence of too nice a sense of honor; some blamed, others praised him for his courage. The King said he had put off his excursion for more than five years, because he was aware that it would be attended with infinite trouble, and told the Prince that he ought to have had but two tables, and not have been at the expense of so many, and declared he would never suffer him to do so again; but all this was too late for poor Vatel. However, Gourville endeavored to supply the loss of Vatel; which he did in great measure.

Escoffier: Chef of Chefs

by Craig Claiborne
(from the New York Times *Magazine)*

THERE IS MORE than one Cassandra in the field of food who says that the world's fine chefs are destined to be replaced by machines, cake mixes and frozen food lockers. In view of such a grim prospect it is heartening to note that a gastronomic society called Les Amis d'Escoffier is establishing an Escoffier Museum and Culinary School at the master's birthplace in Villeneuve-Loubet, France, thus assuring that his culinary principles will survive "to meet the conditions of a changing world."

Georges Auguste Escoffier had a greater influence on fine cuisine than any other chef in history. His kitchens at the Ritz hotels in Paris and London elevated those hotels to gastronomic shrines never equalled before or since. Literally thousands of chefs were trained in his kitchens and their disciples are working all over the world.

What makes a great chef such as Escoffier? There are many chefs (although the breed is fast disappearing) who are possessed of sound techniques. But truly inspired cuisine depends upon an exquisiteness of palate that is denied to all but a few.

The ultimate chef rarely cooks by the book. He works through the senses of taste, touch and sight, in that order. A cook of Escoffier's caliber instinctively supplies the magic ingredient—that extra grain of salt, that inspired garnish, that extra iota of glaze—which cannot be written into any recipe.

Those who knew Escoffier say that his was a genius that could have made a thistle palatable. He is best remembered, of course, for his Peach Melba, which appears more frequently on international menus than anything else he created. But he originated upwards of seven thousand other dishes, ranging from many now reserved for state occasions—*Médaillons de Volaille à l'Isabelle, Célestine de Homard à la Mogador* and *Aspic de Langouste à la Cléopâtre*—to the plainer pleasures of Melba toast.

While he was an expert in formal decorations, Escoffier taught and practiced the art of simplicity in cuisine. Once he said, "It is the plain cooking that counts. If you would live long, leave the cooking to the wife. My wife is still the best cook in the family, in spite of the thousands of recipes I have originated."

Like most great chefs, he himself ate frugally. Even at the height of his glory, with a corps of sixty chefs working for him, he almost invariably dined alone in the evening. He would have soup with a sprinkling of rice, and fruit for dessert, and then return to his office to continue working.

He abhorred the American habit of drinking cocktails before meals and cold water during them. The former, he claimed, insults the palate; the latter stuns it. As for American cuisine, his impressions had been summed up during a visit here in 1908, when the *New York Times* quoted him as saying, "This is the greatest country in the world for the appreciation of the good, square meal."

Because of his world-wide fame as a master chef, Escoffier was frequently badgered by wealthy and admiring patrons to produce new taste sensations.

"What feats of ingenuity," he once wrote in despair "have we not been forced to perform, at times, to produce our customer's wishes! Personally, I have stopped counting the nights spent in attempting to discover new combinations when, completely broken with fatigue of a tiring day, my body should have been at rest."

Many of his culinary inventions were named for women. Among them were the dramatic actress Rachel, and singers Mary Garden, Adelina Patti and, of course, Nellie Melba. For Sarah Bernhardt, a frequent visitor to the Escoffier kitchens, a favorite dish was the master chef's scrambled eggs, for which he was renowned. He died without disclosing the secret, if he had one, of how he made them. It does not help to know that they were cooked in a silver skillet.

Melba and Bernhardt, as well as Marcel Proust, were among the many great artists of the era whom Escoffier counted among his friends. He himself, a most patrician-looking man, though very short, could easily have passed as a member of the French aristocracy. Actually, he was the son of a peasant blacksmith.

He had been born in the tiny village of Villeneuve-Loubet on the Côte d'Azur, on Oct. 28, 1846. When he was thirteen he became an apprentice in his uncle's restaurant at Nice. The hours were punishing, the kitchen a furnace, vulgarity rife, the work back-breaking.

It has been suggested that the rugged discipline of this early training was what developed his genius. Certainly, it inspired the social reforms he later introduced into his own kitchens, and his efforts to improve working conditions in his profession were felt throughout Europe.

After six years of apprenticeship, Escoffier joined the staff of one of the most popular restaurants in Paris, Le Restaurant du Petit Moulin Rouge. His career—interrupted for army service during the Franco-Prussian War of 1870—advanced steadily. In 1883, César Ritz, the fabled hotelier, hired him as head chef in the fashionable Grand at Monte Carlo. Thus began a partnership for the gods. The liaison produced several of the most luxurious hotels in the world, including the Savoy and Carlton in London, the Grand in Rome and the Ritz Hotels in New York, Paris, London, Philadelphia, Budapest, Montreal and Madrid.

The Savoy's restaurant, in particular, became the nightly meeting place of the cream of English and international society. American oil barons and the royalty of all lands sought Escoffier out in the steam of his kitchens to give him crested cuff links and ribboned crosses. High official honors were bestowed upon him by Italy and the Republic of France. He was called prince, king and emperor of chefs.

He died, at eighty-nine, on Feb. 12, 1935, only a few days after the death of his wife, and was buried in the family vault at Villeneuve-Loubet. He had been fond of quoting Brillat-Savarin, and is said to have jokingly remarked that one of that great gastronomer's sayings might be his own epitaph: "Beasts feed, man eats, but only the man of intelligence and true perceptiveness really dines."

* * *

LUXURIES OF THE TABLE

Among the luxuries of the table in greatest request, Gellius quotes out of Varro, the peacock from Samos, the Phrygian turkey, cranes from Melos, Ambracian kids, the Tartesian mullet, trouts from Persenumtium, Tartine oysters, crabs from Chios, Tatian nuts, Egyptian dates, Iberian chestnuts; all which institutions of bills of fare were invented for the wicked wantonness of luxury and gluttony.

—DICK HUMELBERGIUS SECUNDUS, *Apician Morsels*

A DRINK CALLED COFFEE

They have in Turkey a drink called Coffee, made of a Berry of the same name, as Black as Soot, and of a Strong Scent, but not Aromatical; which they take, beaten into Powder, in Water, as Hot as they can Drink it; and they take it, and sit at it in their Coffee Houses, which are like our Taverns. The Drink comforteth the Brain and Heart and helpeth Digestion.

—FRANCIS BACON

Whoever says "truffles" pronounces a great word, sure to awaken sentimental and succulent memories among the sex in petticoats, and succulent and passionate memories among the sex sporting a mustache.

That distinguished duplication comes from the fact that that eminent tuber is not only recognized delicious as to taste, but again because it is believed that it increases a power whose exercise is accompanied by the sweetest of pleasures.

—Brillat-Savarin

PART 6

SOME CURIOUS RECIPES

Chapter Nineteen

SEASON TO TASTE

SINCE THIS IS NOT in any sense a cookbook, we have omitted recipes except as they occur in the natural course of literary work. Some recipes, however, are literary works in their own right, and many have a flavor of the curious about them that makes them fun to read even when they provide no slightest inspiration for the kitchen. These are the kinds of recipes we mean to sample in this shortest section of our book—only a pinch, one might say, for seasoning.

There is nothing especially "curious" about the first excerpt, from a contemporary English food book titled, "Herbs,

Salads and Seasonings," by a writer we have met before, X. Marcel Boulestin, this time working with a collaborator, Jason Hill. But "mixed spices" is far from being a familiar item even in sophisticated cuisines, so it seems worth preserving.

Definitely in the "curious" category, however, is the poet John Gay's recipe for stewing a knuckle of veal, as is the ancient Scottish recipe for "todday" which George Saintsbury, the revered wine expert, gives us, from his classic "Notes on a Cellar-Book," certainly one of the most famous volumes on wine ever written.

It may be that everyone who makes a salad has his own way of doing it, as some say. Here are three which could scarcely be more various: our friend Thomas Walker's version, the Reverend Sydney Smith's winter salad, and John Evelyn's idea of flavoring "sallet," as he called the dish in his discourse.

Everyone will know the "receipts," we think, but for those who did not grow up with Edward Lear's "Nonsense Verses," we offer them as the ultimate length to which recipes may be carried.

The recipe for bouillabaisse (and there are undoubtedly as many as there are for salads) is by an obscure French writer named Joseph Mery (1798-1865), born at Aygalades, Bouche-du-Rhone. We are unable to discover anything else he wrote, gastronomic or otherwise.

"Lettuse is much used in salets in the sommer tyme with vinegar, oyle, and sugar and salt, and is formed to procure appetite for meate, and to temper the heate of the stomach and liver."

—COGAN, HAVEN OF HEALTH

Recipe for Mixed Spices

from Herbs, Salads, and Seasonings

by X. Marcel Boulestin and Jason Hill

ONE CANNOT OVER-RATE the importance of herbs and seasonings: they are essential to good food and well used, that is discriminately and discreetly, as delicious as the dusty packets are nasty. Pepper, for instance (another dusty packet, as a rule) should never be used except fresh out of a grinder, when its taste is clean and fragrant. And the concoction known as "mixed spices" is usually lamentable. Yet a pinch of good spicing in a dish makes the whole difference in the world. There again the garden and not the grocer's shop can and ought to help the kitchen. There are many recipes for making spices, including the one from the famous Carême. This one will serve many purposes: pound in a mortar three parts of Peppercorns (white and black in equal quantities), one part composed of Cloves, grated Nutmeg, Cinnamon, dried Thyme and Bayleaf. Add a small quantity of Ginger and Mace. These ingredients should be very finely pounded, then passed through a fine hair sieve and kept in a well-closed tin or a bottle with a glass stopper, in a dry place.

This type of seasoning is absolutely indispensable when making a gelantine or a *terrine,* also for the kind of cooking known as *en papillotes,* where inside the buttered paper, herbes, spices combine with mushrooms and streaky bacon chopped finely to the sapidity of the dish. There is, in fact, hardly any French recipe for which some herb or other is not prescribed: the specific smell of this one or that one may not be felt in the dish, but its presence is necessary to the harmonious balance of ingredients, to the final general flavor, which makes the perfect whole.

How to Stew a Knuckle of Veal

by John Gay

TAKE A KNUCKLE of veal,
You may buy it or steal;
In a few pieces cut it,
In a stewing pan put it;
Salt, pepper, and mace,
Must season this knuckle;
Then what's joined to a place (i.e. celery, *vulgo* salary,)
With other herbs muckle;
That which kill'd King Will (i.e. sorrel),
And what never stands still (i.e. thyme),
Some springs from that bed
Where children are bred, (i.e. parsley),
Which much will mend, if
Both spinach and endive,
And lettice and beet
With marygold meet.
Put no water at all,
For it maketh things small,
Which lest it should happen,
A close cover clap on;
Put this pot of wood metal (i.e. copper),
In a boiling hot kettle,
And there let it be
(Mark the doctrine I teach)
Above, let me see,
Thrice as long as you preach.
So skimming the fat off,
Say grace with your hat off,
Oh! then with what rapture
Will it fill Dean and Chapter!

Todday, a Prehistoric Compound

from Notes on a Cellar-Book
by George Saintsbury

THIS, EVEN IN Scotland, now almost prehistoric compound, ought to be made, according to Morayshire rules, in a fashion opposite to that usually imagined to be correct. You put in the hot water, sweetened to taste, first, and let the sugar melt thoroughly; *then* you add the whisky. And, of course, you do not "swig" it brutally from the rummer or tumbler, but ladle it genteelly, as required, with a special instrument made and provided for the purpose, into a wine-glass which has been brought, again speccially inverted beforehand in the rummer or tumbler itself.

Mr. Walker's Salad

from The Original
by Thomas Walker

AS I AM on the subject of receipts, I will give another, which is also applicable to the season. It is a receipt for a salad, which I have seen at a few houses, but I think it deserves to be much more common.

Boil one or two large onions, till soft and perfectly mild. When cold, mix the onion with celery, and sliced beetroot, roasted in the oven, which has more flavor than when boiled. Dress this salad with oil, vinegar, salt, and pepper. The onion and beetroot are very good without celery. Roast beef with this salad and potatoes browned in the dripping-pan, or in the oven, is a dish to delight the constitution of an Englishman in the winter months.

Recipe for a Winter Salad

by Rev. Sydney Smith

TWO LARGE POTATOES, passed through kitchen sieve,
Unwonted softness to the salad give.
Of mordant mustard add a single spoon;
Distrust the condiment which bites so soon;
But deem it not, thou man of herbs, a fault
To add a double quantity of salt.
Three times the spoon with oil of Lucca crown,
And once with vinegar procured from town.
True flavor needs it, and the poet begs,
The pounded yellow of two well-boiled eggs.
Let onion atoms lurk within the bowl,
And (scarce suspected), animate the whole;
And lastly, on the flavored compound toss
A magic teaspoon of anchovy sauce.
Then, though green turtle fail, though venison's tough,
And ham and turkey are not boiled enough,
Serenely full the Epicure may say—
Fate cannot harm me—I have dined today.

To Make an Amblongus Pie

Take 4 pounds (say 4½ pounds) of fresh Amblongusses, and put them in a small pipkin.

Cover them with water and boil them for 8 hours incessantly; after which add 2 pints of new milk, and proceed to boil for 4 hours more.

When you have ascertained that the Amblongusses are quite soft, take them out, and place them in a wide pan, taking care to shake them well previously.

Grate some nutmeg over the surface, and cover them carefully with powdered ginger bread, curry-powder, and a sufficient quantity of Cayenne pepper.

Remove the pan into the next room, and place it on the floor. Bring it back again, and let it simmer for three-quarters of an hour. Shake the pan violently till all the Amblongusses have become of a pale purple color.

Then, having prepared the paste, insert the whole carefully; adding at the same time a small pigeon, 2 slices of beef, 4 cauliflowers, and any number of oysters.

Watch patiently till the crust begins to rise, and add a pinch of salt from time to time.

Serve up in a clean dish, and throw the whole out of the window as fast as possible.

—EDWARD LEAR

To Make Gosky Patties

Take a pig three or four years of age, and tie him by the off hind-leg to a post. Place 5 pounds of currants, 3 of sugar, 2 pecks of peas, 18 roast chestnuts, a candle, and 6 bushels of turnips, within his reach: if he eats these, constantly provide him with more.

Then procure some cream, some slices of Cheshire cheese, 4 quires of foolscap paper, and a packet of black pins. Work the whole into a paste, and spread it out to dry on a sheet of clean brown waterproof linen.

When the paste is perfectly dry, but not before, proceed to beat the pig violently with the handle of a large broom. If he squeals, beat him again.

Visit the paste and beat the pig alternately for some days, and ascertain if, at the end of that period, the whole is about to turn into Gosky Patties.

If it does not then, it never will; and in that case the pig may be let loose, and the whole process may be considered as finished.

—EDWARD LEAR

How to Flavor a Sallet

from A Discourse on Sallets

by John Evelyn

EVERY PLANT should bear its part without being overpower'd by some Herb of stronger taste, so as to endanger the native Savor and Vertue of the rest; but fall into their places like Notes in Music, in which should be nothing harsh or grating and tho admitting some discords (to distinguish and illustrate the next) striking in the more sprightly and sometimes gentler notes reconcile all dissonances and melt them into an agreeable composition.

Recipe for Bouillabaisse

by Joseph Mery

BEFORE YOUR EPIC starts, turn to and cook
A savant stock, the Preface to your book.
And what a stock! To baby fish and "fry"
Of scores of kinds . . . that morning's catch . . . apply
The slow, distilling heat of embers clear
And precious, spicy gravy will appear.
Steep in this sauce, with fine discrimination,
The this-and-that designed for titillation,
Manilla pepper, saffron, and bouquet!
Of fennel, with a crackling leaf of bay,
Salt, friend of man, and urchins from their bed
In warm Arenc, well-flavored and well fed.
When this great brew blows bubbles, sheds its skins,
And all is nicely done, your ode begins.

One thing is sure . . . this fine Phocaean dish
Is not the same without one master fish,
The vulgar hogfish, scorpion of the seas,
Which, lonely on its grill, could never please
The crudest tastes. Yet in a bouillabaisse
It has no peer, and nothing can replace
Its subtle odors. If, indeed, they fail,
No other art of cunning will prevail;
Hogfish alone, from chinks in shifting sand
Where bays and myrtles fringe the tenuous land,
Or from some shadowed shelf of thymy cliff,
Provide such wafts for avid guests to sniff.

Next come such fish as choose a deeper stream
And hug the reefs: fine mullet, gilthead, bream,
Saint Peter's fish, embalmers of the stew
(Such game, in fact, as greedy perch pursue).
And last, the gurnard, with Booptic eyes,
And some the ichthyologists despise,
Grand fish which Neptune, under flaming sky,
Chooses with table-forks, lays trident by.

You heedless trippers, do not judge the case
From any one-and-tuppenny bouillabaisse.
Go to the Chateau-Vert. Say: "Something nice.
I'm not a haggler . . . never mind the price.
Dispatch your diver, let him burrow well
Around those rocks of heady ocean smell,
From Greece and Rome "thys" and "parangry" borrow,
And skip the cost. We'll talk of that tomorrow."

SYMBOL OF RESURRECTION

Bless, O, Lord! we beseech thee, this thy creature of eggs, that it may be a whole sustenance to thy faithful servants, eating it in thankfulness to thee, on account of the resurrection.

—PAUL THE FIFTH, *Ritual for England, Ireland, and Scotland*

PART 7

THE PHILOSOPHIC EPICURE

Chapter Twenty

BEFORE THE MEAL

BY THE TIME the last course arrives, the time for philosophy and meditation has arrived with it. The true epicure is a philosopher, it is said, and who can doubt it when he settles back after a fine meal and considers the human condition, particularly his own. It is a state that leads to lofty thoughts, the forgiveness of one's enemies, and the hope of even better things to come.

The contemplation of food itself has led to some of the best philosophic prose in English literature, not to mention the French, and much more lately, the American. It is difficult to discern a pattern in this literature, but we have tried here to make one, arbitrarily for our purposes, to demonstrate perhaps the variety of epicurean philosophy, more than for any other purpose.

Let us approach our philosophic meal with a grace, then, as we would any other. Lamb, in his essays, has inquired into the matter of who should say it, and Jeaffreson has appended some historical observations on the subject.

Thackeray's admonition to respect our dinners—and no man ever respected his more—is followed by Thomas Walker on the art of dining, or as he calls it, aristology. It is worth remembering that when Walker wrote his book on this theme in 1835, he was a police magistrate at Lambeth Court, and a bachelor. With these grains of salt for seasoning, one may read his charming preachments on the virtues of simplicity in dining. We close the chapter with John Ruskin, on the meaning of cookery.

Who Shall Say Grace?

from The Essays of Elia
by Charles Lamb

I AM NO QUAKER at my food. I confess I am not indifferent to the kinds of it. Those unctuous morsels of deer's flesh were not made to be received with dispassionate services. I hate a man who swallows it, affecting not to know what he is eating. I suspect his taste in higher matters. I shrink instinctively from one who professes to like minced veal. There is a physiognomical character in the tastes for food. C— holds that a man cannot have a pure mind who refuses apple dumplings. I am not certain but he is right. With the decay of my first innocence, I confess a less and less relish daily for those innocuous cates. The whole vegetable tribe have lost their gust with me. Only I stick to asparagus, which still seems to inspire gentle thoughts. I am impatient and querulous over culinary disappointments, as to come home at the dinner hour, for instance, expecting some savory mess, and to find one quite tasteless and sapidless. Butter ill melted—that commonest of kitchen failures—puts me beside my tenor. The author of the Rambler used to make inarticulate animal noises over a favorite food. Was this the music quite proper to be preceded by the grace? or would the pious man have done better to postpone his devotions to a season when the blessing might be contemplated with less perturbation? I quarrel with no man's tastes, nor would set my thin face against those excellent things, in their way, jollity and feasting. But as these exercises, however laudable, have little in them of grace or gracefulness, a man should be sure, before he ventures so to grace them, that while he is pretending his devotions otherwise, he is not secretly kissing his hand to some great fish—his Dagon—with a special consecration of no ark but the fat tureen before him. Graces are the sweet preluding strains to the banquets of angels and children; to the roots and severer repasts of the Chartreuse; to the slender, but not slenderly acknowledged, refection of the poor and humble man but at the heaped-up boards of the pampered and the luxurious they become of dissonant mood, less timed and tuned to the occasion, methinks, than the noise of those better befitting organs would be which children hear tales of, at Hog's Norton. We sit too long at our meals, or are too curious in the study of them, or too disordered in our application to them, or engross too great a portion of those good things (which should be common) to our share, to be able with any grace to say grace. To be thankful for what we grasp exceeding our proportion, is to add hypocrisy to injustice. A lurking sense of this truth is what makes the performance of this duty so cold and spiritless a service at most tables. In houses where the grace is as indispensable as the napkin, who has not seen that never-settled question arise, as to *who shall say it?* while the good man of the house and the visitor clergyman, or some other guest, belike of next authority, from years or gravity, shall be bandying about the office between them as a matter of compliment, each of them not unwilling to shift the awkward burthen of an equivocal duty from his own shoulders? . . .

A short form upon these occasions is felt to want reverence; a long one, I am afraid, cannot escape the charge of impertinence. I do not quite approve of the epigrammatic conciseness with which that equivocal wag (but my pleasant schoolfellow) C. V. L., when importuned for a grace, use to inquire, first slyly leering down the table, "Is there no clergyman here?"—significantly adding, "Thank G- -."

Grace at Table

from A Book About the Table

by John Cordy Jeaffreson

MEN MAY LIVE to eat. They must eat to live. This fact is obvious alike to the prig who thinks it unphilosophic, and to the ascetic who deems it sinful, to enjoy a good dinner. Food is the foundation of all human felicity. Though its immediate pleasures are inferior to several enjoyments, it is the root of all mundane blessings. With it, all the finer joys are, under favorable conditions, attainable. Without it, all enjoyment ceases. Elia, deprived of food, would soon have lost all strength for "pleasant walk" and "moonlight ramble," all yearning for "friendly meetings," all appetite for "spiritual repasts." That he relished the ethereal cases for which he required new forms of grace, was due to those grosser ailments for which he was half-ashamed to say "Thank God." Though deep enough for the humorist's purposes his view of the whole question was superficial. Nor can much be said for the historical suggestion at the opening of his paper. It is far more probable that the custom of saying grace at meals originated in an intelligent recognition of the universal importance of food, as the foundation and source of earthly well-being, than that it had its birth in the clamorous exultation of tribes of savages hastening to satisfy their wolfish hunger with long-desired flesh of deer and goats. Charles Lamb, usually so wise with his wit and drollery, was guilty of nonsense when, after stating his theory of the origin of graces, he wrote gravely, "It is not otherwise easy to be understood why the blessing of food—the act of eating—should have had a particular expression of thanksgiving annexed to it, distinct from that implied and silent gratitude with which we are expected to enter upon the enjoyment of the many other various and good things of existence."

No doubt, the sense of thankfulness for blessings is weakened in some natures—by the sense of secure possession. We are all too prone to regard as matters of course, and therefore as no affairs for special gratitude, the comforts which come to us regularly, without forethought, or toil, or anxiety on our part. . . .

The rich men, at whose tables Elia sometimes sat a *rarus hospes*, could be counted by tens, whilst their poor neighbors, to each of whom a savory dinner was a windfall, numbered thousands. And who holds his prosperity by so sure a tenure that no enemy can wrest it from him? The very conditions of civilized life, which, under ordinary circumstances, give us the advantage over savages, may become instruments for reducing us to famine. The Prussians march on Paris; and ere six months have passed, the besieged multitude grow lean and gaunt from hunger, and luxurious epicures, to whom hippophagy had been a mere jest or curious subject of speculation, are glad to fill themselves with sawdust and vermin. Moreover, grace for meat is not limited to the material "creatures" of the abundant board, which in seasons of peace and plenty are easily attainable. It covers the power to enjoy, as well as the substantial means of enjoyment. There is no feast to be thankful for in the absence of desire for food, or if good digestion fails to wait on appetite. And who can say how long he may retain the physical conditions, which are no less needful than sufficient dishes, for the enjoyment of our daily bread? Regarded as the chief type of all material comforts, food will continue to be the subject and occasion for universal thankfulness. Wits may be smart against the grateful usage, but simple men will not depart from their old way at the order of flippancy. And even though the custom of saying them audibly should pass from us, grace at meals will rise silently from thankful hearts.

Respect Your Dinner

by William Makepeace Thackeray

SIR, RESPECT YOUR dinner; idolize it, enjoy it properly. You will be by many hours in the week, many weeks in the year, and many years in your life the happier if you do.

Don't tell us that it is not worthy of a man. All a man's senses are worthy of employment, and should be cultivated as a duty. The senses are the arts. What glorious feasts does Nature prepare for your eye in animal form, in landscape, and painting! Are you to put out your eyes and not see? What royal dishes of melody does her bounty provide for you in the shape of poetry, music, whether windy or wiry, notes of the human voice, or ravishing song of birds! Are you to stuff your ears with cotton, and vow that the sense of hearing is unmanly?—you obstinate dolt you! No, surely; nor must you be so absurd as to fancy that the art of eating is in any way less worthy than the other two. You like your dinner, man; never be ashamed to say so. If you don't like your victuals, pass on to the next article; but remember that every man who has been worth a fig in this world, as poet, painter, or musician, has had a good appetite and a good taste. Ah, what a poet Byron would have been had he taken his meals properly, and allowed himself to grow fat—if nature intended him to grow fat—and not have physicked his intellect with wretched opium pills and acrid vinegar, that sent his principles to sleep, and turned his feelings sour! If that man had respected his dinner, he never would have written "Don Juan."

Allons donc! enough sermonizing; let us sit down and fall to at once.

Aristology

from The Art of Dining

by Thomas Walker

According to the lexicons, the Greek for dinner is Ariston, and therefore, for the convenience of the terms, and without entering into any inquiry, critical or antiquarian, I call the art of dining Aristology, and those who study it, Aristologists. The maxim, that practice makes perfect, does not apply to our daily habits; for, so far as they are concerned, we are ordinarily content with the standard of mediocrity, or something rather below. Where study is not absolutely necessary, it is by most people altogether dispensed with; but it is only by a union of study and practice, that we can attain anything like perfection. Anybody can dine, but very few know how to dine, so as to ensure the greatest quantity of health and enjoyment—indeed many people contrive to destroy their health; and as to enjoyment, I shudder when I think how often I have been doomed to only a solemn mockery of it; how often I have sat in durance stately, to go through the ceremony of dinner, the essence of which is to be without ceremony, and how often in this land of liberty I have felt myself a slave!

There are three kinds of dinners—solitary dinners, every-day social dinners, and set dinners; all three involving the consideration of cheer, and the last two of society also. Solitary dinners, I think, ought to be avoided as much as possible, because solitude tends to produce thought, and thought tends to the suspension of the digestive powers. When, however, dining alone is necessary, the mind should be disposed to cheerfulness by a previous interval of relaxation from whatever has seriously occupied the attention, and by directing it to some agreeable object. As contentment ought to be an accompaniment to every meal, punctuality is essential, and the diner and the dinner should be ready at the same time. A chief maxim in dining with comfort is, to have what you want when you want it. It is ruinous to have to wait for first one thing and then another, and to have the little additions brought, when what they belong to is half or entirely finished. To avoid this a little foresight is good, and, by way of instance, it is sound practical philosophy to have mustard upon the table before the arrival of toasted cheese. This very omission has caused as many small vexations in the world, as would by this time make a mountain of misery. Indeed, I recommend an habitual consideration of what adjuncts will be required to the main matters; and I think an attention to this, on the part of females, might often be preventive of sour looks and cross words, and their anti-conjugal consequences. There are not only the usual adjuncts, but to those who have anything of a genius for dinner, little additions will sometimes suggest themselves, which give a sort of poetry to a repast, and please the palate to the promotion of health. As our senses were made for our enjoyment, and as the vast variety of good things in the world were designed for the same end, it seems a sort of impiety not to put them to their best uses, provided it does not cause us to neglect higher considerations. The different products of the different seasons, and of the different parts of the earth, afford endless proofs of bounty, which it is as unreasonable to reject, as it is to abuse. It has happened, that those who have made the gratification of the appetite a study, have generally gone so to excess, and to the exclusion of nobler pursuits; whilst, on the other hand, such study has been held to be incompatible with moral refinement and elevation. But there is a happy mean, and as upon the due regulation of the appetite assuredly depends our physical well-being, and upon that, in a great measure, our mental energies, it seems to me that the subject is worthy of attention, for reasons of more importance than is ordinarily supposed.

The Meaning of Cookery

by John Ruskin

COOKERY MEANS the knowledge of Medea and of Circe and of Helen and of the Queen of Sheba.

It means the knowledge of all herbs and fruits and balms and spices, and all that is healing and sweet in the fields and groves, and savory in meats.

It means carefulness and inventiveness, and willingness, and readiness of appliances.

It means the economy of your grandmothers and the science of the modern chemist; it means much tasting and no wasting; it means English thoroughness and French art and Arabian hospitality; and, in fine, it means that you are to be perfectly and always ladies—loaf givers.

Chapter Twenty-one

SOME GENERAL OBSERVATIONS

UNDER A TITLE large as a circus tent, this chapter samples the range of food philosophizing. We begin with a curiosity four centuries old, an excerpt from "A Delectable Garden," by Bernard Palissy, published in 1563 and republished in 1931 in an edition set by hand and printed at The Watch Hill Press by Crosby Gaige, whose graceful prose enriched so much modern writing about food. Palissy subtitled his work: "True Receipts by Which All Frenchmen Can Learn to Multiply and Augment Their Treasure."

To those unfamiliar with "The Anatomy of Melancholy,"

Robert Burton seems an unlikely food philosophizer, but here he is with his elegant style and wisdom, to be followed by Juvenal on hospitality. Here the ancient Roman satirist describes a dinner party at which the patron, Virro, eats and drinks of the best, while Trebius, the parasite, is insulted by the servants and starved upon bad food.

Following this appetizing episode, we have two excerpts from a mid-nineteenth century book called "How to Live," by Solon Robinson, a familiar essayist whose work often appeared in the New York papers of the day. Robinson described his book as "a pleasant tale of real life, full of useful lessons in housekeeping, and hints how to live, how to have, how to gain, and how to be happy." "Waste" and "A Dime A Day" are two of the lessons.

The brief morsel from "Our Mutual Friend" is much less familiar Dickens to most of us, but unmistakable.

Coming down to our own times, we have first a tidbit that the late Carl Van Doren wrote for the New York *Herald Tribune,* a piece about sweet corn which has its own charm and sounds little like the scholarly biographer of Franklin.

Of the Chinese cuisine, much has been eaten but much less written. It is a cuisine more and more admired in America, where some gourmets have been known to swear that if they had to forsake all others for the rest of their lives and choose only one, they would elect the Chinese table, in all its infinite variety. The essay by Lin Yutang given here, from his "My Country and My People," is a classic one on the subject, and not likely to be surpassed.

Dear old friend Thackeray adds a characteristic, tongue-in-cheek fillip to the whole subject of dining. No tablecloth? Excellent, says W. M. It means good food followed by good wine.

Of the Rock or Mountain

from A Delectable Garden
by Bernard Palissy

I HAVE TO DISCOURSE to thee now of an object which there will be in my garden, marvellously useful, beautiful, and pleasing. And when I shall have told it to thee, thou wilt know it was not without reason that I sought to build my garden adjoining the rocks.

Because the two sides of my garden, the one towards the north wind and the one towards the west, shall be encircled, closed, and surrounded by rocks and mountains, this will enable me to make my garden marvellously delectable. For along the two sides of the mountain I will have a great number of rooms dug out of the rock, whereof some shall serve as places in which to store the plants and herbs that are subject to frost on winter nights. Some of these plants will be carried thither in vessels of earth, others on engines made in the form of wheelbarrows, and some in vessels of wood, set up on wheels. Some of the aforesaid rooms will serve also to store seeds which are still on their stalks; some of the rooms will serve to store a large quantity of garden stakes, pitchforks, and withes, and all such tools required for the husbanding of the garden . . . also some of the rooms will serve to store the agricultural utensils, others to store for awhile the turnips, garlic, chestnuts, acorns, and such like objects necessary and proper to the ordering of a household. . . .

Now thou must note that I am going to discourse on something most useful and pleasing, which is, that above the aforesaid chambers I will also build in the rock a number of upper rooms along the platform which shall be built over the said lower rooms; and these upper rooms, being thus dug out of the mountain and the rock, will be most useful and pleasing; for one will be hewn in the fashion of a room with a reading desk to serve as a library and study; another will be shaped in another manner from that of the desk, and will be fashioned to hold distilled waters and divers vinegars; another will be fashioned with little closets to hold and harbor the seeds. There will be another which shall be made like the shelves of a merchant to hold a diversity of fruits, such as plums, cherries, figs, and other similar kinds. Also there will be one, which shall be most useful, in which to set up furnaces to distil waters and essences of sweet smelling herbs. There will be other rooms useful for the storing of fruits and all sorts of vegetables, such as beans, peas, lentils, and others of the same kind. All these chambers will be in a moderately warm and well aired place so they shall be suitable for these purposes.

Now thou seest the reason why the said chambers and mountains will be very useful, pleasing, and beautiful. In the first place, thou must note that in front of the said upper chambers there will be a wide and spacious alley, which shall be above the lower chambers, built for the convenience of the gardeners, as I told thee above. This alley will serve as a gallery in front of the aforesaid upper chambers. And to make it resemble a gallery more closely, I will build a wall along the front of the alley, facing the garden. Flowers will be planted in front of the wall on the garden side and between the entrances to the lower chambers. . . And in order to render the structure more pleasing and admirable, I will plant a large number of hawthorns and other shrubs bearing fruits good for the nourishment of birds, above the doors and windows of the upper chambers and along the hill. The aforesaid hawthornes and other shrubs will serve as a pergola above the doors and windows of the upper chambers, indeed, and will cover the whole length of the alley of the platform or gallery, and in this way those who could be in the upper chambers and those who would stroll in front of them will commonly have the pleasure of various ditties, which shall be sung by the birds in the aforesaid shrubs. . . .

And in addition to these things, the balustrade, which shall be erected towards the garden side, will be a very useful place upon which to ripen the plums, figs, cherries, and other fruits, which one is accustomed to ripen in the sun, because this place will be oriented in such a way that the sun will send out its rays to it all the day long; for the rocks, chambers, and galleries face towards the side of the east and south wind. And see how those who are busied with studing, distilling, and other labors in the aforesaid chambers, when they shall wish to rest, will come out onto the platform or gallery, and as they stroll along they will have the shrubs and little birds above their heads. And afterwards, wishing to gaze upon the beauty of the garden, they will come and lean on the rail, which shall be made purposely for this, and leaning there on their elbows they will see at one glance the whole beauty of the garden, and what is going on in it; also they will have the scent of certain damask roses, violets, sweet marjoram, sweet basil, and other such kinds of herbs, which shall be on the rail, planted in certain pottery vases glazed in different colors. These vases, spaced equally apart, will decorate and add greatly to the beauty of the garden and the aforesaid gallery.

Pleasures of the Simple Life

from The Anatomy of Melancholy
by Robert Burton

A POOR MAN TAKES more delight in an ordinary meal's meat, which he hath but seldom, than they do with all their exotic dainties and continual viands; 'tis the rarity and necessity that makes a thing acceptable and pleasant. Darius, put to flight by Alexander, drank puddle water to quench his thirst; and it was pleasanter, he swore, than any wine or mead. All excess, as Epictetus argues, will cause a dislike; sweet will be sour, which made that temperate Epicurus sometimes voluntarily fast. But they, being always accustomed to the same dishes (which are nastily dressed by slovenly cooks, that after their obscenities never wash their bawdy hands) be they fish, flesh, compounded, made dishes, or whatever else, are therefore cloyed; nectar's self grows loathsome to them, they are weary of all their fine palaces, they are to them but as so many prisons. A poor man drinks in a wooden dish, and eats his meat in wooden spoons, wooden platters, earthen vessels, and such homely stuff: the other in gold, silver, and precious stones; but with what success? . . . fear of poison in the one, security in the other. . .

Cleopatra hath whole boars and sheep served up to her table at once, drinks jewels dissolved, 40,000 sesterces in value, but to what end? *Num tibi cum fauces urit sitis, aurea quaeris Pucula?* Doth a man that is adry desire to drink in gold?

Juvenal on Hospitality

from the Fifth Satire
by Juvenal

For first, of this be sure, whene'er your lord
Thinks proper to invite you to his board,
He pays, or thinks he pays, the total sum
Of all your pains, past, present, and to come. . .

If, after two long months, he condescend
To waste a thought upon a humble friend,
Reminded by a vacant seat, and write,
"You, Master Trebius, sup with me tonight.". . .

Before your patron cups of price are placed,
Amber and gold, with rows of beryls graced:
Cups you can only at a distance view,
And never trusted to such a guest as you! . . .

If Virro's veins with indigestion glow,
They bring him water cooled in Scythian snow:
What! Did I late complain a different wine
Fell to thy share? A different water's thine!
Getulian slaves your vile potations pour,
Or the coarse paws of some huge, raw-boned Moor,
Whose hideous form the stoutest would affray,
If met, by moonlight, near the Latian way:
On him, a youth, the flower of Asia waits,
So dearly purchased that the joint estates
Of Tullus, Ancus, would not yield the sum,
Nor all the wealth of all the Kings of Rome! . . .

Mark with what insolence another thrusts
Before your plate, th' impenetrable crusts,
Black, mouldy, fragments which defy the saw,
The mere despair of every aching jaw! . . .

But lo! a lobster introduced in state
Stretches, enormous, o'er the bending plate!
Proud of a length of tail, he seems to eye
The humbler guests with scorn, as towering by,
He takes the place of honor at the board,
And, crowned with costly pickles, greets his lord!
A crab is yours, ill-garnished, and ill-fed,
With half an egg—a supper for the dead!
He pours Venafran oil upon his flesh,
While the stale coleworts in your wooden dish
Stink of the lamp; for such to you is thrown
Such rancid grease as Africk sends to town. . .

Vain hope! Near him a goose's liver lies,
A capon equal to a goose in size;
A boar, too, smokes, like that which fell, of old,
By the famed hero, with the locks of gold.
Last, if the spring its genial influence shed
And welcome thunders call them from their bed,
Large mushrooms enter: Ravish'd with their size,
"O Libya, keep thy grain!" Alledius cries,
And bid thy oxen to their stalls retreat,
Nor, while thou grow'st such mushrooms think of wheat!"
Meanwhile, to put your patience to the test,
Lo! the spruce carver to his task addrest,
Skips, like a harlequin, from place to place,
And waves his knife with pantomimick grace,
Till every dish be ranged, and every joint
Severed, by nicest rules, from point to point.
You think this folly—'tis a simple thought—
To such perfection, now, is carving brought,
That different gestures, by our curious men,
Are used for different dishes, hare and hen...

You champ on spongy toadstools, hateful treat!
Fearful of poison in each bite you eat:
He feasts secure on mushrooms fine as those
Which Claudius for his special eating chose,
Till one more fine, provided by his wife,
Finished at once, his feasting, and his life!
Apples as fragrant and as bright of hue
As those which in Alcinous' gardens grew,
Mellowed by constant sunshine; or as those
Which graced the Hesperides in burnished rows;
Apples which you may smell, but never taste,
Before your lord and his great friends are placed:
While you enjoy mere windfalls; such stale fruit
As serves to mortify the raw recruit...
Your palate still beguiles you! Ah, how nice
That smoking haunch! Now we shall have a slice!

Now that half hare is coming! Now a bit
Of that young pullet! Now—and thus you sit,
Thumbing your bread in silence; watching still
For what has never reached you, never will!
No more of freedom! 'Tis a vain pretense:
Your patron treats you like a man of sense.
For if you can, without a murmur, bear
You well deserve the insults which you share.
Anon, like voluntary slaves, you'll throw
Your humbled necks beneath the oppressor's blow,
Nay, with bare backs, solicit to be beat,
And merit such a friend, and such a treat!

Waste

from How to Live

by Solon Robinson

WHAT A LITTLE word this is; but what a big meaning it has! It seems to be in some way inseparably connected with every transaction and every act of our lives. Even life itself is one continual waste—animals and plants, from maturity to death; but that is natural waste—nature obeying nature's laws. The waste that we commit is unnatural and contrary to the laws of propriety and common sense.

Look into every kitchen; not only at the fat in the fire, but at the wasteful manner in which all of our cooking is done; besides the waste of food at the table. See how that delicate appetite—made delicate by waste—picks out a few choice morsels and carelessly casts the rest aside to go to waste.

It is safe to say that more food is wasted every day in this city than is eaten; not alone in the kitchen or at the table, but in our markets and store-houses, where whole cargoes of grain, meal, flour, meat, fish, fruit, and vegetables are continually being wasted through bad packing or bad management.

What a waste, too, are all of our retail purchases; and, because it is fashionable, buying food that wastes the most.

Is it any wonder that the poor suffer for food after committing such extravagant waste? Look at that man paying a dollar and a half—the price of a whole day's work—for a rib-roast of beef, to be cooked in the most wasteful way, when one half the money expended in a cheaper piece of meat, cooked in a different manner, with vegetables, bread, and gravy, would serve his family twice as long. But not so fashionable and genteel. No, and not so wasteful. Almost the whole system of American cookery is based upon a state of things that existed when we had such a surplus of food that the idea of waste was not taken into account.

There was a time, within but a few years past, at the West, when wheat could be purchased for twenty-five to forty cents a bushel, corn for ten or fifteen cents, pork for one to two cents a pound, and other things in proportion. It would be idle to talk to people about saving every iota of such cheap food.

To some extent the same cheapness has prevailed all over America, until the people have fallen into wasteful habits, both in keeping, cooking, and eating their food, that need reform.

It is probable that one half of the cooking in the kitchens of private families, in this city, is done by Irish servants, who possessed no higher art when they landed upon our shores than is required to boil and roast potatoes, or make an oatmeal cake or mess of porridge. The only art of saving they have any knowledge of is not to have anything to save. All that should be saved is hurried out of sight in the basket of some of their own countrymen at the basement door, thereby encouraging another great waste—the waste of time of these lazy beggars.

Some men waste their lives in finding out cunning inventions, which they hide under a bushel, or in some other wasteful place, where their light never can shine out upon the world, for he wastes both time and money in not letting the world know where he keeps his wares for sale. Neglecting to advertise is a waste of common sense, and of that there is a greater waste than of all other commodities in this great community.

A Dime a Day

from How to Live
by Solon Robinson

ONE DIME— 'Tis a little sum— 'tis often given for a drink or a cigar— 'tis soon burned out and wasted. It takes ten dimes to make a dollar, and a dollar is a common price for a single meal. It is soon eaten—its effects are not lasting, except when it produces dyspepsia, and then it often costs a hundred dimes to purchase medicine that does *not* cure the disease.

To those who never dine for less than a dollar, how unsatisfactory would be a dinner for a Dime! Reader, have you ever reflected how many entire families in this city, where food is so dear, dine, every day, for less than one Dime? Did you ever think of bestowing one Dime for charitable purposes, and how much good it would do? What if every subscriber to the *Weekly Tribune* should give one Dime, with his subscription, to be applied to the necessities of the needy, and deserving poor, in this city—did you ever consider what a sum it would be? Look at it—175,000 subscribers, at one Dime each, is $17,500! What if it were applied to purchase bread, say at five cents a loaf! It would buy 35,000 loaves of bread. What if we should announce that such a quantity of bread was about to be given to the poor in this city! The whole land would rejoice. How much can be done with one Dime!

Let us see what we would do with it if we had but one—only one Dime in the world—and yet with that must provide for a family consisting of a mother and four children for a whole day. We would not buy bakers' bread at sixpence a loaf—very small loaves, too, never weighing over a pound, however moist or however adulterated with corn, potatoes, or buckwheat, which are harmless—or with plaster of Paris, lime, alum, sulphate of zinc, ground bones, and we do not know how many other deleterious substances. No, we would not buy bakers' bread with our Dime, nor would we buy fine flour at six or seven cents a pound, else some of the children would go hungry. We might buy corn meal and make a cheap cake, or a pot of mush, or a larger pot of porridge, or we might buy two pounds of hominy, and then our Dime would feed the family one full meal; but to this latter article there is one objection. Where is the fuel to come from to cook this mess? for corn, more than any other grain, requires cooking to make it palatable and wholesome. Two, three, or even four hours of slow boiling is not too much. Our Dime will not cook as well as buy the corn meal or hominy. What then? Potatoes! Let us see. They require least cooking; but they cost, with all their water—and they are more than half water—two cents and a half a pound at retail.

Then they are not cheap food after all. It will not do to spend our Dime for potatoes. What then? It is no easy study to learn how to procure the most human food for a Dime; to ascertain how many hungry mouths may be fed—how many empty stomachs satisfied, for one Dime. It is a study too much neglected. It should be taught in all Public Schools. . . . What better wisdom could you teach them than how to procure the most food for a Dime? It is a little coin, but can be made to expand. It would be real charity—genuine charity—practical charity—to teach such scholars economy in food; not how to eat less, to live upon less—for Heaven knows some of them live upon little enough now—but to teach them what to buy, in case of emergency, with a little coin—only one Dime. We have lately learned that lesson, and we will teach it to you. We learned it of a woman—that is, the practical operation of it—though she says she learned it of us, from something she read about economizing food, in the *Tribune*.

"I had," said she, "one day last week, only one Dime in the world, and that was to feed me and my four children all day; for I would not ask for credit, and I would not borrow, and I never did beg. I did live through the day, and I did not go hungry. I fed myself and my family with one Dime."

"How?"

"Oh, that was not all. I bought fuel, too."

"What, with one Dime?"

"Yes, with one Dime! I bought two cents' worth of coke, because that is cheaper than coal, and because I could kindle it with a piece of paper in my little furnace, with two or three little bits of charcoal that some careless boy had dropped in the street just in my path. With three cents I bought a scraggy piece of salt pork, half fat and half lean. There might have been half a pound of it—the man did not weigh it. Now half my money was gone, and the show for breakfast, dinner, and supper was certainly a very poor one. With the rest of my Dime I bought four cents' worth of white beans. By-the-by, I got these at night, and soaked them in tepid water on a neighbor's stove till morning. I had one cent left. I bought one cent's worth of corn meal, and the grocery man gave me a red-pepper pod."

"What was that for?"

"Wait a little—you shall know. Of all things, peppers and onions are appreciated by the poor in winter, because they help to keep them warm. With my meal I made three dumplings, and these, with the pork and the pepper-pod, I put into the pot with the beans and plenty of water (for the pork was salt), and boiled the whole two hours; and then we had breakfast, for it was time for the children to go to school. We ate one of the dumplings, and each had a plate of the soup for breakfast, and a very good breakfast it was.

"I kept the pot boiling as long as my coke lasted, and at dinner we ate half the meat, half the soup, and one of the dumplings. We had the same allowance for supper; and the children were better satisfied than I have sometimes seen them when our food has cost five times as much. The next day we had another Dime—it was all I could earn for all I could get to do—two pairs of men's drawers each day at five cents a pair—and on that we lived—lived well. We had a change too, for instead of the corn meal and beans I got four cents' worth of oat-meal and one cent's worth of potatoes—small potatoes, because I could get more of them. I washed them clean, so as not to waste anything by paring, and cut them up and boiled them all to pieces with the meat and meal."

"Which went furthest?"

"I can't say. We ate it all each day, and didn't feel the want of more. . . ."

Economy in food would save all from want.

Economy in clothes would clothe all the destitute.

Economy in drink would make all rich, for that is all waste.

Mellering to the Organ

from Our Mutual Friend

by Charles Dickens

SORRY TO DEPRIVE you of a pipe, Wegg," he said, filling his own, "but you can't do both together. Oh! and another thing I forgot to name! When you come in here of an evening, and look round you, and notice anything on a shelf that happens to catch your fancy, mention it."

Wegg, who had been going to put on his spectacles, immediately laid them down, with the sprightly observation:

"You read my thoughts, sir. Do my eyes deceive me, or is that object up there a—a pie? It can't be a pie."

"Yes, it's a pie, Wegg," replied Mr. Boffin, with a glance of some little discomfiture at the Decline and Fall.

"*Have* I lost my smell for fruits, or is it an apple pie, sir?" asked Wegg.

"It's a veal and ham pie," said Mr. Boffin.

"Is it, indeed, sir? And it would be hard, sir, to name the pie that is a better pie than a weal and hammer," said Mr. Wegg, nodding his head emotionally.

"Have some, Wegg?"

"Thank you, Mr. Boffin, I think I will, at your invitation. I wouldn't at any other party's at the present juncture; but at yours, sir!—And meaty jelly too, especially when a little salt, which is the case where there's ham, is mellering to the organ, is wery mellering to the organ." Mr. Wegg did not say what organ, but spoke with a cheerful generality.

Cannes and Sweet Corn

by Carl Van Doren

from the New York Herald Tribune

THERE IS NO use talking about it one way or the other: what a man has eaten, that he remains. Red meats have left their robust trail in him. Vegetables have modified his native toughness. Fruit, no doubt, reaches to his very character, touching it with charm. Without salads, who can be better than a savage? While as for the various mixtures and combinations of alcohol, brewed or distilled from whatever rich essences of nature and allied with whatever proportions of water, they may rouse or satisfy or change the man, but they do form him, give them time and room enough.

Take me, for instance. Here I sit in a paradise of Amateurs of Food, and Eden of Eaters—in other words, in the town of Cannes on the most beautiful coast of France. I look out of my window at the Mediterranean not thirty yards away. For three days the mistral has been blowing as if all Africa were trying to get at Europe. The mistral has had its effect on my appetite. It has cooled the air, or at least has seemed to. It has kept the water in such paroxysms of motion and such panoramas of color that I have had to go swimming half a dozen times day, if only to pay proper homage to an element so beautiful. Well, cool air and exercise have made me hungry. At this very moment I am hungry, though I have just had my lunch.

Yet that is no reflection on the excellent chef of the Hotel Royal. My lunch began with a merlan fried to the turn which only art and experience could have given it. Very likely the fish came in this morning on one of the boats I can see from my window. His last state was thoroughly worthy of his first. After the merlan came an egg poached in the manner of Mornay (whoever or whatever Mornay was), riding on its customary toast and dripping with better than customary cheese. Then veal, of course—how many calves die each day that men may live on the Riviera! But this veal came in the company of small onions and new potatoes and a sauce, including mustard, to make Diogenes's tongue itch. The cheese was Gorgonzola, and nothing more, but I ate it with a ripe pear and followed it with a cluster of grapes, not too sweet. Then coffee and a mild Virginia cigarette. I really have no excuse for being hungry.

No excuse, that is to say, as a cosmopolitan. There happen, however, to be parts of me which are imperfectly cosmopolitan. It is forty years or so of American food which have done this thing to me. . .

And sweet corn. I shiver in the mistral as I think of what pleasure it would be to pluck ears of corn from their stalks and hurry them shrieking to the pot of boiling water destined for them. Not ears too young, of course. No silly rows of white grains. No protruding naked length of cob at the smaller end. Nothing immature, nothing unformed. The ears must be all at an even flush of growth, the rows close set, the grains full and well rooted. The color must be gold. Then minutes in boiling water are enough, but not too much. Then butter and salt on three rows at a time—not two, which is childish; not four, which is gluttonous—and the three rows eaten steadily from left to right as one reads poetry. Have not the teeth, which can neither taste nor smell, their peculiar sensation when they are plunged into choice morsels? And is any sensation which they ever have more grateful than this, when they feel themselves measuring off the three rows, taking a preliminary hold of them, and then sinking to the cob, cleanly carrying away their booty?

If there is a sensation more grateful it is only when the sweet corn has not been boiled, but has been roasted in its own husks in hot embers, so that it has the taste of smoke about it and here and there a part of the ear a little charred by the heat.

The Chinese Cuisine

from My Country and My People
by Lin Yutang

THE QUESTION HAS often been asked as to what we eat. The answer is that we eat all the edible things on this earth. We eat crabs by preference, and often eat barks by necessity. Economic necessity is the mother of our inventions in food. We are too overpopulated and famine is too common for us not to eat everything we can lay our hands on. And it stands to reason that that in this positively exhaustive experiment on edibles we should have stumbled upon important discoveries, as most scientific or medical discoveries have been stumbled upon. For one thing, we have discovered the magic tonic and building qualities of ginseng, for which I am willing to give personal testimony as to its being the most enduring and most energy-giving tonic known to mankind, distinguished by the slowness and gentleness of its action. But apart from such accidental discoveries of medical or culinary importance, we are undoubtedly the only truly omnivorous animals on earth, and so long as our teeth last, we should continue to occupy that position. Some day a dentist will yet discover that we have the best teeth as a nation. Gifted with these teeth and driven by famine, there is no reason why we should not at some particular time of our national life suddenly discover that roasted beetles and fried bee's chrysalis are great delicacies. The only thing we have not discovered and will not eat is cheese. The Mongols could not persuade us to eat cheese, and the Europeans do not have a greater chance of doing so.

It is useless to use logical reasoning in the matter of our food, which is determined by prejudices. On both sides of the Atlantic Ocean two shellfish are common, the soft-shelled clam, *Mya Arenaria*, and the edible mussel, *Mytilus edulis*. The species of these two mollusks are the same on both sides of the water. In Europe, mussels are eaten freely but not clams, while the reverse is the case on the American side, according to the authority of Dr. Charles W. Townsend (*Scientific Monthly*, July, 1928). Dr. Townsend also mentions the fact that flounders fetch high prices in England and in Boston but are considered "not fit to eat" by Newfoundland villagers. We eat mussels with the Europeans and eat clams with the Americans, but we don't eat oysters raw as the Americans do. It is useless, for instance, for anybody to convince me that snake's meat tastes like chicken. I have lived in China forty years without eating a snake, or seeing any of my relatives do so. Tales of eating snakes travel faster than tales of eating chicken, but actually we eat more chickens and better chickens than the white people, and snake-eating is as much a curiosity to the Chinese as it is to the foreigners.

All one can say is that we are very catholic in our tastes, and that any rational man can take anything off a Chinese table without any qualm of conscience. What famine dictates is not for us human mortals to choose. There is nothing that a man will not eat when pressed by hunger. And no one is entitled to condemn until he knows what famine means. Some of us have been forced in times of famine to eat babies—and even this must be humanly rare—but, thank God, we do not eat them raw as the English eat their beef!

If there is anything we are serious about, it is neither religion nor learning, but food. We openly acclaim eating as one of the few joys of this human life. This question of attitude is very important, for unless we are honest about it we will never be able to lift eating and cooking into an art. The difference of attitude regarding the problem of food is represented in Europe by the French and the English. The French eat enthusiastically, while the English eat apologetically.

The Chinese national genius decidedly leans toward the French in the matter of feeding ourselves.

The danger of not taking food seriously and allowing it to degenerate into a slipshod business may be studied in the English national life. If they had known any taste for food their language would reveal it. The English language does not provide a word for cuisine: they call it just "cooking." They have no proper word for *chef:* they just call him a cook. They do not speak about their *menu,* but know only what are called "dishes." And they have no word for *gourmet:* they just call him "Greedy Gut" in their nursery rhymes. The truth is, the English do not admit that they have a stomach. No stomach is fit for conversation unless it happens to be "sick" or "aching." The result is that while the Frenchman will talk about the *cuisine* of his *chef* with—what seems to the English mind—immodest gestures, the Englishman can hardly venture to talk about the "food" of his "cook" without impairing the beauty of his language. When hard pressed by his French host he might be willing to mutter between his teeth that "that pudding is awfully good" and there let the matter rest. Now if a pudding is good it is good for some definite reasons, and about these problems the Englishman does not bother himself. All the English are interested in is how to strengthen themselves against influenza, as with Bovril, and save the doctor's bills.

Now you cannot develop a national culinary art unless you are willing to discuss it and exchange your opinions on it. The first condition of learning how to eat is to talk about it. Only in a society wherein people of culture and refinement inquire after their cooks' health, instead of talking about the weather, can the art of *cuisine* be developed. No food is really enjoyed unless it is keenly anticipated, discussed, eaten, and then commented upon. Preachers should not be afraid to condemn a bad steak from their pulpits and scholars should write essays on the culinary art as the Chinese scholars do. Long before we have any special food, we think about it, rotate it in our minds, anticipate it as a secret pleasure to be shared with some of our closest friends, and write notes about it in our invitation letters, like the following: "my nephew just brought some special vinegar from Chinkiang and a real Nanking salted duck from Laoyuchai," or this, "This is the end of June, and if you don't come, you won't taste another shad till next May." Long before the autumn moon rises, a real scholar, like Li Liweng as himself confesses, would plan and save money for the crabs, decide upon an historical place where he could have the crab dinner with his friends under the mid-autumn moon or in a wilderness of chrysanthemums, negotiate with some of his friends to bring wine from Governor Tuan Fang's cellar, and meditate upon it as the English meditate upon their champion sweepstakes number. Only in this spirit can the matter of feeding ourselves be elevated into the level of an art.

We are unashamed of our eating. We have "Su Tungp'o pork" and "Kiang bean-curd." In England, a Wordsworth steak or Galsworthy cutlet would be unimaginable. Wordsworth sang about "simple living and high thinking," but he failed to note that good food, especially fresh-cut bamboo-shoots and mushrooms, counts among the real joys of a simple rural life. The Chinese poets, with a more utilitarian philosophy, have frankly sung about the "minced perch and *shun*-vegetable soup" of their native home. This thought is regarded as so poetic that officials in their petition for resignment will say that they are "thinking of *shun*-vegetable" as a most elegant expression. Actually our love of fatherland is largely a matter of recollection of the keen sensual pleasures of our childhood. The loyalty to Uncle Sam is the loyalty to American doughnuts, and the loyalty to the *Vaterland* is the loyalty to *Pfannkuchen* and *Stollen*, but the Americans and the Germans will not admit it. Many Americans while abroad sigh for their ham and sweet potatoes at home, but they will not admit that this makes them think of home, nor will they put it in their poetry.

The seriousness with which we regard eating can be shown in many ways. Anyone who opens the pages of the *Red Chamber Dream* or of any Chinese novel will be struck by the detailed and constant descriptions of the entire menu of what Taiyü had for breakfast or what Paoyü had at midnight. Cheng Panch'iao apotheosized rice congee in his letter to his brother:

On cold days, when poor relatives or friends arrive, first hand them a bowl of fried rice in boiling water, with a small dish of ginger or pickles. It is the most effective means of warming up old people and the poor. In your days of leisure, swallow cakes made of broken rice, or cook "slipslop congee," and hold the bowl between your two hands and eat it with shrugged shoulders. On a cold frosty morning, this will make your whole body warm. Alas! Alas! I think I'll become a farmer for the remainder of my days!

The Chinese accept food as they accept sex, women, and life in general. No great English poet or writer would condescend to write a Cook Book, which they regard as belonging outside the realms of literature and worthy of the efforts of Aunt Susan only. But the great poet-dramatist Li Liweng did not consider it beneath his dignity to write about the cooking of mushrooms and all kinds of vegetarian and non-vegetarian foods. Another great poet and scholar, Yüan Mei, wrote a whole book on cooking, besides writing a most wonderful essay on his cook. He described his cook as Henry James described the English butler, as a man carrying himself with dignity and understanding in his profession. But H. G. Wells, who of all English minds is the one most likely to write about English food, evidently cannot write it, and no hope is to be expected from the less encyclopedic minds. Anatole France was the type that might have left us some wonderful recipe for frying calf's liver or cooking mushrooms, possibly in his intimate letters, but I doubt very much whether he has left it as part of his literary heritage.

Two principles distinguish Chinese from European cooking. One is that we eat food for its *texture,* the elastic or crisp effect it has on our teeth, as well as for fragrance, flavor, and color. Li Liweng said that he was a slave to crabs, because they had the combination of fragrance, flavor, and color. The idea of texture is seldom understood, but a great part of the popularity of bamboo-shoots is due to the fine resistance the young shoots give to our teeth. The appreciation of bamboo-shoots is probably the most typical example of our taste. Being not oily, it has a certain fairy-like "fugitive" quality about it. But the most important principle is that it lends flavor to meat (especially pork) cooked with it, and, on the other hand, it receives the flavor of the pork itself. This is the second principle, that of mixing of flavors. The whole culinary art of China depends on the art of mixture. While the Chinese recognize that many things, like fresh fish, must be cooked in their own juice, in general they mix flavors a great deal more than Western cooks do. No one, for instance, knows how cabbage tastes until he has tasted it when properly cooked with chicken, and the chicken flavor has gone into the cabbage and the cabbage flavor has gone into the chicken. From this principle of mixture, any number of fine and delicate combinations can be developed. Celery, for instance, may be eaten raw and alone, but when Chinese see, in a foreign dinner, vegetables like spinach or carrots cooked separately and then served on the same plate with pork or roast goose, they smile at the barbarians.

The Chinese, whose sense of proportion is so wonderfully acute in painting and architecture, seem to have completely lost it in the matter of food, to which they give themselves wholeheartedly when they seat themselves around a dinner table. Any big course, like the fat duck, coming after twelve or thirteen other courses should be a sufficient meal in itself for any human being. This is due to a false standard of courtesy, and to the fact that as course after course is served during dinners, the people are supposed to be occupied in different wine-games or contests of poetry during the intervals, which naturally lengthens the time required and gives more time for the stomach to assimilate the food. Most probably the relatively lower efficiency of Chinese government officials is due directly to the fact that all of them are subjected to an inhuman routine of three or four dinners a night. One-fourth of their food goes to nourish them, and three-fourths to kill them. That accounts for the prevalence of rich men's ailments, like diseases of the liver and the kidney, which are periodically announced in the newspapers when these officials see fit to retire from the political arena for reasons of convenience.

Although the Chinese may learn from the West a great deal about a sense of proportion in arranging for feasts, they have, in this field as in medicine, many famous and wonderful recipes to teach the Westerners. In the cooking of ordinary things like vegetables and chickens, the Chinese have a rich store to hand to the West, when the West is ready and humble enough to learn it. . . .

But enough has been said to show that the Chinese, in their moments of sanity, know essentially how to live. The art of living is with them a second instinct and a religion. Whoever said that the Chinese civilization is a spiritual civilization is a liar.

Naked Mahogany Means Good Food, Good Wine

from Barmecide Banquets

by William Makepeace Thackeray

LET US SEE the naked mahogany; it means, I think, not only a good dinner, but a *good drink after dinner*. In houses where they leave the cloth down you know they are going to shirk their wine. And what is a dinner without a subsequent drink? A mockery—an incomplete enjoyment at least. Do you and I go out to dine that we may have the pleasure of drinking tea in the drawing-room, and hearing Miss Anne or Miss Jane sing? Fiddlededee! I can get the best singing in the world for half a guinea! Do we expend money in cabs, kid-gloves, and awful waist-coats, in order to get muffins and tea? Bah! Nay, does any man of sense declare honestly that he likes ladies' conversation? I have read in novels that it was pleasant, the refinement of woman's society—the delightful influence of a female presence, and so forth; but say now, as a man of the world and an honest fellow, did you ever get any good out of women's talk? What a bore a clever woman is!—what a frightful bore a mediocre, respectable woman is! And every woman who is worth anything will confess as much. There is no woman but *one* after all. But mum! I am getting away from the dinner-table; they it was who dragged me from it, and it was for parsimony's sake, and to pleasure them, that the practice of leaving on the cloth for dessert was invented.

This I honestly say as a diner-out in the world. If I accept an invitation to a house where the dessert-cloth practice is maintained (it must be, I fear, in large dinners of *apparat* now, but I mean in common *reunions* of ten or fourteen)—if I accept a dessert-cloth invitation, and a mahogany invitation subsequently comes, I fling over dessert-cloth. To ask you to a dinner without a drink is to ask you to half a dinner.

MADAME EGLENTINE

"At mete was she wele ytaughte withalle;
She lette no morsel from lippes falle,
Ne weete hire fingeres with her sauce depe.
Wel coulde she carie a morsel, and wel kepe,
That no drope ne fell upon hire brest.
In curtesie was sette full moche hire lest,
Hire over-lippe wiped she so clene,
That in hire cuppe was no ferthing sene
Of grese, when she dronken hadde hire draught.
Ful semely after hire mete she raught."

—Geoffrey Chaucer

THE MASTER SPEAKS

Brillat-Savarin is well distributed in this volume, as he is in every other collection of writing about food, and deservedly so because it is quite possible no other writer on the subject is his equal. Following are two of his philosophical observations (most of what he wrote was, indeed, philosophical in the large sense), encompassing the act of dining itself, and the senses which make possible its enjoyment. They are extracted from the books by which he is best remembered.

Reflections on the Pleasures of the Table

from The Physiology of Taste
by Brillat-Savarin

THE PLEASURE OF eating is common to us with animals; it merely supposes hunger, and that which is necessary to satisfy it. The pleasure of the table is peculiar to the human species; it supposes antecedent attention to the preparation of the repast, to the choice of place, and the assembling of guests. The pleasure of eating requires, if not hunger, at least appetite; the pleasure of the table is most frequently independent of both.

Some poets complained that the neck, by reason of its shortness, was opposed to the duration of the pleasure of tasting; others deplored the limited capacity of the stomach which will not hold, upon the average, more than two quarts of pulp; and Roman dignitaries went the length of sparing it the trouble of digesting the first meal, to have the pleasure of swallowing a second. . . The delicacy of our manners would not endure this practice; but we have done better, and we have arrived at the same end by means recognized by good taste. Dishes have been invented so attractive, that they unceasingly renew the appetite, and which are at the same time so light, that they flatter the palate without loading the stomach. Seneca would have called them *Nubes Esculentas*. We are, indeed, arrived at such a degree of alimentary progression, that if the calls of business did not compel us to rise from table, or if the want of sleep did not interpose, the duration of meals might be almost indefinite, and there would be no sure *data* for determining the time that might elapse between the first glass of Madeira and the last glass of punch.

The Senses

from Handbook of Dining

by Brillat-Savarin

THE SENSES ARE the organs by which man is brought into contact with external objects.

Sight, which embraces space, and informs us, through the medium of light, of the existence and of the color of the bodies which surround us.

Hearing, which receives, through the intermedium of the air, the vibration caused by noisy or sonorous bodies.

Smell, by the means of which we appreciate the odor of bodies that possess it.

Taste, by which we appreciate every thing sapid or exculent.

Touch, the object of which is the consistency and surface of bodies.

If we may be allowed to carry back our imagination to the first moments of the existence of the human species, we may also be allowed to fancy that the first sensations were purely direct, that is to say that man saw without precision, heard confusedly, smelt without discernment, ate without savor, and was in fact little better than a brute in all his enjoyments.

But as all these sensations have the soul as a common center—the especial distinction of the human species—and the ever active cause of a striving toward perfection, they become modified, swayed by judgment and comparison, and soon all the senses came to the aid of each other for the benefit of the sensitive being or individual.

Thus the sense of touch rectified the errors of sight; sound, by means of articulated words, became the interpreter of every sentiment; taste became benefited by sight and smell; hearing compared sounds and appreciated distances.

The torrent of centuries rolling over the human race has incessantly engendered new perfections, the cause of which, though almost invisible, is to be found in the play of the senses, which, in rotation, exact agreeable employment.

Thus sight gave rise to painting, sculpture, and all sorts of displays.

Sound gave birth to melody, to harmony, to dance, and music, and their branches.

Smell to the discovery and cultivation of perfumes.

Taste to the production, selection, and preparation of every species of food.

Touch gave birth to every branch of industry.

A man who has dined at a sumptuous table, in a hall resplendent with mirrors, pictures, statuary, flowers, delicate perfumes, adorned with beautiful women, and enlivened by the sound of soft music, will not need much mental effort to be convinced that all the sciences have been placed under contribution to heighten and crown the enjoyments of taste.

Taste is that one of our senses which brings us in contact with sapid substances, through the medium of the sensation they produce upon the organ destined to appreciate them.

Taste is aroused by appetite, hunger, and thirst; it is the basis of many operations, the result of which is that the individual grows, develops, lives, and repairs the losses caused by vital evaporations....

Taste appears to have two principal functions:

1. It invites us by pleasure to repair the continual losses we incur by the action of life.

2. It aids us to select amongst the various substances which nature offers us those most suitable for food.

In this selection, taste is powerfully aided by smell, as we shall see further on; for it may be asserted as a general maxim that nutritious substances are not repulsive either to taste or smell.

The number of flavors is infinite, for every substance capable of solution has a peculiar flavor of its own.

The sense of smell has a great influence on taste. I am inclined to believe that taste and smell are one and the same sense, the laboratory of which is the mouth, and the nose the chimney. The nose is a sentinel, and is always on the alert to cry, *Who's there?*

Take away the sense of smell, and that of taste goes with it....

The man who eats a peach is first agreeably struck by its fragrance; he puts a slice in his mouth, and experiences a sensation of freshness and acidity, which induces him to continue; but it is only at the moment he swallows that the real perfume of the peach is revealed: this is the complete sensation caused by a peach.

Finally, it is only when he has swallowed the morsel that he can exclaim, "That was delicious!"

The same may be said of a man who drinks a good glass of wine. As long as the wine is in his mouth he experiences an agreeable, but not a perfect impression. It is only when he has swallowed the liquid that he really can taste, appreciate, and discern the particular perfume of the wine; and then a few minutes must be allowed to the *gourmet* to give vent to his feelings by: *"Peste, c'est du Chambertin!"* or, *"Mon Dieu! c'est du Surêne!"*

This will suffice to prove that your real connoisseur sips his wine; at every sip he takes he has the sum total of the pleasure which another man enjoys when he swallows a whole glass. . . .

Let us now take a philosophical glance at the pleasure or unpleasantness taste may occasion.

We first find the application of that, unhappily, too general truth, that man is more organized for suffering than for experiencing pleasure.

In fact, the injection of very bitter, acid, or tart substance may cause us the sensation of excruciating pain. It is even supposed that hydrocyanic acid only kills so rapidly because it causes such excruciating agony that the vital powers cannot support it.

Agreeable sensations, on the contrary, are on a limited scale; and though there is a marked difference between what is insipid and what is palatable, there is no great interval between what is admitted to be good and what is reputed excellent; for example: 1st term, hard-boiled beef; 2nd term, a piece of veal; 3rd term, a pheasant roasted to a turn.

Yet taste, such as nature has awarded it to us, is still that sense which, well considered, procures us the greatest degree of enjoyment.

1st. Because the pleasure of eating is the only one which, done in moderation, is not followed by fatigue.

2nd. Because it is of all times, all ages, all conditions.

3rd. Because it returns necessarily, at least once a day, and may be repeated without inconvenience two or three times within the same period of time.

4th. Because it may be enjoyed with other enjoyments, and even console us for their absence.

5th. Because its impressions are more durable and more dependent on our will; and,

6th, and finally. Because in eating we experience a certain indescribably keen sensation of pleasure, by what we eat we repair the losses we have sustained, and prolong life.

GRACE AT MEALS

In houses where the grace is as indispensable as the napkin, who has not seen that never settled question as to who shall say it? while the good man of the house and the visitor clergyman, or some other guest, belike of next authority from years or gravity, shall be bandying about the office between them as a matter of compliment, each not unwilling to shift the burden of an equivocal duty from his own shoulders.

—Charles Lamb

ST. PAUL'S ADVICE TO TIMOTHY

Drink no longer water, but use a little wine for
thy stomach's sake and thine often infirmities.

—Timothy, V

How admirable and beautiful are eating and drinking, and what a great invention the human digestive system is! How much better to be a man than an alligator! The alligator can fast for a year and half, whereas five hours' abstinence will set an edge on the most pampered human appetite. Nature has advanced a little since Mesozoic times. I feel certain that there are whole South Seas of discovery yet to be made in the art and science of eating and drinking.

—John Davidson

In short the world is but a Ragou, or a large dish of Varieties, prepared by inevitable Fate to treat and regale Death with.

—from *Miscellanies: or a Variety of Notion and Thought,* by H. W. (Gent.) (Henry Waring), 1708.

Chapter Twenty-two

DRAMA AND POETRY

FOOD LENDS ITSELF to poetry, less so to drama, but sometimes happily to both, as in the case of Shakespeare, from whose numerous meditations on the subject we have snipped two morsels.

Swift, in his satiric way, used the pleasures of the table sometimes to dissect further the personalities of the diners, as he does in a passage from "Polite Conversation." Athenaeus, on the other hand, has Machon dissecting himself in his poem on the art of fish-eating, while Ovid deplores Erisichthon's voracity and Oliver Goldsmith satirizes a whole list of his distinguished contemporary fellow eaters, wryly including himself.

Alexander Pope, imitating Horace, counsels on the wisdom of moderation and cites the poet's simple life as model, a sharp contrast to the lusty Captain Charles Morris, who celebrates the virtues of "Honest Ned," a pugilist who drew his last breath in the dining room of the Society of the Sublime Steaks. Ned's real name, should there be a sports historian in the audience, was Edward Heardson. Morris somehow sums up the philosophy of food in the simplest way when he tells us lyrically, "I like what is good."

A Cake of Wheat

from Troilus and Cressida

by William Shakespeare

PANDARUS: He that will have a cake out of the wheat must needs tarry the grinding.

Troilus: Have I not tarried?

Pandarus: Ay, the grinding; but you must tarry the bolting.

Troilus: Have I not tarried?

Pandarus: Ay, the bolting; but you must tarry the leavening.

Troilus: Still have I tarried.

Pandarus: Ay, to the leavening; but here's yet in the word 'hereafter' the kneading, the making of the cake, the heating of the oven, and the baking; nay, you must stay the cooling too, or you may chance to burn your lips.

No Skill in Grass

from All's Well That Ends Well
by William Shakespeare

LAFEU: 'Twas a good lady, 'twas a good lady; we may pick a thousand salads, ere we light on such another herb.
Clown: Indeed, Sir, she was the sweet marjoram of the salad, or rather the herb of grace.
Lafeu: They are not salad-herbs, you knave, they are nose-herbs.
Clown: I am no great Nebuchadnezzar, Sir, I have not much skill in grass.

Fish Should Swim Thrice

MISS (to Lady Answ.): Madame, will your Ladyship help me to some Fish?
Ld. Smart (to Neverout): Tom, they say Fish should swim thrice.
Neverout: How is that, my Lord?
Ld. Smart: Why, Tom, first it should swim in the Sea (Do you mind me?), then it should swim in Butter; and at last, Sirrah, it should swim in good Claret. I think I have made it out.

—JONATHAN SWIFT, in *Polite Conversation*

Machon, on the Art of Fish-Eating

from The Deipnosophists

by Athenaeus

I AM A fish-eater, and this is now
The whole foundation of the art we practice.
And he who wishes not to spoil the dishes
Served up to others, should be pleased himself.
For he who rightly cares for his own eating
Will not be a bad cook. And if you keep
Your organs, sense and taste, in proper order,
You will not err. But often taste your dishes
While you are boiling them. Do they want salt?
Add some;—is any other seasoning needed?
Add it, and taste again—till you've arrived
At harmony of flavor; like a man
Who tunes a lyre till it rightly sounds.
And then, when everything is well in tune,
Bring in a troop of willing damsels fair;
Equal in number to the banqueters.

The Voracity of Erisichthon

by Ovid

Without delay, what sea, what earth, what air,
Affords at his commands, they straight prepare;
Yet at full tables he complains of hunger,
And for a feast of feasts he calls, in anger.
What a whole city or a lord supplies,
For the content of one will not suffice.
The more his guts devour, the more he craves,
As rivers are exhausted by the waves,
While the insatiate sea, and thirsty sands,
Drinks up the floods, still rolling from the lands;
Or, as the fire no nourishment refuses,
Burns all that comes, but neither picks nor chooses,
And still the more 'tis fed, it feeds the more:
Thus Erisichthon's profane chops devour
All sorts of food; in him food is the cause
Of hunger; and he'll employ his jams
To whet his appetite.

A United Feast

from Retaliation

by Oliver Goldsmith

OF OLD, when Scarron his companions invited,
Each guest brought his dish, and the feast was united.
If our landlord supplies us with beef and with fish,
Let each guest bring himself, and he brings the best dish;
Our Dean shall be venison, just fresh from the plains;
Our Burke shall be tongue, with a garnish of brains;
Our Will shall be wild fowl, of excellent flavor,
And Dick with his pepper shall heighten the savor;
Our Cumberland's sweet-bread its place shall obtain,
And Douglas is pudding substantial and plain;
Our Garrick's a salad, for in him we see
Oil, vinegar, sugar, and saltness agree:
To make out the dinner, full certain I am
That Ridge is anchovy, and Reynolds is lamb;
That Hickey's a capon, and by the same rule,
Magnanimous Goldsmith a gooseberry fool.

On Moderation

from Imitations of the Satires of Horace
by Alexander Pope

WHAT, and how great, the Virtue and the Art
To live on little with a cheerful heart
(A Doctrine sage, but truly none of mine),
Let's talk my friends, but talk before we dine:
Not when a gilt Buffet's reflected pride
Turns you from sound Philosophy aside;
Not when from Plate to Plate your eyeballs roll,
And the brain dances to the mantling bowl . . .

Go work, hunt, exercise! (he thus began)
Then scorn a homely dinner if you can.
Your wine locked up, your Butler strolled abroad,
Or kept from fish (the River yet un-thaw'd)
If then plain bread and milk will do the feat
The pleasure lies in you, not in the meat.
Preach as I please, I doubt our curious men
Will chuse a Pheasant still before a Hen;
Yet Hens of Guinea full as good I hold,
Except you eat the feathers green and gold.
Of Carps and Mullets, why prefer the great,
(Tho' cut in pieces e'er my Lord can eat),
Yet for small Turbots such esteem profess?
Because God made these large, the other less.

Oldfield, with more than happy throat endu'd
Cries, "Send me Gods! a whole Hog barbecu'd!"
Oh blast it, South winds, till a stench exhale
Rank as the ripeness of a Rabbit's tail
By what Criterion do ye eat, d'ye think,
If this is prized for sweetness, that for stink?
When the tired Glutton labors thro' a Treat
He'll find no relish in the sweetest Meat,
He calls for something bitter, something sour,
And the rich feast concludes extremely poor;
Cheap eggs, and herbs, and herbs, and olives, still we see.
This much is left of old Simplicity!
The robin-red-breast till of late had rest,
And children sacred held a Martin's nest
Till Becca-ficos sold so devilish dear,
To one that was, or would have been, a Peer.
Let me extoll a Cat on Oysters fed,
I'll have a Party at the Bedford Head,
Or even to crack live Crawfish recommend
I'd never doubt at Court to make a friend . . .

Between Excess and Famine lies a mean,
Plain, but not sordid, tho' not splendid, clean.
Avidian and his Wife (no matter which
For him you'll call a dog, and her a bitch)
Sell their presented Partridges and Fruits,
And humbly live on Rabbits and on Roots:
One half-pint bottle serves them both to dine,
And is at once their vinegar and wine . . .
He knows to live who keeps the middle state
And neither leans on this side or on that:
Nor stops for one bad Cork his butler's pay,
Swears, like Albutius, a good Cook away;
Nor lets, like Naevius, every error pass,
The measly wine, foul cloth, or greasy glass.

A *Poet's Simple Fare*

from the Imitations
by Alexander Pope

CONTENT WITH LITTLE I can piddle here
On broccoli and mutton round the year;
But ancient friends, tho' poor, or out of play,
That touch my bell, I cannot turn away.
'Tis true, no turbots dignify my boards,
But gudgeons, flounders, what my Thames affords:
To Hounslow Heath I point, the Bansted-Down,
Thence comes your mutton, and these chicks my own.
From yon walnut-tree a shower shall fall;
And grapes, long lingering on my only wall;
And figs from standard and espalier join;
The devil is in you if you cannot dine.
Then chearful healths, (your mistress shall have place)
And, what's more rare, a poet shall say grace.

Epitaph to Honest Ned

by Captain Charles Morris

HIS LAST STEAK DONE, his fire raked out and dead,
Dish'd for the worms himself, lies Honest Ned.
We, who partook of all his fleshly toils,
Received his bastings, too, and shared his broils.
Now in our turn a mouthful carve and trim,
And dress at Phoebus' fire our steak for him.
His heart, which well deserved a noble grave,
Was watchful, patient, modest, just, and brave,
And never did earth's wide maw a morsel gain,
Of kindlier juices or more tender grain.
His tongue, where duteous friendship humbly dwelt,
Charm'd all who heard the faithful zeal he felt.
Still, to whatever end his chops he moved,
'Twas all well seasoned, relished, and approved.
This room his heaven! when threatening fate drew nigh,
And death's chill shade had dimmed his lingering eye,
His fondest hopes, betrayed with many a tear,
Were that his life's last spark might glimmer here;
And the last words that choked his parting sigh,
'Oh, at your feet, dear masters, let me die!' "

I Like What Is Good

from Songs

by Captain Charles Morris

OLD LUCULLUS, they say
Forty cooks had each day,
And Vitellius's meals cost a million;
But I like what is good
When or where be my food,
In a chop-house or royal pavillion.

At all feasts (if enough)
I most heartily stuff,
And a song at my heart alike rushes,
Though I've not fed my lungs
Upon nightingales' tongues,
Nor the brains of goldfinches and thrushes.

FIGURE OF A FEAST

Ingenious Lister, were a picture drawn
With Cynthia's face, but with a neck like brawn,
With wings of turkey, and with feet of calf,
Tho' drawn by Kneller, it would make you laugh!
Such is (good Sir) the figure of a feast,
By some rich farmer's wife and sister drest.
Which, were it not for plenty and for steam,
Might be resembled to a sick man's dream,
Where all ideas huddling run so fast,
That syllabubs come first and soups the last.

—KING's *Art of Cookery*

Chapter Twenty-three

PROVERBS, ADAGES AND MAXIMS

ONE MAN'S ADAGE may be another man's cliché, but it is true that the old familiar saying abounds in cookery as much as it does in any other human activity. Somehow, too, food lends itself to the well turned maxim, as in "Apologies butter no parsnips."

Not all of this advice can be recommended. Modern medicine would take a poor view of such a simple remedy as "An apple, an egg, and a nut, you may eat after a slut," and not every married man is likely to agree that "Good cooks always have good tempers." But we say, "If the adage fits, put it on."

ENOUGH is as good as a feast.

There is little difference between a feast and a belly-full.

Eat to live, but do not live to eat.

Much meat, much maladies.

More meat, less manners.

Spare dinner, spare doctor.

Too much pudding will choke a dog.

Feed sparingly, and defy the physician.

Dry bread at home is better than roast meat abroad.

A bean at liberty is better than a comfit in prison.

He that eats the king's goose shall be choked with the feathers.

Scald not your lips with another man's pottage.

The wholesomest meat is at another's man's cost.

The belly is not filled with fair words.

Apologies butter no parsnips.

Great boast and small roast make unsavory mouths.

There is no great banquet but some fare ill.

The more the merrier, the fewer the better cheer.

Better be meals many than one too merry.

A fat housekeeper made lean executors.

A fat kitchen, a lean will.

Silks and satins put out the kitchen fire.

To pinch the belly in order to flatter the back.

He that would live for aye must eat sage (or salad) in May.

Like lips like lettuce: a thistle is a salad fit for an ass's mouth.

A donkey likes thistles, because he is an ass.

Butter is gold in the morning, silver at noon, lead at night.

An egg and to bed.

They that have no other meat, bread-and-butter are glad to eat.

That which will not be butter, must be made into cheese.

Good kail (pottage) is half a meal.

Poor folks are glad of pottage.

Prettiness makes no pottage.

But to make good pottage it is not necessary that a woman should be ugly.

All flesh is not venison.

All flesh is grass.

The nearer the bone the sweeter the meat.

When the shoulder of mutton is going, it is good to take a slice.

The cut that is worst of a leg is the first.

There's no deceit in a bag-pudding.

Two plum-puddings are better than one.

In time for pudding.

Oh, bother your books and all their receipting,
The proof of the pudding is in the eating.

After cheese comes nothing.

A bit in the morning was better than nothing all day long.

Often and little eating makes a man fat.

A child and a chicken must always be picking.

If I were to fast for my life, I would eat a good breakfast in the morning.

He that would eat a good dinner, let him eat a good breakfast.

Dinners cannot be long where dainties want.

He that saveth his dinner will have more for supper.

Who goes to bed supperless, all night tumbles and tosses.

Meat is much, but manners are more.

It was good to be merry at meat.

None but fools and fiddlers sing at their meat.

Cease your chatter and mind your platter.

The edge of the table as everyone knows, was never made for little elbows.

The ass that brays most eats least.

Never be ashamed to eat your meat.

Who gives the capon, give him the leg and wing.

The wing with the liver for him who's the giver.

He can give little to his servant who licks his own trancher.

Go early to the fish-market and late to the shambles.

He who would have a hare for breakfast must hunt overnight.

If thou hast not a capon, feed on an onion.

He who hathe much pease may put more in the pot.

New meat needs new appetite.

He who boils his pot with chips, makes his broth smell of smoke.

An apple, an egg, and a nut, you may eat after a slut.

There's no use crying over spilt milk.

Don't swear, or the butter won't come.

The watched pot boileth not.

Sweet meat must have sour sauce.

Good cooks always have good tempers.

Take heed of enemies reconciled and meat twice boiled.

The first dish pleaseth all.

A good salad is the prologue to a bad supper.

He would live for aye must eat sallet in May.

A fool can pick a sallet as well as a wiser man.

Four persons are wanted to make a good salad, a spendthrift for oil, a miser for vinegar, a counselor for salt, and a madman to stir all up.

DESSERT

" 'Tis the dessert that graces all the feast,
For an ill end disparages the rest;
A thousand things well done, and one forgot,
Defaces obligation with a blot."

—Dr. King, *Art of Cookery*

A cook is quite as useful as a poet
And quite as wise, and these anchovies show it.

—Euphron

"But the bold Briton ne'er in earnest dines,
Without sustantial haunches and surloins,
In wit, as well as war, they give us vigor;
Cressy was lost by kickshaws and soup-meagre."

—FENTON, *Spartan Dame*

"That all-softening, overpowering knell,
The tocsin of the soul,—the dinner bell."

—DON JUAN

Chapter Twenty-four

THE PHILOSOPHY OF LIQUIDS

MOST OF THE philosophy of liquids has to do with wines, as the large library of books on the subject attests. We have not omitted wines from our sampling here, but have tried to represent them with relatively unfamiliar comments rather than repeat the notable. For the rest, we have gathered a collection of random notes on several liquids, written by those who could be considered expert in their use.

Thus we begin with Dickens on punch, speaking through Mr. Micawber, a combination difficult to beat. There follows an authoritative piece on coffee, written by a turn-of-the-century connoisseur, Arthur Gray, and excerpted from his book on the brew. Alexander Pope and Ben Jonson offer poetic tributes to coffee and Brillat-Savarin, who probably drank it every morning of his life, speaks of the regenerative properties of chocolate.

Turning to sterner matters, we begin with Robert Burns's paean to John Barleycorn, after which Rabelais provides us with a reeling ode to serious drinking, enough to stagger the senses and leave the reader with a hangover.

Wine, as we have said, has engaged the serious attention of a great many serious writers. A few of them are here. First, George Meredith's fictional essay on old and great wines, from "The Egoist." Then a final word from Thomas Walker, this on the necessity of serving champagne for a successful party. Keats on claret and his own drinking habits, and Dr. Johnson on brandy, lead us to the most unlikely entry of all in our anthology, Thomas Jefferson—a connoisseur of both food and wine, among his panoply of talents—who argues for a nation of wine drinkers, at reasonable prices.

Punch Waits for No Man

from David Copperfield

by Charles Dickens

TO DIVERT HIS thoughts from this melancholy subject, I informed Mr. Micawber that I relied upon him for a bowl of punch, and led him to the lemons. His recent despondency, not to say despair, was gone in a moment. I never saw a man so thoroughly enjoy himself amid the fragrance of lemon-peel and sugar, the odor of burning rum, and the steam of boiling water, as Mr. Micawber did that afternoon. It was wonderful to see his face shining at us out of a thin cloud of these delicate fumes, as he stirred, and mixed, and tasted, and looked as if he were making, instead of punch, a fortune for his family down to the latest posterity . . .

"But punch, my dear Copperfield," said Mr. Micawber, tasting it, "like time and tide, waits for no man."

Coffee, a Robust Beverage

from Over the Black Coffee

by Arthur Gray

SINCE THE REAL civilizing of coffee as a drink—we will have to thank Constantinople for that—no beverage has compared with it in the social and companionable qualities it imports. Tea has always been, and will always be, a soft, soothing purring, gossipy decoction for gentle women and men of mild power and peaceful walks. It suggests the Celestial and his low browed laundry, side ringlets, respectability, and the fireside cat.

Coffee, on the other hand, has ever been associated with the robust, daring, and the adventurous. The scenes in which this little brown berry plays its part are those of the sea and the saddle, the mess room, the end of the long march, the camp in the woods, the lone prospector over the mountain range at dusk, the weary traveler in the wayside inn, visions of Venuses in railroad restaurants and lightning-change landscapes, en route.

What man is there among us who has not passed through some of these experiences?

Who can successfully deny that coffee has not been a great factor in the making and unmaking of nations?

Who does not know that in the famous coffee-houses of the past many a leader found his first voice; many a good and many a bad plot have been hatched, many a strong and many a weak cup of coffee have been responsible for these plots? And they are history, and men are the cause of it.

BEN JONSON AND ALEXANDER POPE ON COFFEE

They drank pure nectar as the gods drink too,
Sublimed with rich *Canary;* say, shall then
These less than coffee's self, these coffee-men,
These sons of nothing, that can hardly make
Their broth for laughing, how the jest doth take,
Yet grin, and give for the vine's pure blood
A loathsome potion—not yet understood,
Syrup of soot, or essence of old shoes,
Dasht with diurnals or the book of news!

—BEN JONSON

As long as Mocha's happy tree shall grow,
While berries crackle, or while mills shall go;
While smoking streams from silver spouts shall glide,
Or China's earth receive the sable tide,
While coffee shall to British nymphs be dear,
While fragrant steams the bended head shall cheer,
Or grateful bitters shall delight the taste,
So long her honors, name and praise shall last.

—ALEXANDER POPE

Regenerative Properties of Chocolate

from The Physiology of Taste
by Brillat-Savarin

WHEN HAVING WELL and abundantly lunched, you drink, to top the whole, a good size cup of fine chocolate, digestion will be complete three hours later and dinner will be welcomed . . . Due to a zeal for science, and making use of eloquence, I have had that experiment made by a good many ladies, who first assured me they would die, but they felt marvelously well afterward, and they showered their praises upon the professor.

People who make use of chocolate enjoy a state of health most likely to be equable, they are the least subject to the numerous light ailments that help to make life miserable, and their embonpoint is more rational; these are twin advantages easy to observe in any one's entourage, specially among those whose regimen is well-known. . . .

Now then let any man who has already been too much of a voluptuary; let any man who has spent much of the time intended for sleep at work; let any man of wit temporarily become dull; let any man who finds the atmosphere depressing, time hanging on his hands, and the air hard to breathe; let any man who finds himself hounded with a fixed idea, robbing him of his free thinking; let all these, we dare say, administer to themselves a good pint of amber-flavored chocolate, at the rate of seventy-two grains of amber for each pound avoirdupois, and they will experience marvels.

On Claret

from A letter to his brother and sister-in-law, 1819

by John Keats

I NEVER DRINK ABOVE three glasses of wine, and never any spirits and water; though, by the bye, the other day Woodhouse took me to his coffee-house, and ordered a bottle of claret. How I like claret! when I can get claret, I must drink it. 'Tis the only palate affair that I am at all sensual in. Would it not be a good spec. to send you some vine-roots? Could it be done? I'll inquire. If you could make some wine like claret, to drink on summer evenings in an arbor! It fills one's mouth with a gushing freshness, then goes down cool and feverless: then, you do not feel it quarreling with one's liver. No; 'tis rather a peacemaker and lies as quiet as it did in the grape. Then it is as fragrant as the Queen Bee, and the more ethereal part mounts into the brain, not assaulting the cerebral apartments, like a bully looking for his trull, and hurrying from door to door, bouncing against the wainscot, but rather walks like Aladdin about his enchanted palace, so gently that you do not feel his step. Other wines of a heavy and spirituous nature transform a man into a Silenus, this makes him a Hermes, and gives a woman the soul and immortality of an Ariadne, for whom Bacchus always kept a good cellar of claret, and even of that he could never persuade her to take above two cups. I said this same claret is the only palate-passion I have; I forgot game; I must plead guilty to the breast of a partridge, the back of a hare, the back-bone of a grouse, the wing and side of a pheasant, and a woodcock *passim*.

John Barleycorn

by Robert Burns

THERE WERE three Kings come from the east
Their victory to try;
And they have taken a solemn oath
John Barleycorn must die.

They took a plough and ploughed him in,
Laid clods upon his head;
And they have taken a solemn oath
John Barleycorn was dead.

There he lay sleeping in the ground
Till the dew on him did fall;
Then Barleycorn sprung up his head
And so amazed them all.

There he remained till mid-summer
And looked both pale and wan;
Then Barleycorn he got a beard
And so became a man.

Then they sent men with scythes so sharp,
To cut him off at knee.
Alas, poor Johnny Barleycorn!
They served him barbarously.

Then they sent men with pitchforks strong,
To pierce him through the heart;
And like a dreadful tragedy
They bound him to a cart.

Then they sent men with holly clubs
To beat the flesh from bones;
The miller he served him worse than that,
He ground him betwixt two stones.

O, Barleycorn is the choicest grain
That's ever grown on land.
It will do more than any grain
To the turning of your hand.

It will put sack into a glass
And claret in a car;
And it will cause a man to drink
Till he neither go nor stand.

How They Chirped over Their Cups

by François Rabelais

THEN DID THEY fall upon the chat of the afternoon's collation; and forthwith began flaggons to go, gammons to trot, goblets to fly, great bowls to ting, glasses to ring, draw, reach, fill, mix, give it me without water, so my friend, so, whip me off this glass neatly, bring me hither some claret, a full weeping glass till it run over, a cessation and truce with thirst, Ha! thou false fever, wilt thou not be gone? By my figgings, godmother, I cannot as yet enter in the humor of being merry, nor drink so currently as I would; you have catched a cold, Grammer; yea, forsooth, sir; by the belly of Sanct Bluff let us talk of our drink, I never drink but at my hours, like the pope's mule; and I never drink but in my breviary, like good father Gardian. Which was first, thirst or drinking? Thirst, for who in the time of innocence would have drunk without being a thirst? nay, sir, it was drinking; for privatic *praesupponit habitum*. I am learned, you see. *Foecundi calices guem non fecere disertum?* We poor innocents drink but not too much without thirst, either present or future, to prevent it (as you know) I drink for the thirst to come; I drink eternally, this is to me an eternity of drinking, and drinking of an eternity. Let us sing, let us drink, now for a catch, dust it away, where is my noggin? what, it seems I do not drink but by proxy. Do you wet yourselves to dry, or do you dry to wet you? Pish, I understand not the rhetoric (theoric I should say), but I help myself somewhat by the practice.—Enough; I sup, I wet, I humect, I moisten my gullet, I drink, and all for the fear of dying; drink always and you shall never die. If I drink not, I am aground, and lost. I am stark dead without drink, and my soul ready to fly into some marsh amongst frogs; the soul never dwells in a dry place.

O, you butlers, creators of new forms, make me of no drinker a drinker: a perennity and everlastingness of springling and bedewing me through these my parched and sinewy bowels. He drinks in vain that feels not the pleasure of it: this entereth into my veins, the pissing tool shall have none of it. I would willingly wash the tripes of the calf which I reared this morning. I have pretty well now ballasted my stomach. If the paper of my bonds and bills could drink as well as I do, my creditors would have their hands full. Hold up your dagger-hand; that hand of yours spoils your nose. O how many other such will go in there before this go out; what, drink at so shallow a ford? It is enough to break both girths and breast leather. This is called a cup of dissimulation. What difference is there between a bottle and a flaggon? great difference: the bottle is stopped with a stopple, and a *Flaccon à vis*. Our fathers drank lustily, and emptied their cans; this is *bien chie chante*, well cacked, well sung. Come let us drink: will you send nothing to the river? Here is one going to wash the tripes. I drink no more than a sponge, I drink like a templar knight. And I *tanquam sponsus*. And I *sicut terra sine aqua*. Give me a synonym for a gammon of bacon; it is the compulsory of drinkers; it is a pulley; by a pulley-rope wine is let down into a cellar, and by a gammon into the stomach. Ha, now boys hither; some drink, some drink; there is no trouble in it. *Respice personam; pone pro duo, bus non est in usu*. If I could get up as well as I can swallow down, I had been long ere now very high in the air. Thus became Tom Tosspot rich; thus went in the Taylor's stitch; thus did Bacchus conquer India; thus philosophy, Melinda. A little rain allays a great deal of wind; long tippling breaks the thunder. But if there came such liquor from my buttock, would you not suck the udder? here, page, fill, I prithee forget me not when it comes to my turn; and I will enter the election I have made of thee into the very register of my heart. Sup, Simon; pull away; there is somewhat in the pot. I appeal from thirst, and disclaim it jurisdiction. Page, sue out my appeal in form. This remnant in the bottom of the glass must follow its leader. I was wont heretofore to drink out all, but now I leave nothing. Make not such haste; we must carry all along with us. Hey-day, here are tripes fit for our sport; godebillios of the dun ox with the black streak. O, for God's sake, let us lash them soundly, yet thriftily. Drink, or I will . . .

No, no, drink, I beseech you; sparrows will not eat unless you bob them on the tail; nor can I drink if I be not fairly spoke to. *Lagonaedatera,* there is not a cunniborow in all my body, where this wine does not ferret out my thirst. Ho, this will bang it soundly, but this shall banish it utterly. Let us make proclamation by the sound of flaggons and bottles, that whoever hath his thirst come not hither to seek it. Long spirits are to be voided without doors. The great God made the planets, and we make the platters neat. I have the word of the Gospel in my mouth, Sitio. The stone called Asbestos, is not more unquenchable than the thirst of my paternity. Appetite comes with eating, says Angeston; but the thirst, goes away with drinking. I have a remedy against thirst, quite contrary to that which is good against the biting of a mad dog: keep running after a dog and he will never bite you; drink always before the thirst, and it will never come upon you. There I catch you, I awake you. Argus had a hundred eyes for his sight; a butler should have (like Briarius) a hundred hands wherewith to fill us wine indefatigably. Ha, now lads, let us wet, it will be time to dry hereafter. White wine, here, wine boys, pour out all, *per le diable,* fill, I say, fill and fill till it be full. My tongue peels. *Lans tringue:* to thee, countryman, I drink to thee, good fellow. Comrade, to thee, lusty, lively, ha, la, la, that was drunk to some purpose, and bravely gulped over. O *lachryma Christi,* it is of the best grape; I faith, pure Greek, Greek. O the fine white wine! upon my conscience it is a kind of taffetas wine, him, hij, it is of one ear, well wrought, and of good wool. Courage, comrade; up thy heart, Billy: we will not be bested at this bout, for I have got one trick. *Ex hoc in hoc.* There is no enchantment nor charm there; everyone of you hath seen it; my prenticeship is out; I am a free man at this trade. I am an abbot. (Pshaw, I should say.) O, the drinkers, those that are a dry; O, poor thirsty souls! Good page, my friend, fill me here some, and crown the cup, I prithee, *à la cardinale; natura abhorret vacuum.* Would you say that a fly could drink in this? *À la mode de Bretagne.* —Clear off neat, *super*naculum, swill it over heartily, no deceit in a brimmer; nectar and ambrosia.

A *Venerable and Great Wine*

from The Egoist

by George Meredith

A CHIRRUP WAS IN the Rev. Doctor's tone: "Hocks, too, have compassed age. I have tasted senior Hocks. Their flavors are as a brook of many voices; they have depth also. Senatorial Port! we say. We cannot say that of any other wine. Port is deep-sea deep. It is in its flavor deep; mark the difference. It is like a classic tragedy; organix in conception. An ancient Hermitage has the light of the antique; the merit. Neither of Hermitage nor of Hock can you say that it is the blood of those long years, retaining the strength of youth with the wisdom of age. To Port for that! Port is our noblest legacy! Observe, I do not compare the wines; I distinguish the qualities. Let them live together for our enrichment; they are not rivals like Idawan Three. Were they rival, a fourth would challenge them. Burgundy has great genius. It does wonders within its period; it does all except to keep up in the race; it is short-lived. An aged Burgundy runs with a beardless Port. I cherish the fancy that Port speaks the sentences of wisdom, Port is the Homeric hexameter, Burgundy the Pindaric dithyramb. What do you say?"

"The comparison is excellent, sir."

"The distinction, you would remark. Pindar astounds. But his elder brings us the more sustaining cup. One is a fountain of prodigious ascent. One is the unsounded purple sea of marching billows."

"A very fine distinction." . . .

Of all our venerable British of the two Isles professing a suckling attachment to an ancient port-wine, lawyer, doctor, squire, rosy admiral, city merchant, the classic scholar is he whose blood is most nuptial to the webbed bottle. The reason must be, that he is full of the old poets. He has their spirit to sing with, and the best that Time has done on earth to feed it. He may also perceive a resemblance in the wine to the studious mind, which is the obverse of our mortality, and throws off acids and crusty particles in the piling of the years, until it is fulgent by clarity. Port hymns to his conservatism. It is magical: at one sip he is off swimming in the purple flood of the very-youthful antique.

By comparison, then, the enjoyment of other is brutish; they have not the soul for it; but he is worthy of the wine, as are poets of Beauty. In truth, these should be severally apportioned to them, scholar and poet, as his own good thing. Let it be so.

Meanwhile Dr. Middleton sipped. . . .

"Your opinion of the wine is favorable, sir?"

"I will say this: shallow souls run to rhapsody:—I will say, that I am consoled for not having lived ninety years back, or at any period but the present, by this one glass of your ancestral wine."

"I am careful of it," Sir Willoughby said modestly; "still its natural destination is to those who can appreciate it. You do, sir."

"Still, my good friend, still! It is a charge: it is a possession, but part in trusteeship. Though we cannot declare it an entailed estate, our consciences are in some sort pledged that it shall be a succession not too considerably diminished."

"You will not object to drink it, sir, to the health of your grandchildren. And may you live to toast them in it on their marriage-day!"

"You color the idea of a prolonged existence in seductive hues. Ha! It is a wine for Tithonus. This wine would speed him to the rosy Morning—aha!"

"I will undertake to sit you through it up to morning," said Sir Willoughby, innocent of the Bacchic nuptiality of the allusion.

Dr. Middleton eyed the decanter. There is a grief in gladness, for a premonition of our mortal state. The amount of wine in the decanter did not promise to sustain the starry roof of night and greet the dawn. "Old wine, my friend, denies us the full bottle!"

For a Successful Party, Serve Champagne

from The Art of Dining

by Thomas Walker

Of whatever materials composed, I never knew a party that could be said to go off ill where there was a judicious liberal supply of good champagne. I say judiciously liberal because there may be too much as well as too little, though the error, comparatively, speaking, is seldom on the side of excess; but I have seen, when a party has been raised to what I call the champagne point of conviviality, that an extra quantity has caused a retrograde movement, by clogging the digestive powers. In this, as in all other matters relating to the table, but here especially, much depends upon the eye, the judgment, and the resolution of the master. He must have liberality to give, attention and skill to regulate, and courage to stop. There are two classes of dinner-givers, to whom I do not address myself on this subject, because I know it would be in vain. The first is that class who began their career and had their habits formed during the war, when champagne was double the price it is now. They gave it then like drops of blood, and I have never yet seen an instance of liberalization. The second class is that who merely give it as a part of their state, and deal it out to the state prisoners round their table only to tantalize them. I have no hope, then, of producing any effect except upon those who date their assumption of table government on this side the battle of Waterloo, and who have or are capable of acquiring the same contempt of show that I myself have.

To give champagne fair play it ought to be produced at the very beginning of dinner, or at any rate after one glass of sherry or madeira. Any other wines rather unfit the palate for it. The usual mode is, as with other delicacies, to produce it after the appetite is somewhat palled, and I have often thought it particularly ungallant and ungracious, where there are ladies, to keep it back till a late period of dinner, and such a practice often presents an absurd contrast of calculation and display. According to my doctrines, the champagne should be placed upon the able, so that all may take what they like, when they like, till the presiding genius pronounces in his own mind that there has been enough, which is not difficult to a practiced eye. This supposes a supply at discretion up to the champagne point, which is very agreeable on particular occasions, or now and then without a particular occasion, but would not be convenient to most people, or even desirable, if convenient. I am far from objecting to a limited supply, even the most limited—that is, one glass round; but I do object to the period when it is usually served, and to the uncertainty with which it is served. Where it is handed round, and meant to be so only once, twice, or any greater fixed number of times, to which there can be no objection, the rule I would lay down is, that it should be handed round after the first glass of sherry, and if more than once, without any other wine between, and that it should be contrived to notify beforehand what the supply will be. It might be thought rather awkward to make the communication. That, I think, would depend on custom and tact. I am sure I should have no hesitation in making it, and, at any rate, the awkward effects often arising from uncertainty would be much greater. What can exceed the awkwardness of two persons who are going to take wine together beating about the bush to get each the other to propose champagne—a scene I have frequently witnessed between the best bred people? What can exceed the awkwardness of asking for it when there is no more, or of waiting till a fresh supply is brought, contrary to the original intention? All these awkwardnesses are the consequences of uncertainty, and are much at variance with the ease that is essential to conviviality. An annunciation that there is champagne without limit, or that it will be handed round once or twice, or oftener, saves these embarrassments. If it is placed upon the table, I would make a similar annunciation, as indeed I always do, that there is to be one bottle or two, or more, or at discretion. Then people know what they are about, are at their ease, for want of which there is no compensation. By means of previous annunciation, even the entertainers of the old school, and the men of state, might make their calculation available to a satisfactory purpose. The advantages of giving champagne, with whatever limit, at the beginning of dinner, are these: that it has the greatest relish, that its exhilarating quality serves to start the guests, after which they seldom flag, and that it disposes people to take less of other wines after, which is a relative and sometimes even an absolute, saving to the pocket of the host, and it is undoubtedly a saving to the constitutions of his guests. With wines, as the meats, serving the most delicate first, diminishes consumption—a desirable effect in all respects. I know that a couple of glasses round of champagne at the beginning of dinner will cause a less consumption, and with better effect than the same quantity, or more, at a later period; and where there are ladies, the portion they choose to take is most grateful to them upon this plan, and often the only wine they wish to accept. At the present price of champagne, if it is judiciously given, I believe it is on many occasions little or no additional expense, and its effect is always contributive of exhilaration. By promoting exhilaration it promotes digestion, and by diminishing the consumption of other and perhaps stronger wines is consequently favorable to health. No other wine produces an equal effect in increasing the success of a party; and a judicious champagne-giver is sure to win the goodwill and respect even of those who can command it at pleasure, because a great deal depends upon the mode of dispensing it. If it is handed round often, it should not be handed round quick, at least after the second glass, but at such intervals as the host points out. If it is placed upon the table within every one's reach, his nicely regulating power is necessary to give it sufficient, but to restrain over-circulation. As the only anxiety of many, who give parties regardless of expense, is that they should go off well, I must repeat that they cannot fail, if there is a liberal supply of good champagne, heartily given. Of course there will be various degrees of success upon various circumstances, but champagne can always turn the balance to the favorable side, and heartiness in giving will compensate for many defects in other particulars. I must here add, that in little *fêtes champêtres* champagne has great efficacy, and is a specific against that want of spirit that not unfrequently occurs; also on any convivial occasion, where there is an absence of something desirable in the way of comfort or convenience, or where any disappointment has happened, champagne is the most powerful auxiliary in remedying the omission, and making it forgotten. In short, where champagne goes right, nothing can well go wrong. I think it quite a waste to produce it unless it is iced, or at least of the temperature of cold spring water, and in hot weather its coldness is one of its most effective qualities. The less it is mixed with other wines the better it agrees with any one, and the objectionable effects attributed to it are often in reality the result of too much combination with other liquids. Taken simply and in due quantity, I think there are few constitutions to which it would not be beneficial, and I have frequently seen invalids who I have thought would have been all the better for an alterative course of it.

Brandy for Heroes

from The Life of Samuel Johnson

by James Boswell

ON WEDNESDAY, APRIL 7, I dined with him at Sir Joshua Reynolds'. I have not marked what company was there. Johnson harangued upon the quality of liquors; and spoke with great contempt of claret, as so weak, that "a man would be drowned by it before it made him drunk." He was persuaded to drink one glass of it, that he might judge, not from recollection, which might be dim, but from immediate sensation. He shook his head, and said: "Poor stuff! No, Sir, claret is the liquor for boys; port for men, but he who aspires to be a hero (smiling) must drink brandy. In the first place, the flavor of brandy is most grateful to the palate; and then brandy will do soonest for a man what drinking *can* do for him. There are, indeed, few who are able to drink brandy. That is a power rather to be wished for than attained. And yet, (proceeded he) as in all pleasure hope is a considerable part, I know not but fruition comes too quick by brandy. Florence wine I think the worst; it is wine only to the eye; it is wine neither while you are drinking it, nor after you have drunk it; it neither pleases the taste, nor exhilarates the spirit." I reminded him how heartily he and I used to drink wine together, when we were first acquainted; and how I used to have a headache after sitting up with him. He did not like to have this recalled, or, perhaps, thinking that I boasted improperly, resolved to have a witty stroke at me: "Nay, Sir, it was not the *wine* that made your head ache, but the *sense* that I put into it." BOSWELL. "What, Sir! will sense make the head ache?" JOHNSON. "Yes, Sir, (with a smile) when it is not used to it."

A Tax on Wine

by Thomas Jefferson

I REJOICE AS A moralist at the prospect of a reduction of the duties on wine, by our national legislature. It is an error to view a tax on that liquor as merely a tax on the rich. It is a prohibition of its use to the middling class of our citizens, and a condemnation of them to the poison of whiskey, which is desolating their houses. No nation is drunken where wine is cheap; and none sober, where the dearness of wine substitutes ardent spirits as the common beverage. It is, in truth, the only antidote to the bane of whiskey. Fix but the duty at the rate of other merchandise, and we can drink wine here as cheap as we do grog; and who will not prefer it? Its extended use will carry health and comfort to a much enlarged circle. Every one in easy circumstances (as the bulk of our citizens are) will prefer it to the poison to which they are now driven by their government. And the treasury itself will find that a penny apiece from a dozen, is more than a groat from a single one. This reformation, however, will require time.

. . . for drink the Grape
She crushes, inoffensive moust, and meates
From many a berrie, and from sweet kernels prest
She tempers dulcet creams . . .

—John Milton

Better to die of good wine and good company than of slow disease and doctors' doses.

—Thackeray

SAFFRON

Saffron killeth moths if it be sowed in paper bags verie thin, and laid up in presses amongst tapistrie or apparell.

—HARRISON'S *Introduction* to HOLINSHED'S *Chronicles*

July 23, 1670. This is in Saffron Walden parish, famous for that useful plant, with which all the country is covered.

—JOHN EVELYN'S *Diary*.

Chapter Twenty-five

THE END OF THE MEAL

DINNER IS OVER, the last of the wine has been drunk, and we have come to the end of philosophizing. But have we? There seems to us a need for a final word, a what-does-it-all-mean commentary on the subject of epicureanism. Why have so many men devoted their lives to their stomachs, as this volume shows so clearly they have done for thousands of years? Why have the best poets and scholars and novelists turned out so many millions of words in praise of an everyday fact of life, the ingestion and digestion of food and drink?

The answer to this historic preoccupation, which sometimes seems unreal in an era when instant food threatens properly meditative gastronomy, has been given by many writers, but by none more cogently, we think, than in a preface to "The Epicure's Anthology," by the English writer A. J. A. Symons, a highly literate and sophisticated man.

The anthology itself was collected by Nancy Quennell, and published in Britain by The Golden Cockerel Press, no copyright and no date, but probably a product of the Twenties. Symons called his introductory essay, "The Epicure and the Epicurean." We print it here in its admirable entirety.

Bon appétit!

The Epicure and the Epicurean

from The Epicure's Anthology

by A. J. A. Symons

GASTRONOMY IS ONE of those pleasures that have allied themselves to literature, and therefore are remembered. Many phases of life in classical days have vanished from our knowledge; many of the minutiae of the middle ages can only be surmised; and the record of affairs even as conducted by the Victorians is in some ways already obscure or imperfect. But we know how almost every people of the past, near or remote, has eaten and drunk. What sauces the Greeks used, how the Romans stewed their dormice, what names were given by the Norman conquerors to the divisions and subdivisions of the beasts of the chase, what parts of the human body were preferred by the Congo cannibals, are questions which belong, not to the domain of conjecture, but to that of verified knowledge. We know (at least, those who care to *can* know) what fare was set before the unjust lords of the Star Chamber, how the court of Louis XIV was fed, what, and even where, Nelson, Wellington and Marlborough ate. "I dined today with your Mr. Sterne by invitation and drank Irish wine," wrote Swift to Stella, and we know what he meant. "I dined again yesterday at Blackwall as a guest, and observed that my theory as to adjuncts was carefully put into practice," remarks Thomas Walker, and we know what the theory was. And, though he said nothing aloud, we know what Professor Saintsbury said to himself when his twelve guests, who had all refused an excellent soufflé, changed their minds one by one when the Professor, to whom it was served last, helped himself. We have his own authority: he said "Sheep."

But, despite this vast accumulation of gastronomic detail and knowledge, in which there is material for a whole library of anthologies, we are still strangely ill-informed concerning the epicure himself. He has been accepted rather than defined; and though, as a type, he is perpetual, and renewed in every generation, his appearances in fiction are few and unsatisfactory. Even to this day the associations that are thought to cling to his character make him, in England at least, an unpopular figure, subject to disapproval and distrust. To confess oneself an epicure is to invite a tinge of that suspicion which has for so long attached itself to the Epicurean. Is it a survival of our Puritanism that the English terms for the table-lover are both contemptuous: glutton and gorbelly? Dr. Johnson admitted to his dictionary another unfavorable term, "gormand": it is typical that he did not include "gourmet." "Epicure" he defined as "a man given wholly to luxury."

Modern usage, however, recognizes a distinction between the epicure and Epicurean—a distinction which must be emphasized if the former is ever to be freed from the reproach that shadows his name. Originally the two words were merely variants of one term describing a follower of Epicurus (320-270 B.C.), a believer in his teachings. But, in the strictest sense, its use in that connection was short-lived, since the disciples of Epicurus very early reversed his doctrines by exaggerating one part and abandoning another. Epicurus taught that pleasure is the supreme good, the end of life; but he taught also that pleasure consists in serenity of mind and absence of pain, and can best be obtained by the man who is ready to refect dangerous or disturbing gratifications in favor of permanent and tranquil well-being. In effect he asserted that not only is pleasure the only good, but also that good is the only source of pleasure. He was an apostle of moderation, and, as might be expected, his moderation did not commend itself to his followers, who, though they knew their own desires well enough, could not tell which pleasures were likely to carry a sting in their tail—or, when they could tell, were prepared to take the risk. Their reversed doctrine proved far more acceptable than the austere original. Men distrust moderation. "The golden mean is that there is no golden mean"; and pleasures which are recommended by lack of penalty pale before those which are positive and supreme in their own moments. Gradually the name of Epicurus became attached to a philosophic system he had never promoted, and an attitude to life which he denied. In the seventeenth century St. Evremond and Cowley, among others, made vain efforts to restore his name to the teachings truly his, but failed, and false associations of the word "Epicurean" remained current and universal.

For centuries the imaginary figure of the epicurean, consciously devoting his life to the pursuit of pleasure, bending all his powers to that end, has attracted and repelled the Western mind. "Every age of European thought has had its Cyrenaics or Epicureans, under many disguises, even under the hood of the monk" observes Pater. Faust is one of the many figures in whom the pleasure-seeker is personified; but what he seeks is shown as being procurable only at the price of damnation, at the cost of himself, of his soul. Bradley has summarized the general answer: "Common opinion repeats its old song, that the search for pleasure is the coarsest form of vulgar delusion, that if you want to be happy in the sense of being pleased, you must not think of pleasure, but, taking up some accredited form of living, must make that your end, and in that case, with moderately good fortune, you will be happy."

Although there can be no final answer to such questions, it is clear that the man who makes pleasure his sole principle must face the distrust, if also the envy, of the world. And it is in this distrust, this denial, that the opposition to the epicure is wrongly rooted. He falls under the same ban as the Epicurean. But the ban is unjust, for the two characters seek different goals. The Epicurean is a skeptic who values nothing save his own sensations, and suborns his intelligence to the unending task of refining and intensifying them; whereas the epicure is, or at least may be, a man of faith who affirms and enjoys the gastronomic pleasures as a justification of life.

The epicure is most frequently a man of affairs, who has distinguished himself by talent, or played some prominent part in the world's administration, to whom care in eating and drinking is a relaxation, a hobby, or an inspiration. The modern definition "one who cultivates a refined taste for the pleasures of the table" is explicit and sufficient; and no qualification should be added to it. The epicure is not a man who thinks of, and lives for, his belly alone; he is not a sensualist for whom dinner is merely an elaborate prelude to sexual passion; he is not a hedonist who sees life as a succession of pleasurable sensations to be obtained by hook, crook, or levitation; he is not a table bore who rams his one subject down your throat; he is not a pride-starved victim of insufficiency striving to assert a false superiority by making undue fuss over wine and food. He is simply "one who cultivates a refined taste for the pleasures of the table." No more. He may profess any of a dozen religions (though not those of Mahomet or Confucius, which forbid wine), he may be a carpenter in Surrey or a Burgundy cooper, a colonel of infantry or a private detective; all that we can predict or expect of him is that, as an epicure, he conforms to the definition already quoted.

Indeed, instead of suspecting and distrusting the epicure, we should revere him. His attention to what he eats and drinks is the demand that encourages good cooks; and the dishes that his palate appreciates and creates pass from his table to those of countless others who are unaware of their benefactor. High among philanthropists, the devotee of an absorbing and harmless faith, he deserves our appreciation as one of the few enthusiasts whose hobby can have no evil effect either upon himself or on others.

Against Faust let us set the sturdy figure of George Saintsbury, certainly one of the half dozen most notable epicures in the English scene, who enshrined the memory of his cellar in discerning and expressive prose twenty years after he had ceased to drink wine, telling over again, bottle by bottle almost, and with a scholar's patience and care, the vanished contents of his empty bins. No one acquainted with Saintsbury's life and work can doubt that, so far from losing his soul, his character was benefited and his life enriched, by his gastronomic zeal. Instances might be multiplied, by the score, of distinguished men whose appreciation of the pleasures of the table has not been inconsistent with a life of worth and work. Whistler, Rossini, Lamb, Thackeray, Keats rush at once to the mind. Brillat-Savarin, the supreme epicure, asserted the four strongholds of his favorite study to be letters, the church, medicine and finance—to which surely, by his own example, we must add law. That general opinion which, according to Bradley, has decided against the epicurean, would, if it could judge the issue fairly, accept the pastime of the epicure as one of the most reasonable and beneficent elements in human existence. . . .

INDEX